❧ MAN'S EVOLUTION ☙

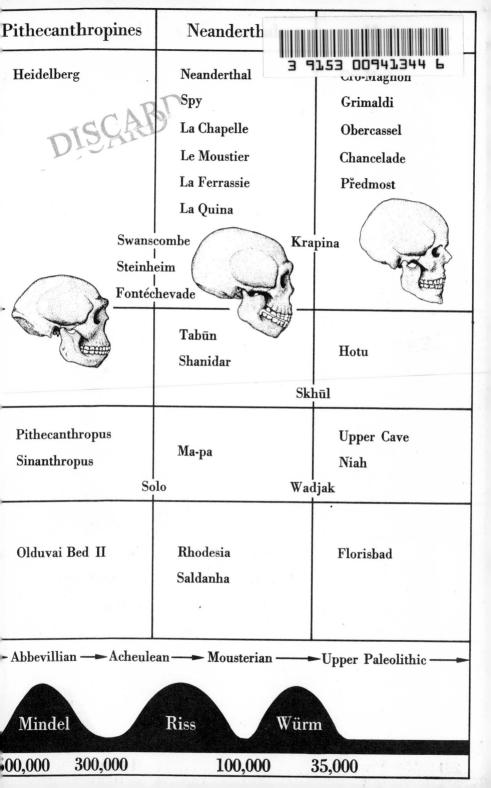

Pithecanthropines	Neanderth...	
Heidelberg	Neanderthal	Cro-Magnon
	Spy	Grimaldi
	La Chapelle	Obercassel
	Le Moustier	Chancelade
	La Ferrassie	Předmost
	La Quina	
	Swanscombe / Steinheim / Fontéchevade	Krapina
	Tabūn / Shanidar	Hotu
		Skhūl
Pithecanthropus / Sinanthropus	Ma-pa	Upper Cave / Niah
	Solo	Wadjak
Olduvai Bed II	Rhodesia / Saldanha	Florisbad

→ Abbevillian → Acheulean → Mousterian → Upper Paleolithic →

Mindel   Riss   Würm

| 00,000 | 300,000 | | 100,000 | 35,000 |

MAN'S EVOLUTION

An Introduction to Physical Anthropology

C. L. BRACE and
M. F. ASHLEY MONTAGU

THE MACMILLAN COMPANY, NEW YORK
COLLIER-MACMILLAN LIMITED, LONDON

Seventh Printing, 1968

Library of Congress catalog card number: 65–14956

THE MACMILLAN COMPANY, NEW YORK
COLLIER-MACMILLAN CANADA, LTD., TORONTO, ONTARIO

Printed in the United States of America

To
RAYMOND DART
In Appreciation

❦ PREFACE ❦

THIS BOOK PRESENTS an interpretation of the data of the human fossil record and of man's variation in the light of contemporary evolutionary theory. As such it attempts to articulate the available data with the evolutionary facts in such a manner as to make evolutionary sense of the facts of man's evolution. It has been our endeavor to present the reader with an operationally effective account of that evolution which not only makes sense but is also meaningful and verifiable, at least as verifiable as possible.

We believe that the facts ought to determine the nature of the theory, rather than the other way round. Adherence to this rule has served us as the guideline by which to find our way among both the thickets of the facts and the clouds of theories. We have endeavored also to bear in mind that theory-free statements of facts do not exist, and that therefore our own presentation of the facts is not altogether free of our theories. What we have striven to do is to make our particular evaluation of both the facts and the theories as fruitful as possible. This approach lends a theoretical and organizational consistency to the volume which, we feel, is lacking in many other works. It is possible, even probable, that some of the views expressed in the present volume may meet with criticism from professional physical anthropologists. Such criticism will be welcomed by the authors. Criticism is the life-blood of science. However, it should at once be said that this book is not designed to be a fully documented attempt to change or modify the long-held viewpoints of professional anthropologists, but rather to afford the beginning student an easily comprehensible text which leaves him enlightened and undismayed by the conflicts, confusions, and unanswered questions which he is likely to encounter in so many other works.

In the present work many issues concerning which there is a wide diversity of opinion are discussed primarily from one point of view, namely, that there has been a progressive evolution of man which can, in its broad outlines, be traced more or less step by step, and that while that evolution has been reticulate we can, as in a scattergram, trace something of its central tendency. There may be some professional disagreement with this view, and to the nature of such possible disagreements we refer in the text. In the suggested readings works are listed which present views diametrically opposed to ours.

With the beginning student in mind we have minimized the amount of traditional descriptive material, leaving this to some extent to be graphically presented in the illustrations. Instead, we have focused attention on an exposition of the processes affecting those traits which have responded to evolutionary forces, and have endeavored to give the reader a developmental account of change through time according to the logically comprehensible evolutionary principles.

It may, perhaps, be complained that we are omitting much of the uncertainty, complexity, and detail of physical anthropology. That may be a just complaint, but it is our strong feeling that a logical and consistent beginning constitutes a far better foundation on which to develop the subtleties of advanced study than one which presents a mass of conflicting data and interpretation to students who have not yet developed the competence or the sophistication to judge the issues for themselves.

The authors wish to express their warmest thanks to Mr. John Dennis Moore, their most efficient editor at The Macmillan Company, who at every stage of the work has been most helpful, patient, and understanding.

C.L.B. and A. M.

❦ CONTENTS ❦

[xi]

PART III
Living People

MAN'S EVOLUTION

INTRODUCTION ❧❧ THE HISTORY OF EVOLUTIONARY THOUGHT AND THE DEVELOPMENT OF PHYSICAL ANTHROPOLOGY

I F ONE CONCEDES the fact that *Homo sapiens* possesses all the attributes of organic life, and especially of animal organic life, it follows that the course of human development should have proceeded in a manner not too different from that of the rest of the animal kingdom. Such a statement seems to us so self-evident it hardly requires emphasis, but this was not always so. Today it takes something of an effort to recall that the nature and development of organic life was viewed in a very different light a century and a half ago. At that time it was generally believed that plants and animals had simply been created in their present form. In accordance with the view that man also is a member of the world of organic reality, it was assumed that he too had been created in his present form.

Special creation does not scientifically explain the existence of life, since it is an idea outside the realm of verifiable knowledge, but at least it does provide an answer to a question which men inevitably ask. Until relatively recently, it was not particularly important that the answer be a correct one, since the problem to which the question was directed was not one of great importance in governing the behavior of man toward man.

The creation myths recorded in the writings of the major religions of the world, and, indeed, the verbal accounts from the religions of nonliterate peoples, indicate by their very arbitrariness the recognition by men of their ignorance concerning the origins of the natural world of their everyday experience. Today the sciences of geology, paleontology, biology, and anthropology have contributed greatly to our knowledge concerning the course of organic development, and, rather than diminishing the wonder conveyed by the various creation myths, they have immeasurably enlarged that wonder. At the same time, they have not only left the basic moral teachings unchanged, but they have also provided solid evidence in their support.

Hence it should come as no surprise that religious thinkers and evolutionary scientists have no basic area of necessary disagreement. In fact, many contributions have been made to the understanding of organic evolution by men who were professionally committed to both religion and science. Much of our knowledge of fossil man in Europe, where more is known of fossil man than in any other region of the world, has been the direct contribution of Roman Catholic priests supported by their church in their prehistoric researches.

For instance, much of our knowledge of Paleolithic art, archeology, and fossil man in Europe is derived from the labors of the Abbé Henri Breuil whose active career spanned the first half of the twentieth century. The work of Hugo Obermaier, also a Jesuit priest, was scarcely less important, and the most complete Neanderthal skeleton found to date, La Chapelle-aux-Saints, was the result of the efforts of the Abbés A. and J. Bouyssonie and L. Bardon.

A century and a half ago, however, the majority of scholars, laymen, and clergy felt that Christian scripture was more than a model for moral teaching. The general view was that the Biblical creation story literally recounted the prehistory of the world, that is, the history of the world before any written records. All attempts to view the present state of the world as the outcome of the operation of natural forces were viewed with suspicion, hostility and fear, as contrary to the teachings of the Scriptures. The suggestion that man himself might have developed in a similar manner was regarded as blasphemous.

A residue of this heightened concern felt by many when their own ancestry is in question is evident in the slip many people make when referring to Charles Darwin's epoch-making work of 1859, *The Origin of Species*. Almost everyone who can read and write is aware that all serious attempts to study human evolution date from the publication of Darwin's book, but many are not aware that Darwin's book scarcely made reference to man, but restricted itself to a consideration of the evidence for evolution in general. Yet in the minds of many individuals, the title of the book is remembered as *The Origin of THE Species*, and it is supposed that *THE Species* upon which attention is focused is man. Nothing could be further from the truth.

While Darwin was aware that the principles set forth in his book could be applied in the investigation of human origins (the theme of his later work *The Descent of Man*, 1871), his concern in *The Origin of Species* was not with man at all. His primary purpose was to document his growing awareness that the species we observe around us were not simply created *de novo*. He had become convinced, by his extensive observations of variation and adaptation in related forms of living plants and animals, as well as by his increasing familiarity with the gradual change in living forms visible in succeeding layers of the fossil record, that all living things had achieved their present form by slowly occurring natural processes. Evidently the common tendency to interpolate the crucial article *THE* into Darwin's title is simply a bit of human egocentricity which, understandable though it may be, underestimates the larger scope of Darwin's actual intention.

We have mentioned that prior to Darwin the majority believed in special creation. The sensation which attended the publication of Darwin's book was due to the fact that the proponents of special creation felt their positions threatened by his mechanistic views. Differences in social class and wealth were inherited in the world of Western civilization, and positions of power in church, school, and politics were monopolized by people with inherited wealth and social position. Understandably such people favored a world view which emphasized the divine and unchanging fixity of the *status quo*—a *status quo* with themselves at the top. Any expression of opinion regarding the world as subject to change in the natural course of events was viewed as a threat to the established order. When things are thought to be as good as they can be, any change is not infrequently considered a change for the worse. The conflict between "religion" and "science" reduces itself to social issues rather distantly removed from any question of fundamental Christian morality.

In this respect, part of the impact of Darwin's work stems from the fact that he himself belonged to a socially prominent and well-to-do family. With such a background, any opinion he might offer would have received due consideration. Even a view thought to be contrary to the interests of his social class could not be ignored and brushed aside. As it was, his views were soberly and cautiously proposed and supported by an overwhelming amount of carefully considered evidence. Finally, the impact was heightened by the firm and convincing manner in which Thomas Henry Huxley—self-elected "bulldog" of Darwin—and Darwin's other supporters defended his position in contrast to the emotional, unethical, and rather un-Christian attacks by many of his critics.

If the mid-nineteenth century clash between "religion" and "science" was basically an issue of social philosophy, the strength of feeling generated on both sides bore testimony to the fact that it had been brewing for some time. It has already been stated that creation myths have adequately served most peoples as an explanation for the origin and existence of the world. Creation myths, however, do not account for changing worlds. They work only if the world to which they apply remains fixed from the point of creation to eternity. In western civilization creation myths were satisfactory enough till the end of the fifteenth century, but from that time on such myths became increasingly unsatisfactory to a small but growing body of thinkers.

Columbus discovered America, Magellan circumnavigated the world, and the universe of man could never again be the same. This vast increase in knowledge of peoples, places, and things produced changes in a no longer static world which did not fail to affect the lives and thought of men. Economic and social changes followed shortly, and the result was the need for a philosophy which could comprehend a changing world. Naturally, no all-encompassing viewpoint could spring into being overnight, but, like so much else, it did initiate the beginnings of a change in thought which continues to this day.

One of the first examples of the development of the change in character and direction of thought, "The New Philosophy," as it came to be called, is to be found in the writings of Francis Bacon (1561–1626). To encompass and give coherence to the vast increases in knowledge at the time, Bacon proposed systematic rules of observation whereby knowledge could be acquired. Little might be unraveled by this means concerning the nature of the world, but by being systematically collected, information would become available. But Bacon did not stop there. He urged, as William Gilbert (1540–1603) had done before him, the necessity of experiment.

And it was not long before a generation of "Bacon-faced" young men took up the challenge. One of these, Isaac Newton (1642–1727), worked out the laws by which he conceived certain facets of the world to operate. Newton's mechanistic insights, coming as they did toward the end of the seventeenth and beginning of the eighteenth centuries, were not of much use for the development of those branches of knowledge dealing with the study of life, since, although a great deal of information had been accumulated, it had not been collected systematically. For many, the world was still populated with dragons, unicorns, sea serpents, and a host of other mythical beings. What was needed was the rigorous application of Baconian principles to the world of animated nature, the phenomena of natural history.

The English comparative anatomist Edward Tyson (1650–1708), his contemporary countryman, the naturalist John Ray (1628–1705), and a number of their contemporaries devoted themselves to this task, but the man whose name is most prominently associated with this phase in the development of science was the Swedish naturalist Karl von Linné, better known by his Latinized name, Carolus von Linnaeus (1707–1778). As a reflection of the thoroughness of his work, he is called a "systematist"

FIGURE 1. Edward Tyson (1650-1708), father of primatology, author of the first comparative anatomy of an ape, *Orang-Outang, Sive Homo Sylvestris*, London, 1699. (Painting by E. Lilly. Courtesy of the Royal College of Physicians, London.)

to this day. In his immortal work, the *Systema Naturae* first published in 1735 and in a tenth edition in 1758, he classified all known living organisms according to the greater or lesser extent of their similarities. Each form was designated by two Latin names, one for Genus, and one for Species, hence the designation "binary nomenclature." From that day to this, man has been officially (and possibly somewhat prematurely) known as *Homo sapiens*.

Precise, controlled observation, as exemplified by Linnaeus, is the foundation for all good natural science and remains so today. Analysis and interpretation have played an increasingly larger role in the public recognition and acceptance of scientific theories, beginning with the tremendous interest generated by the publication of *The Origin of Species*. But what is most notable in Darwin, whose interpretations are among the most convincing in science, is that they are based on an overwhelming quantity of careful observations and systematically collected data.

Late in the eighteenth century, a number of savants, a small minority to be sure, began to suggest developmental schemes, based on the operation of observable forces, to account for the extensive similarities between many organisms for which precise

FIGURE 2. Karl von Linné, better known by the Latinized form of his name, Carolus Linnaeus (1707–1778), the father of taxonomy. (Courtesy of the American Museum of Natural History.)

observations had been recorded. The reaction to this was predictable. Those who had a vested interest in preserving the *status quo* of an unchanging world, created in the form they knew, were outraged. Since education was possible only for the relatively wealthy, it was inevitable that a majority of the educated should oppose the view of an evolving world. Yet, a few of the most able and devoted students of natural science were unable to resist explanations involving changes effected by natural forces.

Significantly, Linnaeus, in the last (1766) edition of his *Systema Naturae,* removed his former statement asserting the fixity of species. Linnaeus' eminent French contemporary, Georges Louis Leclerc, comte de Buffon (1707-1788), commonly referred to as Buffon, had unequivocally clear and definite ideas concerning change in the organic world, but these were buried in his massive *Histoire Naturelle* which ran to 44 volumes. Similarly, Charles Darwin's grandfather, Dr. Erasmus Darwin (1731–1802), clearly expressed ideas which became the foundation of later nineteenth century evolutionary thinking, but his thoughts, recorded mainly in poetry, were ahead of his time, and when not frankly ridiculed, were regarded as too speculative. Nevertheless, Dr. Darwin achieved sufficient recognition during his lifetime so

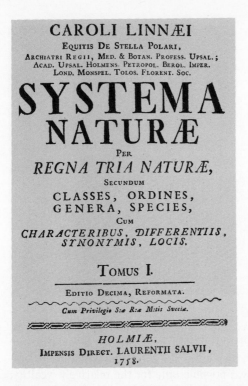

CAROLI LINNÆI

EQUITIS DE STELLA POLARI,
ARCHIATRI REGII, MED. & BOTAN. PROFESS. UPSAL.;
ACAD. UPSAL. HOLMENS. PETROPOL. BEROL. IMPER.
LOND. MONSPEL. TOLOS. FLORENT. SOC.

SYSTEMA NATURÆ

PER

REGNA TRIA NATURÆ,

SECUNDUM

CLASSES, ORDINES, GENERA, SPECIES,

CUM

CHARACTERIBUS, DIFFERENTIIS, SYNONYMIS, LOCIS.

TOMUS I.

EDITIO DECIMA, REFORMATA.

Cum Privilegio S:æ R:æ M:tis Sveciæ.

HOLMIÆ,
IMPENSIS DIRECT. LAURENTII SALVII,
1758.

FIGURE 3. Title page of the 1758 edition of the *Systema Naturae*, the foundation work of systematic biology. (Courtesy of the American Muesum of Natural History.)

that views of organic development were referred to as "Darwinism" even before the birth of his grandson in 1809.

The first really thoroughgoing evolutionist, however, was the French scholar Jean Baptiste Pierre Antoine de Monet, Chevalier de Lamarck (1744–1829), generally known as Lamarck. Today, Lamarck is remembered principally for his view that characteristics developed during the lifetime of a particular organism could be transmitted to succeeding generations. This theory involving the inheritance of acquired characteristics has been conconclusively refuted by twentieth century genetic studies.

Although the scientific basis for the refutation of Lamarck's basic idea did not exist until nearly a century after his death, he was thoroughly discredited during his own lifetime by the sarcastic attacks of his rising young contemporary, Baron Georges Cuvier (1769–1832). Cuvier, with a theatrical and commanding personality, achieved great popularity as a lecturer and public figure, and, by means of ridicule, influenced a whole generation of European scholars against the views of Lamarck. While it is true that the mechanism for moving evolution which Lamarck proposed has now been shown to be incorrect, it is too often forgotten that he clearly understood and documented the fact that evolution must have taken place.

On the positive side, Cuvier rigorously practiced the principles of observation exemplified in the work of Linnaeus, and provided the foundations for the modern sciences of comparative anatomy and paleontology. Ironically, these are the two disciplines that offer the most conclusive direct evidence for evolution.

Because of his work in paleontology, Cuvier was well aware of the sequences of time represented by superimposed layers of sedimentary rock. He was also aware of the graded changes in the fossilized forms of life contained within successive strata. Since he believed that all organisms were the result of special creation, he was forced to postulate a succession of special creations to account for the observable fossil record.

More than half a century earlier, Linnaeus had believed that all life now visible on earth dated from the time of the Biblical flood. Cuvier still held that view, but to it he added a succession of previous deluges and subsequent creations to account for the progression of changes visible in the fossil record. While he still attempted to view the world as fixed, rigid, and unalterable, it is evident that a major concession had been made. Change was recognized, even if it was considered to be of catastrophic and supernatural origin.

Concession, however, is hardly the same as creation in the scientific world (it might be added that the successive catastrophes and creations invoked by Cuvier were not even his own ideas, having enjoyed considerable popularity for many years). The overall influence of Cuvier was to retard creative thinking, and it comes as no surprise, therefore, that a really convincing exposition of evolution and its mechanism (natural selection) was not to be a product of French scientific thought.

The final irony in connection with Cuvier's thought and influence concerns his reaction to questions relating to the possibility of the discovery of fossil man. His pronouncement on this subject was *"L'homme fossile n'existe pas!"* Fossil man does not exist! As fate would have it, more evidence for the existence of fossil man has come from France than from any other part of the world.

It is generally granted that full-scale evolutionary thinking had its first complete expression in the writings of Charles Darwin (1809–1882). Darwin's work represented the culmination of a sequence of intellectual development of quite respectable history. European thinkers of the previous century had clearly expounded evolutionary views when human society was the subject of their concern. Rousseau, Condorcet, Diderot, Kant, and Goethe,

FIGURE 4. Charles Darwin (1809–1882), photograph taken in 1854 at the age of 45. Author of *The Origin of Species*, 1859. (Courtesy of the British Museum, Natural History.)

Hume and Malthus from the French-, German-, and English-speaking worlds, respectively, had written of the natural development of social systems. Since the conditions of human society are so clearly controlled by man's choice of activity, and since written history records great changes in human activities and societies, it is not unexpected that mutability and the forces effecting change should first be appreciated in the social sphere. So that Shelley could write at the beginning of the nineteenth century:

> Man's yesterday may ne'er be like his morrow;
> Naught may endure but mutability.

By the mid-nineteenth century sufficient thought and systematic observation had accumulated to make the time ripe for a synthesis by a powerful mind such as that of Charles Darwin. One could name a number of English scientific workers whose evolutionary views, closely resembling those of Darwin's, appeared during the half century prior to *The Origin of Species* (Blyth, Wells, Lawrence, Prichard, Lyell, Matthew, Chambers, Wallace), but this in no way diminishes the originality and importance of Darwin's great work.

Perhaps it is significant that such a development should occur in England. There the Industrial Revolution started and was already a hundred years old when Darwin's book was published. There changes in the social system had occurred by gradual rather than revolutionary means. Wealth and power could be attained by individual effort and no longer necessarily depended on inherited position. This is not to say that reverence for the *status quo* had disappeared, but the idea of progress, of change for the better, had become a genuine value for the first time. Darwin certainly was greatly stimulated by the expressed ideology of laissez-faire capitalism, and from it took over the idea of competition as a moving force in the world of nature. The result was that the principle of natural selection tended to be viewed in dramatic competitive imagery—"Nature red in tooth and claw." Darwin himself never expressed it in quite such lurid terms, though he did, in *The Origin of Species*, frequently speak of "the warfare of Nature."

Darwin made evolution respectable. His work was presented in a sober and quiet voice with a mass of personally compiled and

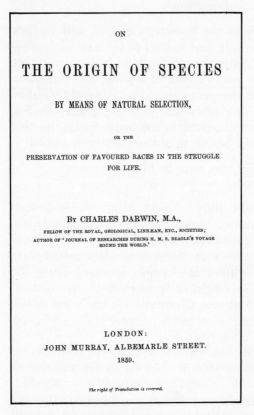

ON

THE ORIGIN OF SPECIES

BY MEANS OF NATURAL SELECTION,

OR THE

PRESERVATION OF FAVOURED RACES IN THE STRUGGLE
FOR LIFE.

BY CHARLES DARWIN, M.A.,

FELLOW OF THE ROYAL, GEOLOGICAL, LINNÆAN, ETC., SOCIETIES;
AUTHOR OF 'JOURNAL OF RESEARCHES DURING H. M. S. BEAGLE'S VOYAGE
ROUND THE WORLD.'

LONDON:
JOHN MURRAY, ALBEMARLE STREET.
1859.

The right of Translation is reserved.

FIGURE 5. Title page of *The Origin of Species,* 1859. (Courtesy of the American Museum of Natural History.)

easily understandable supporting evidence, and with natural selection he furnished a guiding principle. This principle not only constituted an effective means by which evolution could occur, but it was such a simple, obvious, and inevitable process that, once understood, it became impossible to imagine a world in which evolution did not occur.

With these considerations in mind, Darwin's impact on both popular and scientific thinking easily qualifies him for the title of "The father of evolutionary thought." As such, Darwin occupies a position of key importance in many more fields of interest than those merely limited to the field of biology. For example, the science of anthropology, the comparative study of the evolution of peoples and cultures, recognizes his particular importance, although Darwin would not have regarded himself as an anthropologist.

Physical anthropology, the comparative study of the evolution of man as an organism, has been most explicit in its recognition of Darwin's importance, since it is evident that all specifically evolutionary studies must claim him as an intellectual father. Recently, cultural anthropology has been approaching the study of the origin and development of culture from the evolutionary point of view, and, while ideas of social evolution go back to the eighteenth century, Darwin's work has been given increased recognition.

Even though evolutionary thinking now colors all interpretive generalizations in the biological sciences, including physical anthropology, there are many areas of specific and observational studies which do not necessarily depend upon an evolutionary viewpoint, and which historically have their roots in pre-Darwinian times. The accumulation of information contributing to a knowledge of basic human biology dates back to the collection of writings attributed to Hippocrates (c.460–c.370 B.C.), the Greek physician, and even before. Until quite recently, the accumulation of such knowledge was a more or less incidental by-product of the work of medical men. Historians of science can point to the work of the Renaissance anatomist and physician Andreas Vesalius (1514–1564) who laid the foundations for all subsequent investigations in human anatomy, but his contribution was most specifically to medical knowledge, however important it may have been for the advancement of basic human biology.

The individual often given the title "father of physical anthropology" is Johann Friedrich Blumenbach (1752–1840), professor of anatomy at the University of Göttingen, Germany. As a pre-Darwinian savant, Blumenbach's work was not influenced by evolutionary concepts, although it is worth noting that he attempted to explain human differences by viewing them as adaptive responses to differing environments. His writings touch on all aspects of human variation—skeleton, internal organs, hair, skin, teeth, and similarities and differences when compared with nonhuman Primates. With the broad range of utilized knowledge characteristic of his eighteenth-century background, Blumenbach

FIGURE 6. Johann Friedrich Blumenbach (1752–1840), the father of physical anthropology. Author of *De Generis Humani Varietate Nativa*, 1775.

functioned more like a modern physical anthropologist than his increasingly specialized successors in the nineteenth century, despite his generally non-evolutionary viewpoint.

At first thought, it might seem as though the addition of an evolutionary orientation to the kind of interest in human biology, represented by Blumenbach, would have produced a science recognizable as physical anthropology, yet this did not immediately occur. To be sure, interest in human biology, and specifically in human evolution, greatly increased during the latter part of the nineteenth and the first part of the twentieth centuries, to the extent that the term "anthropology" in Germany, and particularly in France, refers to what is called more specifically "physical anthropology" in the English-speaking world. In spite of this heightened interest in man's variations and their origins, the increasing specialization within the different areas of interest meant that professional students of human biology tended to be less and less well grounded in what are now called the social sciences. This growing compartmentalization has progressed to the point where there is actually some feeling of antagonism between the natural and social sciences. Natural scientists, justly proud of the progress made in physics and chemistry during the last half century, have occasionally felt that such fields as general anthropology, sociology, economics, and the like are not true sciences, and the social scientists have tended to react by proliferating increasingly formidable terminologies of their own.

In America the field of anthropology owes its existence largely to the efforts of Franz Boas (1858–1942), who had been trained in the physical, natural, and social sciences at the doctoral level, and who clearly perceived the difficulties which would follow a dismemberment of the science of man. Despite the occasional abrasiveness, the more successful departments of anthropology in the United States have continued to contain both cultural and physical anthropologists.

Where physical anthropology has remained within the medical orbit, as is largely the case in Europe today, there has been less success in understanding the course of human evolution and its mechanics than is the case where physical and cultural anthropologists habitually rub elbows. The reason for this lies in the fact that the key to human survival is in man's culture, and an understanding of culture past and present is necessary before there can be any adequate appreciation of the selective forces which have determined the course of human evolution.

Culture, the component of human possessions and human be-

havior which is derived from the activities and learning of previous generations, can be regarded as man's primary adaptive
mechanism. An understanding of the evolution of any organism
requires an appreciation of its adaptation, and hence the student
of human evolution must be sensitive to the role played by human
culture throughout the course of man's existence. This is a simple
enough concept and quite obvious when stated, but, like so many
other "obvious" concepts, it was not at all obvious until it was
put into words. In this case, this has only been done within the
last few years. So it is, that in spite of a full century of evolu-

FIGURE 7. Franz Boas (1858–1942). Cultural and physical anthropologist.
Founder of the American school of anthropology. Author of *The Mind of
Primitive Man*, 1911. (Courtesy of the late Dr. Ernst Boas.)

FIGURE 8. Aleš Hrdlička (1869–1943), American physical anthropologist. Author of *The Skeletal Remains of Early Man*, 1930. (Courtesy of the Smithsonian Institution.)

tionary studies, and the even longer accumulation of basic biological information, it is only now that a fully coherent picture of human evolution can be developed, and the field of physical anthropology can properly emerge from the union of its essential but diverse components.

SUGGESTED READINGS

Broderick, A. H. *Father of Prehistory: The Abbé Henri Breuil: His Life and Times.* William Morrow, New York, 1963.
Henri Breuil, the leading prehistoric archeologist of his time, was born in 1877 and died in 1961. He thus spanned the periods of maximum archeological discovery in the nineteenth and twentieth centuries. This book tells his story, and since it is told by one who knew him well, it possesses both authority and understanding, and presents an illuminating history of archeology through the life and practice of one of its luminaries.

Casson, S. *The Discovery of Man.* Harper & Bros., New York, 1939.
An excellent history of man's research into his own origins, which traces the growth of both archeology and anthropology from their beginnings to modern times.

Daniel, G. E. *A Hundred Years of Archaeology.* Macmillan, New York, 1950.
Deals with the development of prehistoric archeology in the period 1840–1940.

Darwin, C. *On the Origin of Species.* John Murray, London, 1859.
There are many editions of this famous book. An inexpensive facsimile edition, with a valuable introduction by Ernst Mayr, was published in 1964 by the Harvard University Press.
———. *The Descent of Man.* 2 vols. John Murray, London, 1871.
A fundamental book.

Eiseley, L. *Darwin's Century: Evolution and the Men Who Discovered It.* Doubleday, New York, 1958.
A fine book on the discovery of evolution, written by an anthropologist.

Ellegård, A. *Darwin and the General Reader.* Gothenburg Studies in English, vol. 8, Göteborg, Sweden, 1958.
A study of the reception of Darwin's theory of evolution in the British periodical press, 1859–1872. Indispensable.

Greene, J. *The Death of Adam.* New American Library, New York, 1960.
A history of the development of evolutionary ideas from Newton's day to their fulfillment in Darwin.

Haddon, A. C. *History of Anthropology,* 2nd ed. Watts, London, 1934.
A brief and basic history of anthropology.

Huxley, T. H. *Man's Place in Nature.* Williams & Norgate, London, 1863.
The 1896 edition is the best of this classic work, applying to man the principles that Darwin in the *Origin* had strategically not referred to man.

A good reprint of the 1863 edition, with an introduction by Ashley Montagu, is published by the University of Michigan Press.

Meggers, B. J. (editor). *Evolution and Anthropology: A Centennial Appraisal.* The Anthropological Society of Washington, D.C., Washington, D.C., 1959.
Eight lectures on the influence of evolutionary theory on the various branches of anthropology.

Millhauser, M. *Just Before Darwin.* Wesleyan University Press, Middletown, Connecticut, 1959.
A study of Robert Chambers' *Vestiges of the Natural History of Creation*, 1844, the book that prepared the way for Darwin's *Origin*.

Montagu, M. F. Ashley. *Edward Tyson, M.D., F.R.S.* (1650–1708): *And the Rise of Human and Comparative Anatomy in England.* American Philosophical Society, Philadelphia, 1943.
A study of the development of evolutionary ideas written about the life of the man who wrote the first comparative anatomy of an ape and a man, and who was a cousin, seven generations removed, of Darwin!
———. *Darwin, Competition, and Cooperation.* Schuman, New York, 1952.
A critical examination of the misuse of such terms as "The survival of the fittest," "The warfare of Nature," and "The competitive struggle for existence," and the consideration of the role of cooperation in evolution.

Penniman, T. K. *A Hundred Years of Anthropology,* 3rd ed. Macmillan, New York, 1964.
A good historical survey of anthropology.

Slotkin, J. S. (editors). *Readings in Early Anthropology.* Aldine Publishing Co., Chicago, 1965.
A comprehensive anthology of pre-scientific writings on the nature, origin, history, and behavior of man.

General Biological Background

CHAPTER ONE ❧❧ ORGANIC
CONTINUITY

I N ORDER TO APPRECIATE the operation of natural forces in the
production of cumulative organic change, i.e. evolution, it is necessary to understand something of the normal manner in which
organic life is perpetuated. In an age when special creations and
other supernatural phenomena were accepted as matters of course,
it did not occur to people to question the assumption that worms,
insects, mice, in fact, life itself, arose miraculously by spontaneous
generation in mud or trash or other organic refuse. By the mid-
nineteenth century, however, the investigation of the natural mechanics of the universe had proceeded to such a point that there
was a growing tendency to attempt to explain the operation of
all observable phenomena by logical, natural, and understandable
means. Hence Darwin.

Among the various researches being pursued at that time, some
of the most outstanding were those that were undertaken by the
students and associates of the physiologist Johannes Müller in
Berlin. Two of these, Jakob Schleiden and Theodor Schwann, are

credited with making the scientific world aware of the importance of the cell as a basic building block in all organic life. This interest was epitomized by the statements of another of Müller's protegés who eventually became his successor, Rudolf Virchow, the founder of cellular pathology. Virchow explicitly regarded all organisms as being communities of cells, and he expressed what was to become a guiding biological principle when he said that all cells must arise from other cells. *Omnis cellula e cellula.*

Within a few years Pasteur had performed his famous experiments which forever discredited spontaneous generation, and for the remainder of the nineteenth century the frontiers of basic biological research lay in investigations which were concerned with determining the mechanics of the cell. The egg was recognized as being a single cell, and it became increasingly clear that in order to understand organic growth and differentiation as well as organic perpetuation, the phenomena of cell division had to be investigated.

With the development of improved cytological staining techniques and microscopes of high quality during the 1880's, the various stages of ordinary cell division (mitosis) were observed. In the same period observations were made on the union of sperm and egg cells which universally precede the accumulation of cell divisions involved in the growth and development of a single organism. The presence of chromosomes within the cell nucleus had been known for some time, but with the new staining techniques they could be more easily studied—the very name "chromosomes" means colored bodies—and it was realized that the precise number of chromosomes in the cells of any given plant or animal always remained constant. This, plus the realization that chromosomes were practically the only contribution made by the sperm in transmitting the male half of inheritance, led to the suspicion that the stuff of heredity, the basic genetic material, was located in these chromosomes.

As a final refinement, the Freiburg zoologist, August Weismann, predicted that the cellular division processes which produced the sex cells, the egg and the sperm, must include one stage where the process of chromosomal duplication, which normally accompanies cell division, was inhibited. He realized that if this were not true, then the union of sperm and egg at fertilization would double the number of chromosomes each generation. Observation quickly bore out this prediction, and the 1880's saw the demonstration and verification of the phenomenon of reduction division (meiosis) whereby the sex cells are furnished with only half the normal complement of chromosomes (the haploid set). Fertilization was then observed to restore the full (diploid) set to the developing zygote with half of its genetic material being contributed by each parent (see Figure 13).

By the 1890's, the basic phenomena of cell division and sexual reproduction were well known, and the time was ripe for the development of some scheme which could explain the transmission and assortment of characteristics which were under the control of heredity. A number of such schemes had already been proposed, among them the theory of "pangenesis" offered by Darwin, but the only one of these which was actually correct was almost completely unknown. These were the principles discovered by the Moravian abbot Gregor Mendel (1822–1884), who had published his work in 1866. This appeared in *The Proceedings of the Natural History Society of Brünn* (now Brno, Czechoslovakia) and although this was not a particularly important journal, it was available in most of the major European libraries. In spite of this, and in spite of the fact that Mendel carried on an extensive correspondence with the German botanist von Nägeli, sending him relatively detailed accounts of his experiments and ideas, his work and insights were completely ignored.

Darwin's work of 1859 formally initiated an era in which interest in the possibilities of evolution led to an increasing concern for information on the mechanics of organic perpetuation. Because of the involvement of evolutionary thought with the occurrence of accumulating organic change, much of this concern was directed toward discovering the source of new variations. Darwin himself simply had faith in the sufficiently frequent origin of novelty—a faith supported by an immense amount of personal observation and accumulated evidence.

Critics pointed out that, even with new variants arising occasionally, they would breed with the existing population and the variation would become so diluted within a very short time that

FIGURE 9. Gregor Mendel (1822–1884), Moravian abbot, discoverer of the laws of heredity. (Courtesy of Professor Luigi Gedda.)

it would effectively be lost. This criticism worried Darwin enough so that he devoted a considerable amount of thought to meeting it, and, as a result, produced a theory of inheritance which, although incorrect, had one important element of similarity to that proposed by Mendel. This was the theory of pangenesis, which suggested that each cell of an organism gives off minute particles (Darwin called them gemmules) which are collected via the blood stream and stored in the gonads prior to transmission to the next generation. These particles then supervised the construction of cells similar to those that had produced them. While there were many insurmountable difficulties which eventually deprived this hypothesis of its effectiveness as an explanation of heredity, yet the concept that inherited characters are produced by the action of specific particles or units was essentially correct, and it solved the problems which arose when inheritance was assumed to be a "blending" of the maternal and paternal contributions.

The idea that heredity was particulate in its nature was one of the most important contributions of Mendel, and it is interesting to note that the powerful mind of Charles Darwin had also appreciated the fact that the apparently sporadic transmission of various traits could only be explained by assuming that the hereditary substance was made of discrete particles. The major flaw in pangenesis was the assumption that influences which altered the form of the cells would result in their giving off altered gemmules. This, in fact, was a statement involving the transmission of acquired characteristics, and shows how Darwin came to fall into a Lamarckian position.

Mendel, however, was less concerned with the origin of variation than with the mechanics involved in the transmission of characteristics already a part of the hereditary endowment. Not that he was unaware of evolution or the implications of an understanding of the laws of heredity for evolutionary thought. His library contained a well-read copy of Darwin's work with his own marginal notations, and it is abundantly evident that Mendel's discoveries were not simply fortunate guesses, but rather the result of intelligent, well-planned, and brilliantly executed basic scientific research.

At a time when the origin of change was a major consideration, he was chiefly concerned with the ordinary facts of organic continuity, but it is not so much the subject of his inquiry which accounted for his failure to make an impression, as it was his method of approach. In retrospect this method scarcely seems remarkable since it involved assumptions which form one of the foundation stones of twentieth century science—quantification— but, at the time, this was so novel that virtually no one perceived the significance of what he had done.

While his records show that he performed breeding experiments on several kinds of plants, he is most famous for his work with the garden pea (*Pisum sativum*). The choice of this humble plant was deliberate, and reflects Mendel's intuitive grasp of the problem even before he began his experiments. He chose the pea since, as a self-pollinating plant, the various strains bred true indefinitely, and the only way in which different elements could be introduced was by artificial pollination. Furthermore, the several commercially available varieties possessed a series of traits which differed in easily distinguishable and simply inherited ways. He chose varieties which were distinguished by differences in seven simple traits which occurred either in one condition or another, for example:

> shape of the pea, whether wrinkled or round,
> color of the pea, whether green or yellow,
> length of the stem, whether tall or short,

and so on for the remainder.

When he cross-pollinated differing strains, he did something which biologists were not to do until another generation—he kept careful records and *he counted the results*. As a consequence, he discovered that the ratio of forms of whatever trait he chose remained constant from the second subsequent generation on. In the first generation after the cross, now referred to as the first filial or F_1 generation, he discovered that one form of whatever trait was being considered characterized all of the plants. If, for instance, the parental generation included plants from both tall and short strains, he found that the entire F_1 generation was tall. When this was allowed to pollinate itself and produce a second filial or F_2 generation, he noted that three-quarters of the F_2's were tall but one quarter was short.

Subsequently, the aggregate offspring of all succeeding generations maintained this 3:1 ratio, but, when more detailed examination was made, it transpired that the plants which were short produced only short offspring when allowed to fertilize themselves. Also, one out of every three tall plants was capable of producing only tall offspring, while the remaining two-thirds of the tall plants produced both tall and short offspring in the 3:1 ratio. Thus the external characteristics of his F_2 generation revealed only the two forms present in the original parental strains, but in terms of their potential, there were three kinds of plant present; one of which produced only short, one only tall, and the remainder able to produce both. Geneticists in the twentieth century have given these phenomena labels, the appearance is called the *phenotype*, while the breeding potential is called the *genotype*, and, while Mendel did not use these terms, for our discussion it will be convenient to do so.

Mendel realized that his ratios could be most efficiently explained if one assumed that each trait was controlled by units, or factors, and if an individual inherited one such factor from each parent. In any individual, then, each trait would be controlled by a minimum of two such units. A Danish botanist was to christen these unit characters *genes* early in the twentieth century, and, again, we shall use the term for the sake of convenience.

Figure 10 diagramatically illustrates the preceding. In the parental generation, the true breeding tall strain has a double dose of the tall factor, or, in modern terms, is homozygous for tallness as is illustrated by a genotype of *TT*. The true breeding short strain is given the symbols *tt* to illustrate that, genotypically, it is homozygous for shortness. Since one half of the genetic endowment of the offspring comes from each parent, and the tall parent can only pass on *T*, and the short parent *t*, inevitably the genotype of the first filial generation must be *Tt*, that is, mixed or heterozygous.

Now while the F_1 generation is genotypically mixed, it is phenotypically tall since, in *Pisum sativum*, the edible garden pea, tallness predominates over shortness. This is the phenomenon of dominance, and, in this case, the gene for tallness is dominant and the gene for shortness is called recessive. In all the characters in Mendel's experiment, one condition was dominant over its alternative, and Mendel believed he had discovered a general law of heredity, the law of dominance. Actually he did not take into account the fact that he had deliberately chosen characters that were expressed in an either-or fashion, and had thus predetermined his results.

In later work with other plants, he noticed that in crossing certain strains of red and white flowers, the F_1 generation was pink. The F_2 generation then produced red, pink, and white offspring in the 1:2:1 ratio, and it was evident that the phenotype was an accurate indicator for the genotype. Such instances were called cases of partial dominance, and, in the vast quantity of genetic information which has accumulated since Mendel's time, it has become clear that the phenomenon of dominance does not warrant the status of a general law, as he had assumed.

The other principles which he deduced, however, have been proven by the test of time and repeated experimental confirmation, and are basic to the understanding of all problems related to

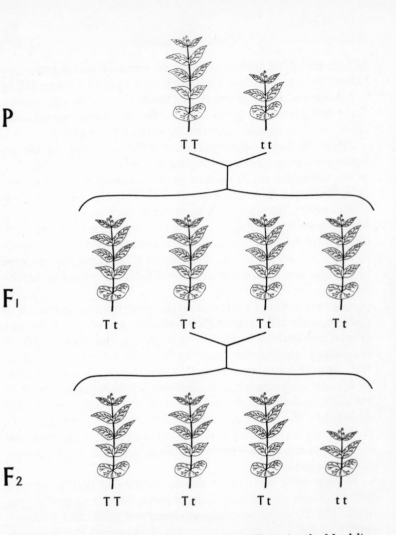

FIGURE 10. The inheritance of height in ,pea plants illustrating the Mendelian ratio. In the parental generation (P) one plant carries two "factors" for height *TT*, while the other plant carries two "factors" for shortness *tt*. The offspring in the first filial generation (F₁) each carry one "factor" from each parent *Tt*. In the second filial generation F₂ there will be 3 tall plants to every short plant, because the "factors" will usually be distributed in the manner illustrated, and because big *T* happens to dominate little *t*. It was from such painstaking observations of the transmission of particulate traits that Mendel was able to derive the basic laws of inheritance.

organic continuity and, ultimately, evolution. His basic contribution can be generalized in the following manner:

1. Heredity is particulate in nature, that is, the hereditary material of any organism is made up of discrete units. Today we call them genes.

2. The distribution of these units among the offspring of any particular mating is entirely a matter of chance.

3. The association of more than one of these units in a given individual or even in successive generations does not influence the unit itself. If any unit (gene) is segregated by chance (according to generalization number 2) it will be fully expressed despite the previous combinations in which it may have occurred.

Since the rediscovery of Mendel's work, some biologists have elevated various of these generalizations to the status of "laws." Actually, according to strict logic, the first one could be regarded as a major principle or law, and the next two as conditions or corollaries, since their expression depends on the existence of the units. Unfortunately for the recognition accorded Mendel during his lifetime, neither the basic nature of cellular reproduction nor the power of a quantitative approach to biological problems was sufficiently understood for the scientific world to have recognized the value of his work. He died in 1884, a respected and beloved ecclesiastical figure, head of the powerful monastery of Altbrünn, widely known for his struggle to preserve the rights of the monastery against the encroachments of Habsburg tyranny, and totally ignored by the world of science.

In 1900, more than fifteen years after Mendel's death and some thirty-five years after his fundamental work had been reported, the accumulation of knowledge in the various branches of biology had advanced to the point where the quantitative predictions of a Mendelian kind of formulation could be appreciated. Inevitably, when the world is ready for a discovery, someone makes it, and the readiness of the biological world for a quantitative genetic formulation was indicated by the fact that three separate workers independently came to the same conclusions as a result of similar courses of research. What is even more interesting, each, having realized the import of his discovery, combed the botanic literature to see whether there was any support for such a formulation, and each independently rediscovered Mendel's classic publication and gave Mendel full credit for the initial discovery. The Dutch botanist Hugo de Vries, the German botanist Karl Correns, and the Austrian botanist Erich Tschermak announced their independent and nearly identical discoveries within the space of four months in papers read before the German Botanical Society, and, as a result of their insistence, the quantitative picture of heredity which underlies twentieth century biology is called Mendelian genetics.

During the decade following the rediscovery of Mendel, it was discovered that his predictive scheme worked for many organisms and not just for peas. Mendel's "factors" were given the name of *genes* by the Danish botanist Johannsen (1857–1927), and it was recognized that chromosomes, as observed under the microscope, behaved in somewhat the same way that Mendelian theory predicted that genes should behave. It was soon realized, however, that there were many more genes than chromosomes. The suggestion was offered that chromosomes were structures which carried the genes, and the experimental work which followed provided ample confirmation. Microscopic investigations of cell structure, cytology, joined with quantitative breeding investigations to create the field of cytogenetics which has given us a far better understanding of the workings of heredity than either field could have done separately.

If genes were carried on the chromosomes and chromosomes were constantly transmitted from one generation to another, then presumably those genes which occurred on the same chromosome would be transmitted as a linked group and would not assort at random as strict Mendelian theory would claim. In individual cases this was partially confirmed, but, for populations as a whole the complete randomness of Mendelian theory was observed. The solution to this problem and to many others was provided by the work of Thomas Hunt Morgan (1866–1945) and his associates at Columbia University. Beginning in 1910, Morgan carried out a series of brilliant experiments using *Drosophila melanogaster*, commonly known as the fruit fly. Hitherto much of the basic information concerning heredity came from work on plants, but the selection of *Drosophila* greatly accelerated things. Thousands

FIGURE 11. Thomas Hunt Morgan (1866–1945) one of the principal founders of modern genetics. (Courtesy of the New York Academy of Medicine.)

of flies can be raised in the laboratory at very little cost, and they produce a new generation every two weeks. *Drosophila* possesses one other great advantage, although this was not discovered until the 1930's, and this is the fact that the salivary glands of the larval form have cells with gigantic chromosomes some one hundred times longer than those of other cells. Eventually this meant that the hard-won conclusions of early *Drosophila* research could be checked microscopically.

By 1915, Morgan's group had observed that certain specific traits were almost always transmitted together. It was postulated that chromosomes were linear arrangements of genes with the loci for traits which are inherited together being adjacent. This tendency to be transmitted together was called genetic linkage, and it was found that there were four linkage groups for *Drosophila* which corresponded to the four chromosome pairs. There are twenty-three such pairs in man, one of these pairs consisting of the sex chromosomes. The components of this particular pair are unmatched, one being the X and the other the Y chromosome. A Y chromosome in association with an X chromosome determines the

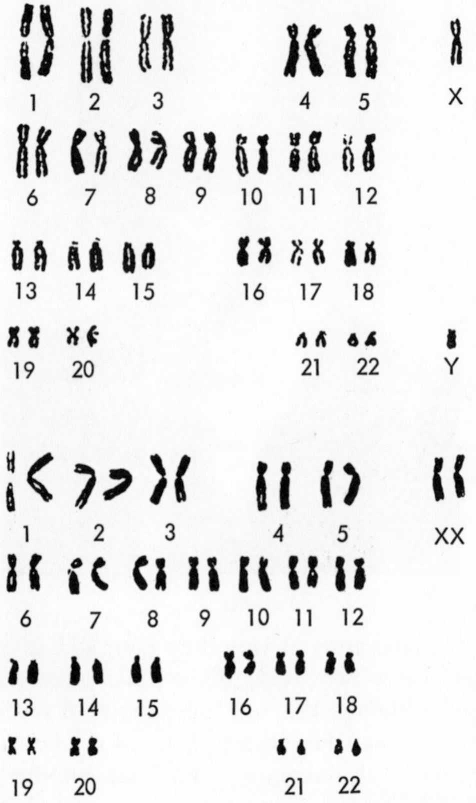

FIGURE 12. The chromosomes of the human male (above). The chromosomes of the human female (below). Arranged according to the Denver Classification. (Courtesy of Dr. Kurt Hirschhorn.)

sex of the individual as male. An X chromosome associated with another X chromosome determines the sex of the individual as female.

Since there were different degrees of the regularity with which traits in the same linkage group (i.e., chromosome) were transmitted together, Morgan postulated that this must be related to their positions on the chromosome. Closely linked characters are controlled by genes which occur side by side. At first it seemed that Mendel's criterion of independent assortment was therefore invalid, but information from whole populations showed that this was not true. Morgan realized that at some time during reduction division when the sex cells were being produced, parts of the

[34]

halves of chromosome pairs must get tangled and exchanged—a process called crossover. Experiments showed that crossover could occur anywhere along the length of a chromosome pair with equal probability. Evidently if one gene locus (position on the chromosome) is right next to another gene locus, crossover will only rarely dissociate the two, but if one investigates genes whose loci occur at opposite ends of the chromosome, any crossover to which the chromosome is subject will separate them.

Within a large population, crossover occurs often enough so that there is no evident association between the various genes on a single chromosome, and since, in evolutionary genetics, it is the survival of the population which is important, it would appear that Mendel's original claim concerning the random assortment of unit characters was correct as far as evolution is concerned. For individual family lines, linkage between loci is an important phenomenon, but, when enough family lines are included in a population, crossover will assure Mendelian randomness.

Ordinary genetic linkage as it has been presented here should not be confused with the phenomenon referred to as sex linkage. This latter refers to loci which are found on that part of the X chromosome which is not matched by the associated Y chromosome. Since there is no Y chromosome locus corresponding to those on the non-homologous part of the X chromosome, any abnormal gene occurring there will be expressed without inhibition. In man, for instance, genes for red and green color-blindness occur on the non-homologous part of the X chromosome. If a male has such a gene on his X chromosome, it will be expressed since the Y chromosome has no corresponding locus or potentially suppressing gene. A female, however, has two X chromosomes, and, if one has an abnormal gene, there is a good chance that the corresponding locus on the other will possess a normal gene which will inhibit its expression. Two abnormal genes on the other hand will be expressed. This is the reason why red and green color-blindness is found more frequently in males than in females. The mechanism has been called sex-linkage.

By the 1920's, the picture of hereditary transmission was quite well understood, although, for various socio-political reasons, it was eventually rejected by Russian biologists who, until recently,

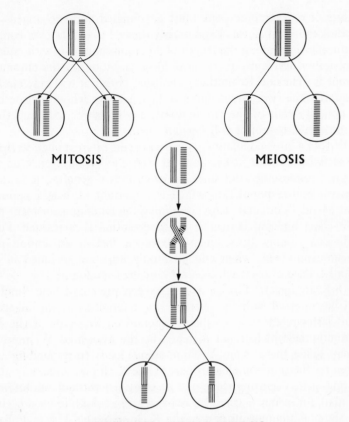

MITOSIS

MEIOSIS

CROSSOVER DURING MEIOSIS

FIGURE 13. Mitosis, Meiosis, and Crossover. In crossover, illustrating how genes on homologous chromosomes can be interchanged. In mitosis there is a duplication of each chromosome so that the daughter cells have one each. During meiosis each chromosome arranges itself in longitudinal contact with the one derived from the opposite parent. In this way each gene is brought into place opposite its corresponding gene (synapsis or conjugation). These chromosomes become closely entwined about each other lengthwise. It is during this crossover process that segments of each chromosome break off and become attached to the broken ends of the opposite chromosome. In this way genes that were originally located in a maternal chromosome become part of one that originally came from the father. Crossover, then, provides a major source of genetic variability.

regarded particulate genetics as an especially evil bit of capitalist mythology. To be sure, no one has ever seen a gene, but then neither has anyone actually seen a neutron or the nucleus of a hydrogen atom, and yet the Russians have shown no reluctance to accept the facts of their existence and use them in the construction of a formidable weaponry.

Because of the wealth of biological phenomena which has occupied the attention of research workers, it has taken biologists a full half century longer than it took physicists to come to grips with the structure of their basic particles. The nature and mode of action of the gene is only now becoming understood. In Morgan's time, however, the grosser effects of genes and chromosomes became generally known, but this did not at first explain the origin of change. Morgan, in exploring the mechanics of organic perpetuation, could not see how this could fit evolutionary interpretations, and for some years he rejected evolutionary thought.

Then in 1927, one of Morgan's former students, Professor H. J. Muller, announced that he had produced permanent heritable changes in the genetic material of *Drosophila* as a result of subjecting them to X-rays. Spontaneously occurring heritable changes had been noticed at the turn of the century by de Vries, one of the rediscoverers of Mendel, and he had called them mutations, suggesting that these were the sources of evolutionary novelty. It was eventually realized that de Vries' changes were rare and rather unusual alterations and not the normal means by which evolution occurred, so the term mutation was given to the simple alterations in single genes observed by Muller. The simple but permanent nature of the change, and the means of its production, led Muller to postulate that a gene was actually a single molecule—reason enough why one has never been seen. Time has shown that Muller was substantially correct, but the proof had to await the development of refinements in research technology and the accumulation of results from a field which had yet to be born—molecular biology.

Research in this direction started slowly and has been picking up speed ever since. Early in the 1930's, workers at the University of California purified and crystallized a virus, the simplest living thing. For some time, viruses were regarded as being possible examples of "naked genes," that is, genes without organisms attached, so there was great interest in the analysis of the crystallized viral material. Subsequent findings have shown that a virus is *not* a naked gene, but this initial theory accounts for the widely held misconception that the basic genetic material is "nucleoprotein" since the analysis of crystallized virus showed that it was entirely composed of only two substances, nucleic acid and protein. At its most basic, living matter is composed of protein and nucleic acid, and there is some justification in the statement that the most significant progress in biological research for the past several decades has come as a result of discoveries relating to the structure and modes of operation of these two classes of substances.

Among other things, the advances in basic biology during the 1940's can be traced to the use of more rapidly breeding experimental organisms. From Mendel's garden peas to Morgan's fruit flies, attention was now turned to bacteria, specifically *Escherichia coli*, the harmless colon bacillus normally found in the human large intestine. With a new generation being produced every twenty minutes, breeding experiments can be carried out in one day which would have required two years if fruit flies had been used, and in the neighborhood of 2,000 years if a subject had been used with approximately the span required for a human generation. In three years, *Escherichia coli* produces nearly as many generations as have occurred for mankind since the very beginning of human history more than a million years ago.

In the mid-1940's it appeared that the simplest genetic changes, the smallest mutations, caused simple changes in the mode of operation of single enzymes. Enzymes themselves are proteins, the most complex of organic molecules, and for a while, as the result of work on *Neurospora*, bread mold, it was postulated that one gene controlled one enzyme. This turned out to be a little too simple, but it had become increasingly obvious that the main function of a gene is the control of protein synthesis. Then in 1952, by experiments with the colon bacillus and with a virus which infects it (a bacteriophage) it was proven that the material which carries the hereditary information is a nucleic acid, specifically deoxyribonucleic acid, generally referred to as DNA. The stage was now set for one of the most important breakthroughs in the history of science, the discovery of the exact structure and mode of action of the basic genetic material.

Until the last decade, it had been felt that the discovery of the significance of the gene was to biology what quantum mechanics was to physics, but it is now apparent that the use of the concept "gene" as a simple unstructured particle was similar to the conception of the atom as a solid irreducible particle which prevailed in pre-twentieth century physics. In 1953, James D. Watson and Francis H. C. Crick, working in the Cavendish Laboratory at Cambridge University, proposed a structure for deoxyribonucleic acid, DNA, which has had an impact on the biological sciences comparable to the effect that nuclear theory had on the physical sciences half a century ago. It is an interesting and not unillumi-

FIGURE 14. Model of a portion of the DNA molecule, showing the two interlocking polynucleotide chains. Only a few of the thousands of turns in the double helix are shown. Each outer helix consists of five carbon-sugar molecules S (deoxyribose), alternating with P phosphate groups —hence, a pair of sugar-phosphate (deoxyribosephosphate) chains wound

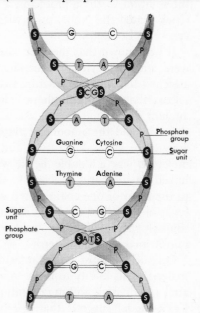

in a double helix. The helical polynucleotide chains are united by the closely-fitting paired nitrogenous bases AT adenine-thymine and GC guanine-cytosine connected by hydrogen bonds (the double lines). A, Adenine; C, Cytosine; G, Guanine; P, Phosphate; S, Sugar; T, Thymine; =, Hydrogen bonds. It has been estimated that if the helical chains (or sugar-phosphate backbones), or tapes, as they are sometimes called, in the human body were placed end-to-end, they would reach beyond the moon. Each unit phosphate-sugar-base represents a nucleotide; hence, each helix is a polynucleotide chain. (Courtesy of Ashley Montagu, *Human Heredity*, and The World Publishing Co.)

nating fact that the Cavendish Laboratory was also the scene of some of the most fundamental work in the development of nuclear physics.

Nucleic acids, like proteins, are polymers. The term polymer (many unit) refers to the fact that these molecules are constructed of relatively simple units attached end-to-end in the form of a long chain. For proteins, the basic units are *amino acids*. There are some twenty amino acids, and all the varied and complex protein molecules are formed by differing numbers of these twenty amino acids in specific orders. Nucleic acids also are formed by sequences of basic units, but in their case, the constituent units are organic bases called *nucleotides* and there are only four of them. One of the problems that plagued investigators for some time was how to use these four building blocks to construct a model which would not only give a clue to the means by which it duplicated itself, but also to the process whereby it could direct the building of protein molecules from the twenty building blocks of which they are constructed. The Watson-Crick model provided the solution to these problems, a solution for which Watson and Crick shared the Nobel prize with M. F. H. Wilkins of the University of London in 1962.

It was known that the four bases of which DNA was composed were adenine, cytosine, guanine, and thymine, and that these attached to a helical structure made of repeating units of a sugar (deoxyribose) and phosphoric acid. Further, it was known that the amount of adenine present was always the same as the amount of thymine, and the amount of cytosine was always the same as the amount of guanine. Watson and Crick proposed that the DNA molecule was a double helix, with two phosphate-sugar chains linked via the bases attached to the sugars. The adenine attached to the sugar of one chain paired with the thymine attached to the sugar of the other chain. With guanine and cytosine behaving in similarly complementary fashion, evidently one chain was the mirror image of the other.

One of the most important characteristics of the basic genetic material is its ability to make exact copies of itself in cell division after cell division and in generation after generation. The Watson-Crick model suggests that the two strands of the usual double

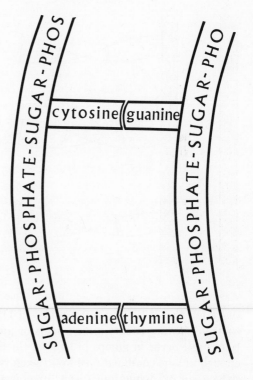

FIGURE 15. The sequence of sub-units in a DNA molecule showing the alternation of sugars and bases in the backbone and the way nucleotide parallel strands couple with each other.

helix must separate during each cell division, with one half going to each daughter cell. There, the guanines pair with cytosine, the adenines with thymine, and the single helix lays down its mirror image exactly reconstituting the form of the DNA molecule of the original cell. There are still some formidable problems to be overcome in detailing the manner in which this process works, but undoubtedly these problems will eventually be solved.

At first it seemed even more difficult to perceive how this model could relate to protein synthesis, since it appeared extraordinary that all of the information necessary for the building and operating of an entire organism could be present within the nucleus of a single cell and written down in a code with only four symbols. Nevertheless, the discoveries of the last decade have shown that this is indeed the case. Shortly after their initial proposal, it was

[41]

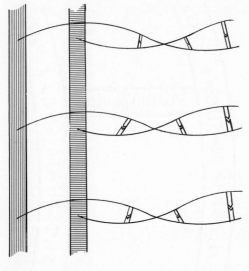

FIGURE 16. Proposed chromosome-DNA relation. A possible model for the way in which the double helix DNA molecules relate to the double structure of a chromosome.

suggested that if the four nucleotides of DNA were to correspond somehow to the twenty amino acids of protein, then the nucleotides must occur in groups of at least three in order that there be enough unique combinations. Four taken two at a time yields only sixteen (or 4^2) while four taken three at a time makes sixty-four, which is more than enough. The group of three adjacent nucleotides is referred to as a nucleotide triplet or occasionally as a *codon*.

There were other problems, too. For example, DNA occurs only in the nucleus, while protein synthesis takes place in minute bodies called ribosomes situated in the cytoplasm. The ribosomes, however, are also the sites where the greatest quantity of the other form of nucleic acid occurs. This is ribonucleic acid, or RNA, which differs in a minor way from DNA. Apparently RNA is laid down on the model of DNA in the nucleus, and from there it moves out into the ribosomes where it directs the synthesis of proteins from the available amino acids in the cytoplasm. Since most proteins are enzymes which catalyze and control subsequent reactions, the production of proteins in the ribosomes influences the speed at which more protein-enzymes are produced. This process, of course, is cumulative and accounts for the fact that tissues differentiate during growth, although the same genetic potential is to be found within the DNA of each cell nucleus of a given organism.

The hypothesis that the four nucleotides taken three at a time— a four-letter alphabet from which words only three letters long are constructed—providing explanation of the means by which the synthesis of protein is coded in the structure of nucleic acid, received brilliant confirmation by the experimental work of two groups in 1962. Research teams at New York University and at the National Institutes of Health in Maryland artificially hooked together nucleotides to form synthetic RNA molecules of known structure. These molecules were then put into an amino acid soup, and in the presence of the necessary enzymes, they managed to synthesize proteins whose structures depended upon the sequence of RNA nucleotides.

Many problems still remain to be cleared up, for instance, the exact relationship between the basic genetic material, DNA, and the chromosome, which is a linear structure of a protein nature. Also the exact mechanics by which the helical DNA molecule unwinds itself and then synthesizes its mirror image remains unknown. Yet with the basic foundations provided by the research of the recent past, there is every reason to expect that the problems that remain will be solved in the relatively near future.

The reader may have noticed that throughout our discussion of nucleic acids and proteins, we have not used the term gene. Rather we have preferred the vaguer phrase "basic genetic material." The concept of the gene, as it developed through the era of Morgan and his followers, was based on the minimal units affected by crossover. During the 1940's, there was some thought that a gene might correspond to a single enzyme. Then, in the case of the important human blood protein, hemoglobin, it was discovered that the difference between normal and abnormal forms of the molecule, inherited as a single gene trait, was simply due to the difference in the identity of one single amino acid unit out of the 600 units present. According to what we have said then, the gene in question should be the nucleotide triplet responsible for the amino acid at that particular site in the protein chain. The difficulty lies in the fact that a change in only one nucleotide can account for the difference in the amino acid called for, but if another nucleotide in the triplet is substituted instead, no change is made in the effect. Some nucleotide alterations act like single gene changes, but under certain circumstances, other such alterations do not. This only serves to illustrate the fact that the concept of the gene is a little too crude to be used effectively when one reaches the molecular level. For much of agricultural, medical, and evolutionary research, however, it remains as effective as when it was developed by Mendel a century ago.

There are many today who predict a time when man will be able to exercise some control over his own heredity. While one may cautiously assert that this does not appear likely within the immediately foreseeable future, yet no one even as recently as twenty years ago could have predicted the spectacular progress made by biochemical genetics in the decade following 1953. With these and other lessons clearly in mind, we shall pursue the better part of valor and refrain from making any predictions at all.

SUGGESTED READINGS

Anfinsen, C. B. *The Molecular Basis of Evolution.* Wiley, New York, 1959.

One of the most provocative attempts yet undertaken to relate the new findings of biochemistry to the fields of genetics and evolution.

Boyer, S. H. IV. (editor). *Papers on Human Genetics.* Prentice-Hall, Englewood Cliffs, N.J., 1963.

A collection of some of the most significant contributions to modern human genetics.

Carter, G. S. *A Hundred Years of Evolution.* Macmillan, New York, 1957.

A survey of the changes of thought in evolutionary theory since the publication of Darwin's *Origin*.

Dunn, L. C. (editor). *Genetics in the 20th Century.* Macmillan, New York, 1951.

Essays by twenty-six leading authorities on the progress of genetics during its first fifty years.

Gillispie, C. C. *Genesis and Geology.* Harvard University Press, Cambridge, 1951.
A study in the relations of scientific thought, natural theology, and social opinion in Great Britain, 1790–1850.

Harris, H. *Human Biochemical Genetics.* Cambridge University Press, New York, 1959.
Demonstrates how many of the traits with known inheritance exist at the level of single molecules.

Montagu, M. F. Ashley. *Human Heredity.* 2nd ed. World Publishing Co., New York, 1964; New American Library, New York, 1964.
An introductory survey of the principles and findings of human genetics.

Sutton, H. E. *Genes, Enzymes, and Inherited Diseases.* Holt, Rinehart and Winston, New York, 1961.
Presents evidence for the basic nature of inherited traits.

CHAPTER TWO ❧❧ PRINCIPLES
OF EVOLUTION

Natural Selection

THE GREAT CONTRIBUTION OF CHARLES DARWIN, in addition to providing the evidence for the evolutionary explanation of the origin of the diversity of organic life, lay, more specifically, in the fact that he proposed the mechanism by which evolution could work. That mechanism is natural selection. To the embarrassment of the natural scientist and the annoyance of the student, natural selection is peculiarly difficult to encompass within a *simple* definition. Yet despite the difficulty in reducing it to a simple definition, there is virtually unanimous agreement in the use of the principle. The physical scientists find similar, difficulties in defining entropy, a concept which is as useful and well understood as natural selection is to the biologist. The anthropologist's concept of culture is similarly useful and equally difficult to encompass within a simple definition.

By natural selection, the biologist means the aggregate of environmental forces which condition the chances for species survival. In the course of time, those variants within a species that are better fitted for survival, in the face of the various environmental forces, will leave a larger progeny of offspring than the less well adapted individuals. Heredity, being what it is, the offspring of the better adapted individuals will tend to exhibit characteristics similar to those that made their parents successful, and, providing that the selective forces have not altered, this will continue to favor the transmission of those characteristics. As a result of natural selection, the variant of today may become the average of tomorrow, at which time, more successful variants may arise by chance and forecast still further change for the species in question.

Nineteenth century advocates of evolution by means of natural selection tended to view the process in rather more violent terms than is customary today. For example, such terms as "the warfare of Nature," "struggle for existence," and "survival of the fittest" became established usage. Today, however, many biologists have pointed out that reproductive success is the final determiner of what the future of a species shall be, and the ability to leave adequate numbers of descendants does not necessarily depend on size, robustness, or intelligence. Individuals with well developed procreative powers, who are otherwise merely adequate for survival, will have far greater influence on succeeding generations than the strong and vigorous but less fertile. The nineteenth century emphasis on the survival of the fittest should therefore be modified to read "the survival of the fit."

While Darwin's opponents could not deny the documentation he produced for the operation of selective forces, they could and did attack him for his assumptions concerning the origin of the variations which were essential if evolution by means of natural selection were to work. Darwin, with the insight built upon a lifetime of careful observation, simply took it on faith that the necessary variation arose by natural means. Long after his death and after the rebirth of the science of genetics, the source for this variation was finally located in those minute modifications of the gene, namely, mutations. In the late 1920's, long before the exact nature of a mutation was known, it was the generally accepted view that "mutations are the raw materials of evolution." They do indeed produce the variation on which naturally occurring forces operate to effect the accumulation of organic change, i.e., evolution.

Although environmental forces are responsible for exerting the selection which produces adaptive responses in organic life, this does not mean that similar environments in different areas necessarily engender identical forms of life. For a variety of reasons, apparently similar selective forces may engender quite different responses. One of the most frequent reasons why this is so is the fact that all organisms bear the traces of their previous evolutionary history, and since this is often radically different, the base on which the forces operate is different enough to have quite diverse results.

To take an extreme example, the requirements for successful survival of a highly mobile organism in an aquatic ecological niche (an ecological niche is the total life way of an organism) are limiting enough to produce a great superficial resemblance between successful sea-going vertebrates. Whether these are whales or fishes or the extinct Mesozoic Ichthyosaurs, they all possess streamlined bodies propelled by powerful tails. Yet there are some striking differences. The fishes, for example, propel themselves by means of side-to-side tail movements while whales and dolphins, with their horizontal tails, move them up and down. Both methods are remarkably efficient, and, at first, it might not seem apparent why one was chosen rather than the other. We cannot even guess why the first fishes adopted a side-to-side movement nearly 500 million years ago since we do not possess the fossil evidence for precursors of the first fishes,* but the reason why the whales, who after all are remote descendants of the earliest fishes, chose the up-and-down motion is apparent when the history of pre-whale development is appreciated.

Whales are mammals with the typical mammalian warm blood and elevated metabolism. The elevated metabolism developed as an adaptation enabling the early mammals to inhabit a cool terrestrial ecological niche where normally cold-blooded reptiles were less likely to be effective. In order to maintain the elevated metabolism, regular food intake was required and regular food intake

---

* It may, however, be that since the first fishes were almost certainly as lateral-eyed as their descendants, perception of food on one side of the visual field would have initiated movements of the fins on the heterolateral side, hence, the development of side-to-side movement.

necessitates a reasonably efficient means of locomotion. Whereas reptiles, being less well adapted to terrestrial locomotion, still preserve the lateral position of their limbs, they tend to crawl with the aid of side-to-side motions of the entire body. This is a sloweddown version of what fish do in the water, and it is less efficient than the characteristic mammalian form of terrestrial locomotion where the limbs are moved in a front-to-back plane directly under and supporting the weight of the body. To aid this movement the mammal typically flexes and extends the backbone in the same plane of motion as the limbs. While mammals are ultimately descended from the early fishes by way of amphibians and reptiles, the pressures conditioning early mammalian development ensured it that the typical movement of the backbone in aiding locomotion was in a vertical rather than a horizontal plane.

Once this development had occurred, it affected all subsequent mammalian history, and when one line reinvaded the oceans in the Cenozoic, its method of meeting the requirements for success in an oceanic ecological niche was conditioned by these previous adaptations. Powerful propelling movements of the tail could be accomplished with fewer changes in the skeletomuscular system by ensuring that the tail was horizontal and the movements up-and-down, rather than by developing a vertical tail with side-to-side movements.

The superficial similarity between whales and fishes is technically a case of convergence. The selection exerted by the environment is strong enough to produce such an effect, although sufficiently radical differences remain to avert any possibility of confusing the two forms.

Genetic Drift

Evolutionary change can also occur by chance. In small populations (about 100 individuals) the *relative* amount of any given individual's contribution to the next generation is much greater than would be the case where the population size is up in the thousands or more. A mutation transmitted in a small population would have a much better chance of becoming generally established than it would in a large population, but at the same time the probability that any given character might fail to be transmitted would also be much greater. The gain or loss of genes simply due to the operation of chance on the reproductive mechanics of small populations has been called genetic drift. Since it simply depends on the accident of transmission, it is unrelated to natural selection, although the fixing or loss of characters in the genetic endowment of a population may ultimately have evolutionary significance.

As far as moving evolutionary change in any persistent direction, genetic drift (often called the Sewall Wright effect in honor of the American geneticist who proposed it) has probably played an unimportant role. Since it is the result of chance only, it is necessarily nondirectional. Genetic drift can accomplish the separation of two populations of the same species that have been isolated from each other for a long time. If, for instance, two populations become separated when a rise in sea level floods the connection between their areas of habitation, then it is possible that the random accumulation of insignificant changes over the generations may proceed to the point where mutual fertility is reduced or absent when contact is re-established. Once this degree of reproductive isolation is reached and it is no longer possible to exchange genetic material by hybridization, then the two populations have reached the level of specific difference and there are two new species. In this way, genetic drift may have played a role in speciation, whereas it has probably been insignificant in the progressive evolution of any particular group.

The selective effect of similar environments on closely related forms may very well ensure that these continue to resemble each other, although they have been separated for long periods of time. One of the classic cases is represented by the monkeys. Both New World and Old World monkeys are recognizably monkeys and quite similar in their adaptation to life in the trees of a tropical forest. However, they have been separated for 50 million years, and neither group looked like monkeys when the separation took place. The fact that they separately reached the Monkey Grade of development is a striking example of parallelism, and while this is not a particularly important principle, it does illustrate the effect that the continued operation of similar selective forces will have on similar basic organisms, despite the influence of genetic drift and other factors tending to produce differences.

Specialized vs. Unspecialized or Adaptation vs. Adaptability

All species must adapt to their environments if they are to survive, and if the environments change, the species must adapt to the changes. This is accomplished in several ways. Some organisms become closely adapted to the particular conditions of their environment. When this adaptation is particularly close, it is termed specialization. For instance, the marsupial koala bear of Australia is specialized for existence on a diet of eucalyptus leaves, which is fine if nothing happens to the eucalyptus trees. Specializations frequently enable organisms to make highly efficient use of a particular resource, but occasionally they mean that this efficiency is attained at the expense of adaptability. The fossil record is littered with the bones of animals which became overspecialized in one way or another and failed to adapt when conditions changed.

At this point we should interject a note of caution. There has been a tendency among paleontologists in the past to record the features of extinct animals which differentiate them from their modern counterparts, label these features "specializations," and attribute their extinction to such "specializations." This has been particularly evident in the literature dealing with fossil man, where every bump on the skull has at one time or another been called a specialization and cited as a reason for excluding the fossil in question from man's ancestry. With this tendency, there has gone the assumption that any specialization is limiting and therefore of doubtful value. The reduced number of digits in a horse's foot is excellent for high-speed locomotion, but it necessarily precludes any manipulative ability. In this case, the specialization is limiting, but the specialized molar teeth of horses have no such disadvantages. With their highly complicated enamel and dentine layering, and the open, continuously growing root, the horse can eat highly abrasive foods for upwards of twenty years without wearing the teeth to the gums. While horse molars are wonderfully specialized, they do not prevent the animals from eating virtually anything they choose. Perhaps the most remarkable specialization in the animal world is the human brain, yet it is just this specialization which has allowed man to devise the means for surviving in a variety of environments possible for no other mammal.

In contrast to specific adaptation, another trend which has been developed with great success by certain organisms is the emphasis on adaptability. Adaptability can be achieved in two ways. Either an organism can possess a morphology suitably generalized so that it can get along adequately in a variety of environments—witness the variety of habitats and diets successfully utilized by the brown rat—or it can preserve the genetic potential for producing variants capable of getting along under specifically differing conditions.

The reader will recall that the F_1 generation of the cross between two pure-breeding strains preserves all the genetic material of both parental lines. The offspring of the F_1, i.e. the F_2, will show the original parental conditions as well as the hybrid or heterozygous state. The preservation of several manifestations of a particular characteristic within the range of variation of a particular species is called polymorphism (many + form + ism). The continuing forces of selection dictate the chances which each manifest character possesses for survival, and the proportion between them is kept in balance. Recent investigations have shown that balanced polymorphism is a relatively common means of preserving the adaptability of a species.

There is another aspect of balanced polymorphism. In many cases it is the heterozygous condition which is the best adaptation. While the heterozygotes have the greater chances for survival (this is sometimes referred to as "hybrid vigor"), in obedience to Mendel's observed 1:2:1 ratio, 50 per cent of each succeeding generation will be homozygous. Natural selection, then, determines the proportion between the survivors, and the polymorphism is therefore in a state of balance. As we shall see when we discuss human variation later on, one of the best known examples of balanced polymorphism exists in the human hemoglobins. The operation of natural selection in discouraging the survival of the various homozygotes often appears to be a rather startling evolutionary waste, but then in the completely opportunistic workings of evolutionary forces, the fate of certain individuals is unimportant provided that enough of the adaptively adequately endowed survive to propagate the species. This is clearly illustrated by the vast quantities of doomed progeny which two fish must produce each generation simply in order that the fish population continues to maintain itself.

Evolution, being opportunistic as well as cumulative, frequently takes advantage of structures developed under certain circumstances, and uses them as the base for adaptation to changed environmental circumstances. Such a condition is referred to as preadaptation. Preadaptation, the reapplication of structures originally developed for other purposes, has accounted for some of the otherwise remarkable developments in evolution, although this should not be taken to indicate that there was any such preordained plan. The four fins of the early Paleozoic fishes were a preadaptation for later life on land, although it should be stressed that their initial appearance was simply to enable the fish to function more efficiently in the water. It was simply a matter of chance that it was later possible to modify fins into the legs of the earliest land tetrapods.

Long before the development of human beings, man's Primate precursors passed through a phase in which the characteristic mode of locomotion was brachiation—hanging beneath tree branches and proceeding hand over hand. This meant that the body developed to function in a vertical rather than a horizontal posture, and, as far as man is concerned, this was a necessary preadaptation to the later adoption of an upright posture on the ground. Actually every organism is a complex of made-over characters, which accounts for the fact that organic adaptations are so frequently complex and inefficient. Man, as we shall see, is a made-over ape. The term preadaptation, however, should be reserved for those structures which can be reapplied in new contexts. The postural preadaptation developed by man's arboreal ancestors represents an appropriate example, as does the hand-eye coordination that successful tree living also produced.

Adaptive Radiation

From time to time in evolutionary history, adaptations have arisen which have been so successful that they have allowed a con-

siderable expansion of the population and in the areas inhabited
by a particular group of organisms. When such an adaptation is
so effective that it allows the possessors successfully to enter previously unoccupied or poorly filled ecological niches, then the
result is what is called adaptive radiation. Birds, for example, inhabit a wide variety of ecological niches, but basically this all
stems from the initial development of the ability to fly.

In the history of the development of evolutionary thought, the
adaptive radiation of a particular group of finches played a crucial
role, for it was this which impressed the young Charles Darwin
with the importance of natural forces in shaping developments
in the organic world. Darwin was occupied as the naturalist aboard
the British brig *Beagle* on its voyage around the world, and, as
such, he spent five years building up the fund of knowledge which
was eventually to form the basis for his immortal work. In 1835,
the *Beagle* visited the Galápagos Archipelago—a string of rocky
islands some 600 miles west of the coast of South America. There
Darwin was fascinated by the various morphological differences
exhibited by the local birds, particularly the finches.

Superficially these appeared to be drab and uninteresting little
birds, but closer inspection revealed that the different species had
undergone modifications in the beak which enabled them to
occupy ecological niches ranging from those of insect eaters similar to warblers, to woodpecker, to parrot-like ones. All these differences were in addition to variations on the normal seed-eating
niche which is characteristic for finches. It occurred to Darwin
that the absence of natural predators and the absence of the usual
occupants of these various ecological niches was a function of the
long geological and geographic isolation of the islands, and that
the chance arrival of stray finches, blown from the mainland long
ago, allowed them to exploit these niches without the normal
competition. Since availability of food was the main limiting factor, those variants which could take advantage of normally un-
finchlike sources of nourishment would flourish. This would account for the fact that these otherwise quite similar birds differ
markedly in their food-getting structures, their beaks. In exploring
the picture of the adaptive radiation of the Galápagos finches and
similar radiations of the other Galápagos animals, Darwin de-

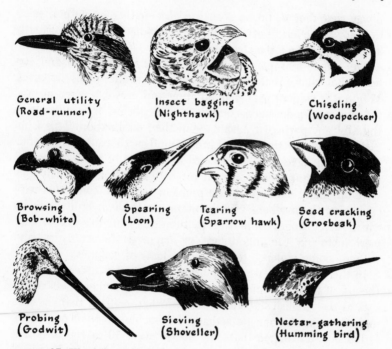

General utility
(Road-runner)

Insect bagging
(Nighthawk)

Chiseling
(Woodpecker)

Browsing
(Bob-white)

Spearing
(Loon)

Tearing
(Sparrow hawk)

Seed cracking
(Grosbeak)

Probing
(Godwit)

Sieving
(Shoveller)

Nectar-gathering
(Humming bird)

FIGURE 17. The bills of birds furnish a good example of adaptive radiation. (Courtesy of G. Hardin, from *Biology: Its Human Implications*, and W. H. Freeman & Co.)

veloped the basis for what he was later to generalize and apply to all life as the theory of evolution by means of natural selection.

The Probable Mutation Effect

In later sections we shall briefly treat the sequence of adaptive radiations which eventually prepared the way for the appearance of man. We have already stated that the major determiner of the course of organic evolution has been natural selection working on the variations supplied by genetic mutation. We have also noted that genetic drift accounts for differences which arise by chance, although it does not allow for development in any consistent direction. For many years, biologists have noted that directional changes have occurred during the course of evolution but in such a way that they could be accounted for neither by natural selection nor by genetic drift, which could not have acted consistently enough to produce the changes.

The classic example is presented by the depigmented and eyeless fishes that inhabit underground rivers and pools in caves. While it is evident that pigmentation and eyes can serve no useful purposes under such conditions, nevertheless it is difficult to think of any particular advantage in their elimination. This is an extreme case, but the fossil record abounds with examples of structures which have become reduced as a result of their ceasing to be as important to the survival of their possessors as when they were originally developed. The problem for those concerned with explaining the mechanics of evolution was to discover a means by which such changes could occur, without resorting to a Lamarckian view involving the inheritance of acquired characteristics, and without doing violence to the known facts of genetics.

In the late 1920's, when evolution began to be interpreted with the aid of the developing field of genetics, a number of scientists, such as the English statistician R. A. Fisher, realized that the vast majority of mutations are actually detrimental to their possessors. It has been estimated that only one in every 50 to 100 thousand replications of a gene will result in its failure to copy itself exactly —hence a mutation—and, out of these, less than 1 per cent will prove advantageous. No wonder, then, that evolution is a slow process.

At the same time that these facts became known, the American geneticist Sewall Wright, who developed the concept of genetic drift, also realized that the vast majority of mutations will result in physiological inactivation. Recalling that the primary role of the basic genetic material is in supervising protein synthesis, and that the vast majority of proteins are those organic catalysts called enzymes, it is not hard to visualize why most mutations should result in physiological inactivation, and how this has effected the reduction of various structures that have ceased to be of adaptive value.

Sewall Wright proposed the term "mutation pressure" to account for the accumulation of mutations which result in structural reduction, but over the years it has been assumed that this meant an unusual or abnormal *rate* of mutation. Wright's original meaning was that, by probability alone, most mutations would decrease the effectiveness of the processes which they control. This of course had nothing to do with abnormal rates at all. One of us (C. L. B.) has therefore proposed that Wright's concept be renamed the Probable Mutation Effect, which recognizes the probable result of randomly produced changes in protein (enzyme) structure.

Genetic mutations involve changes in one or more nucleotides in the triplets (codons) of which a DNA molecule is composed. Since the role of the triplet is the acquisition of an amino acid unit which is then towed to the site of protein synthesis, any such alteration will probably result in the acquisition of the wrong amino acid. This then is assembled along with the other amino acids to produce an enzyme altered at this one site. In turn, the most likely result (probability again) is that the enzyme will not work at all, or, if it does work, it does not work as well as it normally should, and the reaction of which it is a part will be only partially completed.

Organic structures are the end products of growth processes which are controlled by enzyme action, and the probable enzymatic (physiological) inactivation, which is the result of mutation, generally means that the growth process necessary to produce normal structure is not completed, i.e. structure is reduced. In a normally adapted organism, the failure of one of its normal structures to attain complete development usually means that the chances for the survival of that organism are reduced. This was what Fisher meant when he noted that most mutations are detrimental.

However, when a species enters a new ecological niche, or there is a change in the environmental pressures affecting its survival, then there are going to be certain structures which are no longer quite so important. Any chance mutation affecting such a structure will *not* be selected against. As we have seen, most chance mutations produce reductions, and the accumulation of mutations in time will result in the reduction of the structure in question.

For fishes that have inhabited a lightless environment for hundreds of thousands of years, the presence of eyes or of pigmentation is of no importance. Mutations can occur affecting eye or pigment structure without any disadvantage to the fish, and the accumulation of such mutations over the generations dooms the adaptively unimportant characters to eventual reduction. While the blind and depigmented fish are the classic and extreme example, there are many somewhat less dramatic instances which indicate that the probable mutation effect has been a minor but constant force in shaping evolutionary history. Again, our discussion of human diversity will suggest the role that this has played in the course of human evolution.

In Retrospect

The impact evolutionary thinking had upon the complacency of the nineteenth century was unsettling. Many educated people simply could not bring themselves to examine the theory of evolution dispassionately, and still more had the uncomfortable feeling that it was indecent to apply such principles in an attempt to understand the development of man. In fact, many people who accepted general evolutionary thinking did not believe that natural selection was adequate to explain the evolution of man, and among these skeptics was none other than Charles Darwin himself. During the decade following the publication of the *Origin*, he collected information relating to human diversity, and in 1871 he published *The Descent of Man, and Selection in Relation to Sex*, in which he stressed the role played by sexual selection in human evolution. This approach stresses the role played by human choice in influencing the frequency of the variants which would be transmitted. Some biologists still believe that such features as beards, fat padded mammary glands, and various remarkable facets of Hottentot anatomy, can only be explained in this way. It has been assumed that the strongest and most vigorous males would choose the most attractive females as mates and therefore assure the perpetuation of their particular traits.

While such a view was understandable in Darwin's day, enough anthropological information has accumulated since to render such interpretations quite outmoded. Today, it is evident that what constitutes "desirability" varies greatly from culture to culture. Even within a single tradition, such a behavior can scarcely be expected to remain constant over the periods of time required to affect evolutionary development. In addition, the degree to which members of nonliterate societies approach the culturally prescribed ideals of sexual attractiveness has virtually no influence on reproductive behavior. Those who are physically able, indulge in sufficient sexual activities to present all with equal opportunities for reproduction. Ability as a hunter, trapper, food and water finder is more important than features of morphology that may be regarded as sexually desirable. Finally, marriage in most nonliterate societies is not free, but rigidly determined by regulations over which the individual has no control whatever.

Certainly, throughout the greater part of human evolution, sexual selection cannot have been of any importance. Some have noted that, with the lowering of mortality during childbirth produced by modern medicine and the standardization of human ideals of "beauty" as a result of the activities of magazines, motion pictures, and television, perhaps some sort of sexual selection is in fact being practiced at the present time. With more women than men in the world, it is true that greater percentages of women remain unmarried than previously—presumably the men select the more desirable women for marriage partners. The effect of this is easily offset by the fact that the declared paragons of female pulchritude limit the actual extent of their reproductive activities to the point where the mammarian monstrosities of Hollywood fame tend to have had more husbands than children. However much they may inspire imitation by young people, their actual contribution to the future betterment of mankind is disproportionately small. Hence, "serial monogamy" or "sequential polygamy" is not without its eugenic effect.

One final point deserves mention before we leave the subject of evolutionary principles, and this concerns the sources of control over the direction of evolutionary development. Some scientists, even at this late date, are unable to believe that natural selection working on normally occurring mutations has been sufficient to produce the observed evolutionary developments. Some have resorted to an explanation called orthogenesis—straight-line evolution, or development which continues by its own momentum in a single direction without any visible cause. Occasionally a vital force is assumed, while others have tried to defend the idea of a momentum tending to continue a direction of development set in motion originally by selective forces.

These ideas deal with the unknowable, and since they rely on essentially mystical assumptions, they have been rejected by most modern students of evolution. There is overwhelming agreement that natural selection, utilizing the raw material produced by mutation, has been able to create the diversity visible in the organic world as well as the changes hinted at in the fossil record. Less agreement exists concerning the roles of the probable mutation effect and genetic drift, although it is recognized that these have been far less important than natural selection.

In summary, then, we may say that natural selection is the process of diversification of adaptations in a population, and the product of evolution is a diverse but well-adapted population. Evolution, in short, consists of the changes which occur in genotypes, and having a great store of such diverse potentials makes for evolutionary adaptiveness.

Finally, it should be said that while in theory evolution is relatively well understood, in practice there remain a great many problems awaiting the application of as yet undeveloped research techniques and the additions to our knowledge that will come from the efforts of future generations.

SUGGESTED READINGS

Darwin, C. *The Descent of Man,* 2 vols. John Murray, London, 1871.
Darwin impressively but unsuccessfully presents the evidence for evolution by sexual selection.

Dobzhansky, Th. *Genetics and the Origin of Species,* 3rd ed. Columbia University Press, New York, 1951.
The classic work on the genetic processes of evolution.

Huxley, J. *Evolution: The Modern Synthesis.* Harper & Row, New York, 1942, 1964.
The 1964 edition contains a new introduction bringing this standard

work on the evolutionary process up to date since it was first published in 1942.

Lack, D. *Darwin's Finches.* Cambridge University Press, London and New York, 1947.
A study of adaptive radiation in a small self-contained group of birds.

Mayr, E. *Systematics and the Origin of Species.* Columbia University Press, New York, 1942.
A fundamental work on the origin of species.
————. *Animal Species and Evolution.* Harvard University Press, Cambridge, 1963.
A full exposition, synthesis, summation, and critical evaluation of the present state of knowledge of the biology and genetics of animal species and their role in evolution. The chapter on man as a biological species will be of special interest to readers of the present volume.

Moody, P. A. *Introduction to Evolution,* 2nd ed. Harper & Row, New York, 1962.
One of the best all-round general introductions to the subject of organic evolution.

Simpson, G. G. *The Major Features of Evolution.* Columbia University Press, New York, 1953.
A sound and sophisticated presentation of evolutionary theory.
————. *The Meaning of Evolution.* Yale University Press, New Haven, 1949. New American Library, New York, 1951.
The best book on the subject.
————. *This View of Life.* Harcourt, Brace & World, New York, 1964.
A highly stimulating series of essays especially relating to the evolution of man.

CHAPTER THREE ❦❧ TAXONOMY AND PRIMATE CLASSIFICATION

BEFORE THE ADVENT of modern genetically based evolutionary studies, taxonomy (literally, the arrangment of names) constituted the foundation of the biological sciences. The eighteenth century systematists spent their lives devising and revising systems of names to encompass all living organisms. The most complete of these is Linnaeus' system which, with some modifications, survives to the present day. While the form remains substantially the same, the reasoning behind it has undergone change.

Prior to Darwin, taxonomy primarily served to demonstrate the order inherent in creation and was regarded as an end in itself. Today, rather than constituting a picture of the ordained and eternal, formal classification is best considered to represent a summary of evolutionary distances and relationships. Occasionally philosophers of science will attempt to equate the relationships and complexities of the physical and organic worlds with the infinite and eternal of the religious philosophers, and perhaps they have a point, for the immense but logical complexity of organic evolution as revealed by a complete taxonomy is indeed great and wonderful. In this sense, perhaps, there is still some value in regarding classification as being partially justified as an end in itself.

Our primary concern, however, is with the practical results of taxonomy and with the problems involved in constructing an adequate classification. Except at the species level, the units and levels of classification are purely arbitrary and primarily reflect the accumulated opinions of ten generations of classifiers. Even at the species level there are problems which result in the continuous use of compromise and expediency. For example, the continuous evolution of a single line produces an accumulation of changes in time which demands adjustment of the specific designation, but at precisely which point the change in name should go into effect is an unanswerable question. The same sort of question occurs where geographic isolation separates members of an original species. In time, differences in selective pressures and the accidents of genetic drift would change them enough to prevent the possibility of interbreeding, but such a point would be reached after a full continuum of reducing interfertility, and the actual instant when species differentiation occurs is simply an arbitrary decision made by a taxonomist.

With these difficulties in mind, the taxonomic unit species is still a basic and useful concept and the definition which we shall use is this:

> A *species is composed of all those organisms which interbreed to produce viable fertile offspring.*

Some authors prefer the stipulation that the organisms "regularly interbreed" indicating that those populations which experiments show are interfertile but which are geographically isolated in nature should not be included in the same species. For evolutionary purposes it is true that in such a case the initial step toward speciation has occurred. On the other hand, certain authors feel that "those organisms which are capable of interbreeding . . ." should define species, since this refers to anatomical and physiological fact. In our definition, we have attempted to avoid these two extremes by being deliberately vague and using a phrase which could be interpreted either way. These restrictions only allow a limited amount of quibbling and furnish us with a basic evolutionary unit.

The larger and more inclusive divisions are compounded of closely related clusters of the immediately lower divisions, but no criteria have been offered for their exact definition. The standard list of major taxonomic categories with the appropriate name for the placement of man is as follows:

Kingdom	*Animalia*
Phylum	*Chordata*
Class	*Mammalia*
Order	*Primates*
Family	*Hominidae*
Genus	*Homo*
species	*sapiens*

Most of these categories can be further subdivided, but, since our present concern is focused on man and his nearest relatives, we shall only deal with the more important subdivisions of the Order Primates. Most authorities agree in splitting the Order into two suborders, although their exact names occasion some disagreement. The classification we are using is based on that proposed by Professor G. G. Simpson.

The two suborders are *Prosimii* and *Anthropoidea*. The Prosimians include the tree shrews, lorises, lemurs, and tarsiers. *Anthropoidea* includes monkeys, apes, and man. The differences between the varieties of Primates are so numerous that it is reasonable to ask what it is that defines the Primates as an Order. Until recently, taxonomists were inclined to require certain basic characteristics of any organism if it were to warrant inclusion within a particular category. This procedure was a carryover from pre-Darwinian thinking and was based upon the idea of fixed, eternal, and preordained distinctions. If it were possible to make taxonomic judgments on the basis of such rigid requirements, it would make matters easier for the student as well as for the professional scientist, but, unfortunately, there are always exceptions to any rigid scheme, and among the diverse and generalized members of the Order Primates there are sufficient exceptions so that no rigidly defined lists of traits are adequate to define them.

A solution to this dilemma has been offered by the English anatomist and primatologist Sir Wilfrid E. Le Gros Clark, who distinguishes the Primates from the other Orders of Mammals on the basis of a number of evolutionary trends. Our discussion is largely based on that of Professor Le Gros Clark.

The tendencies which characterize the Order Primates involve two areas of the overall anatomy, the locomotor apparatus and the head, and manifestations of the tendencies listed below in both of these areas signifies that the possessors are Primates.

I. Limb structure characterized by:
   A. Retention of generalized or primitive mammalian organization
      1. retention of a well-developed clavicle (collarbone) allowing great mobility of the pectoral appendages (arms).
      2. retention of the primitive vertebrate pentadactyl (five-fingered) appendages.
   B. Emphasis on grasping ability
      1. enhanced mobility of all the digits, but especially of the thumb and big toe.
      2. presence of nails, rather than claws, indicating the development of pads of well-endowed tactile sensory tissue at the ends of the digits.
II. Cranial organs characterized by:
   A. Development of the powers of vision
      1. varying degrees of binocular ability.
   B. Expansion of the choice-making organ—the brain, especially in the cerebral cortex
   C. Reduction of the muzzle
      1. reduction in importance of the sense of smell and its related organs.
      2. reduction in the dentition coincident with its reduced importance as a defensive and manipulative organ. This involves reduction in the primitive mammalian number of teeth and simplification of crown cusp patterns.

The significance of these tendencies will be discussed later when we deal with the evolution of the Primates as seen in the interpretation of the fossil record. At the moment, it is sufficient to note that these are all related to the fact that, early in the age of mammals, the Primates adapted to an arboreal (tree-living) ecological niche.

It is not our intention to discuss the living members of the Primates in any kind of detail, however fascinating they may be, however, in order to convey some idea of the relationships, forms, and habitats of the various Primates, a brief consideration of the Superfamilies will follow.

Order   *Primates*
   Suborder   *Prosimii*
      Infraorder   *Lemuriformes*
         Superfamily   *Tupaioidea*
                     Lemuroidea
                     Daubentonioidea
      Infraorder   *Lorisiformes*
      Infraorder   *Tarsiiformes*
   Suborder   *Anthropoidea*
      Infraorder   *Platyrrhini*
         Superfamily   *Ceboidea*
      Infraorder   *Catarrhini*
         Superfamily   *Cercopithecoidea*
                     Hominoidea

Prosimii

TUPAIOIDEA. This Superfamily today occupies an equivocal position. Following a long taxonomic sojourn among the insectivores, it was promoted to the status of the most primitive of the Primates. This new situation has met with serious criticism from many authorities. Among the tree shrews, to give the tupaiids their common name, placentation is unlike that in any Primate, and there are fundamental differences in ankle and wrist bones, the cartilaginous skull, musculature, viscera, and many other features. It has been suggested, therefore, that the tupaiids be removed from the Order Primates and placed with the lepticid-like insectivores. But if that is done it will not alter the fact, upon which all authorities agree, that the tupaiids constitute the closest relatives of the Primates.

Several forms of tree shrew are known, ranging from India east and south through Southeast Asia and the Indonesian Archipelago. They are small scurrying creatures, living on a variety of insects,

FIGURE 18. Tree shrew, *Urogale everetti*, Philippines. (Courtesy of Dr. Ralph Buschbaum.)

FIGURE 19. Lemur. Brown Lemur (*Lemur fulvus*). (Courtesy of the Zoological Society of Philadelphia.)

although they do eat some fruits and seeds and occasional small mammals, mice for instance. They tend to live in bushes and on the lower branches of trees rather than in the arboreal niche proper.

Tree shrews possess claws on *all* digits, unlike Primates who generally possess flattened nails on their digits. Whatever taxonomic category we choose to view them from, the tree shrews constitute a remarkable living example of a form transitional between the Primates and the primitive, generalized, mammalian stock which the Order Insectivora represents. The tree shrews afford us a clue to the nature of the first step away from the basic mammalian stem toward the evolution of the higher Primates and ultimately man himself.

LEMUROIDEA. The lemurs proper exist only on the island of Madagascar and neighboring smaller islands off the east coast of Africa. There they have been isolated for more than half of the age of mammals, and in the absence of competition from both carnivores and higher, more efficient Primates, they have undergone a minor adaptive radiation of their own. Except for the tree shrews, these are the most primitive of living Primates.

The lemurs have monkey-like limbs with flattened nails on their digits—all except the second toe which preserves a convenient claw for scratching purposes. The cranial development, however, represents a compromise. The brain is larger than that of other mammals of comparable size, but it is not up to monkey standards. The reduction of the snout has not proceeded to the degree it has in monkeys, and with the bare patch of moist skin— the rhinarium—the sense of smell is retained to a greater extent. Sensory whiskers remain on the muzzle, over the eyes, and on the wrists indicating that the sensory equipment of the primitive terrestrial mammal persists. The lemurs also retain the ability to move the ears toward sources of sound, an ability long since lost by higher Primates in spite of the fact that it is retained by some humans who can manage to "wiggle their ears."

DAUBENTONIOIDEA. This Superfamily is represented by only a single species, the curious and specialized aye-aye. Unimportant for building a systematic picture of Primate evolution, it is never-

FIGURE 20. Aye-Aye (*Daubentonia madagascariensis*), an aberrant primate from Madagascar. (Courtesy of the Zoological Society of London.)

theless a curious and interesting creature. It represents, in fact, a part of the lemur adaptive radiation of Madagascar, where the isolation of this refuge area allowed creatures to survive which would long since have been eliminated by natural selection had they been faced with competition from the main stream of mammalian development. Other environmental refuge areas—the Galápagos Islands with their birds and reptiles and Australia with its marsupials—have harbored similar evolutionary curiosities.

The Madagascar aye-aye has diverged to such an extent from the rest of lemur evolution that at one time it was even classed as a rodent. Now it is recognized as a lemur but belonging in a separate Superfamily of its own. It has enlarged rodent-like incisors while the rest of the dentition is greatly reduced, claws on all the digits except the thumb, and a greatly elongated third finger of the hand. This latter is related to its dietary specialization. Its main item of food is a wood-boring grub which it locates in branches by the sound. Having located a grub burrow, the aye-aye gnaws an opening with its specialized incisors and then inserts the long third finger like a flexible wire probe. With this it impales the grub, extracts it, and then pops it into its mouth—lunch. Not really an important Primate, but an interesting one.

LORISIFORMES. Lorises are the mainland equivalents of the lemurs. Anatomists have listed enough distinctions between

FIGURE 21. Loris. The potto (*Perodicticus potto*). (Courtesy of the Zoological Society of Philadelphia.)

lemurs and lorises to separate them into different Infraorders, but because of the similarity in their sensory and motor equipment, they occupy an ecological niche similar to that of the Madagascar lemurs. They range throughout the bush and forest parts of Africa, India, and Southeast Asia, but since these areas are also the locations of the more successful Anthropoidea, the restrictions on loris form and activity have been much more stringent. Among other things, most lorises have sought refuge in nocturnal activities. Admittedly some true lemurs are nocturnal, but the diurnal arboreal ecological niche on Madagascar is also occupied by lemurs. On the mainland, however, competition from the monkeys means that most Prosimians are nocturnal or semi-nocturnal (twilight operators).

TARSIOIDEA. The entire Infraorder Tarsiiformes with its one Superfamily is represented by the single Genus *Tarsius*. The Tarsiers display a unique combination of primitive and advanced features which has given taxonomists trouble for years. A case could be made for regarding them as the most primitive of the

FIGURE 22. Philippine tarsier (*Tarsius syrichta*). (Courtesy of the Zoological Society of Philadelphia.)

Suborder Anthropoidea, as deserving of a special Suborder of their own, or, as is generally felt, the most advanced of the Prosimians.

The center of this taxonomic wrangle is a creature "the size of a small kitten" which inhabits parts of the Indonesian Archipelago, Borneo, and the Philippines. Its name, tarsier, refers to the elongation of the tarsal portion of the foot. This provides the added leverage which allows the little tarsier to make spectacular leaps more than four feet straight up—a remarkable performance for such a small animal. This specialization along with the specialization of the eyes for nocturnal activities and modifications in the dentition prevents the living tarsier from being a good representative of a transition between the Prosimians and the Anthropoidea although it approaches more closely to filling this role than any other living Primate.

Anthropoidea

CEBOIDEA. This is the only Superfamily in the Infraorder Platyrrhini, the New World monkeys that range from southern Mexico down into the tropical parts of South America. Until the arrival of the American Indians beginning a few tens of thousands of years ago, the only Primates in the Western Hemisphere belonged to the Superfamily Ceboidea. The best indications point to a separation from the Primates of the Old World of more than fifty million years. During that time, the New World monkeys have undergone an adaptive radiation which in many ways parallels that of Primates in the Old World.

Two Families are encompassed by the Ceboidea, the Callithricidae and the Cebidae. The Callithricidae include the marmosets: scurrying, scampering, squirrel-like creatures which functionally might be called the Prosimians of the New World. The Family Cebidae is composed of the New World monkeys proper, and includes the only monkeys in the world which can actually hang by their tails. Not even all of the Cebidae have prehensile tails, and even in the case of *Cebus* itself, the capuchin or organ grinder's monkey, (the popular name for the best known of the Cebidae) the tail is not as well developed a weight-supporting organ as it is in the howler monkey or in the woolly and the spider monkeys.

The howler monkey is aptly named, for the enlarged hyoid bone in the throat of both sexes serves as a vocal resonating chamber, and the creature can produce a simply phenomenal amount of noise—audible for several miles on a quiet day. However, from the point of view of the student of primate evolution, the most interesting of the New World monkeys is the spider monkey. Not only does it possess the most thoroughly prehensile tail of any primate, but, it also is the only monkey in either hemisphere which makes more than occasional use of the mode of progression characteristic of the apes — brachiation. As a consequence of this adaptation there has been some selection for

FIGURE 23. Marmoset. Female (front) and male (back) golden marmosets (*Leontocebus rosalia*).

FIGURE 24. Cebus. White-throated capuchin monkey (*Cebus capucinus*). (Both photos courtesy of the Zoological Society of Philadelphia.)

modifications of the pelvis, chest, shoulders, arms, and hands, which show a striking degree of convergence toward the form visible in the same parts of the anatomy of the apes, particularly the gibbon, which, as the smallest of the apes, is not much bigger

FIGURE 25. Spider monkey. Geoffroy's spider monkey (*Ateles geoffroyi*). Note the enormously developed prehensile tail, and the absence of a thumb. (Courtesy of the Zoological Society of Philadelphia.)

than the spider monkey. The spider monkey is the only New World monkey in which the thumbs have been reduced often to a mere tubercle. While the spider monkey, as an interesting example of evolutionary convergence, comes closest to the structure of the anthropoid apes of any of the New World monkeys, the possession of a tail, so useful that it is practically a fifth hand, would prevent one from ever confusing a spider monkey with a genuine ape.

CERCOPITHECOIDEA. The Infraorder Catarrhini includes monkeys, apes, and man, and the Superfamily Cercopithecoidea is its monkey division. The single Family Cercopithecidae includes all the Old World monkeys. This in turn is further subdivided into the Subfamilies Cercopithecinae and Colobinae each of which

FIGURE 26. Baboon. The mandrill (*Mandrillus sphinx*). (Courtesy of the Zoological Society of Philadelphia.)

includes many Genera. The Cercopithecinae embraces the manga-beys, guenons, guerezas, baboons, and macaques, i.e. all the monkeys one generally associates with the Old World and particularly with Africa. Many, such as macaques and baboons, are partly or wholly terrestrial, and as a consequence, tend to have longer muzzles and larger canine teeth than New World monkeys. Some of the baboons get to be quite formidable in size and, the males particularly, are equipped with large canine teeth—necessary defensive equipment for a relatively slow-running quadruped only

FIGURE 27. Green monkey. (*Cercopithecus aethiops sabaeus*). (Courtesy of the Zoological Society of Philadelphia.)

[76]

secondarily adapted to terrestrial living. Members of the Sub-family Cercopithecinae extend as far south and east as the Celebes and as far north and east as Japan, but they are most numerous in Africa.

The Subfamily Colobinae includes the leaf-eating monkeys, the langurs and the proboscis monkey, and is concentrated in Southeast Asia and India, although a few are found in Africa. They are characterized by the possession of complex sacculated stomachs which enable them to derive adequate nourishment from their bulky but relatively un-nutritious diet of leaves and shoots (the nuts, fruits, berries, insects, eggs, etc., of the cercopithecine diet have relatively much higher nutritive values). The Colobinae are strictly arboreal, and, with their gastric specialization, are farther from the evolutionary line which led to the great apes and man than are the other Old World monkeys.

[77]

HOMINOIDEA. Anthropoid apes and man.

Finally we reach the Superfamily to which we ourselves belong, and since it is of greater concern to us, it is worth giving a more complete classification of it and dwelling for a while on each of its genera.

Superfamily   *Hominoidea*
  Family   *Pongidae*
    Subfamily   *Hylobatinae*
      Genus   *Hylobates*, the gibbon
              Symphalangus, the siamang
    Subfamily   *Ponginae*
      Genus   *Pongo*, the orang-utan
              Pan, the chimpanzee
              Gorilla, the gorilla
  Family   *Hominidae*
    Genus   *Homo*, man

All the members of this Superfamily, unlike any other Primates, are utterly devoid of external tails; all are now or show clear evidence that their ancestors were brachiators, and, as such, show various degrees of structural adaptation to an erect posture; all have the same numbers of incisors, canines, premolars and molars, and have the same cusp patterns on the molars and second premolars; and all show varying degrees of cerebral expansion when compared with the other Primates.

HYLOBATES AND SYMPHALANGUS. The siamang is actually just an enlarged version of the gibbon inhabiting Java and Sumatra. The siamang inhabits Sumatra and the mountains of Selangor State in the Malay Peninsula. But since it is not otherwise notable, it will not be treated separately. The gibbons are the most numerous of the anthropoid apes as well as being the most spectacular arboreal acrobats. Exclusively tree-living, they owe at least a part of their acrobatic ability to the fact that they are by far and away the smallest of the anthropoid apes. While adult stature nearly reaches three feet, body weight ranges from not quite fifteen pounds down to well under ten pounds. Obviously the build is exceedingly slender, with the limbs—especially the arms—being enormously elongated in proportion to the general bulk. With such

FIGURE 29. Gibbon. White-handed gibbon (*Hylobates lar*) with young. (Courtesy of the Zoological Society of Philadelphia.)

anatomical equipment, the gibbons are brachiators without peer, flourishing in the forests of Southeast Asia and Indonesia and ranging all the way from sea level up to the frost line in the foothills of the Himalayas.

The brachiating specialization of the gibbon has clearly gone beyond the point reached by man's own remote brachiating ancestor. In the gibbon, the fingers are so elongated that they can only be opposed to the thumb by bending them sharply toward the palm, and, even then, the opposition is weak and ineffective. Evidently to gain such superb powers of locomotion, they have sacrificed a considerable amount of manipulative ability.

PONGO. The orang-utan is the larger of the two Asiatic anthropoid apes and, like the gibbon, is strictly arboreal, in contrast to the two African apes which are largely terrestrial. Today the orang is restricted to the swampy forests of western Borneo and the very northwestern tip of Sumatra, the same species being found in the two areas despite their separation. Extensive fossil remains show that, in the recent past, the orang was common throughout Borneo, Java, Sumatra, and mainland Southeast Asia as far north as China.

It seems likely that its present restricted habitat is at least partially due to competition from the most formidable Primate of

[79]

FIGURE 30. Two immature Sumatran orang-utans (*Pongo pygmaeus*). (Courtesy of the Philadelphia Zoological Society.)

them all, man himself. In the recent past, man has spread and multiplied in Southeast Asia and Indonesia as a result of the utilization of controlled food resources, i.e., agriculture. Even the most primitive slash-and-burn mobile cultivators had a major impact on the extent of fully developed tropical rain forest. With the disappearance of the rain forest, the orang disappeared also. Gibbons, being small and light, are not so seriously affected by the fact that cut and burned rain forest is replaced by brush and bamboo, but one need only make an attempt to imagine several hundred pounds of orang-utan struggling to brachiate in a bamboo thicket and the present limitations of the area inhabited become understandable.

The orang is more of an enigma than any of the other anthropoid apes since less is known about its life in the wild. Physically the male orang stands somewhat less than five feet in height and weighs about 165 pounds, although large males are over five feet and two hundred pounds, making them second in size only to the gorilla. Females, on the other hand, average only half the bulk of the males, being under ninety pounds. The arms are enormously long—over eight feet in span for a large male—and, in conjunction

FIGURE 31. Orang-utan. Sumatran orang-utan (*Pongo pygmaeus*) with young. (Courtesy of the Zoological Society of Philadelphia.)

with their thorough adaptation as arboreal brachiators the bones of both the hands and the feet are curved into permanent hooks. However excellent this may be for supporting bulky bodies with a minimum of muscular effort, it severely limits manipulative ability. These facts and many others are known about orangs, but we have relatively little information about their mode of living in the wild. This is partly due to their solitary habits, but mostly because the remaining areas inhabited make observation difficult. The creatures live hidden in the leafy parts of big trees far above the forest floor, and, as if that did not make things difficult enough, for part of the year the forest floor is neck deep in water so that a boat would be necessary. Hence virtually nothing is known of the family life and social habits of the orang, and, with the tremendous current expansion of the human population in Southeast Asia, it is apparent that serious efforts must be made to secure this information before it is too late.

PAN. Of all the anthropoid apes, the African chimpanzee is the best known, although most of this knowledge was based on chimps in captivity, and only recently, as the outcome of a prolonged and successful attempt to study them in their African habitat, has reliable information been obtained concerning their ways of life under natural conditions. Male chimpanzees weigh in the neighborhood of 110, and females just under 90 pounds on the average, with a wide range of fluctuations. In the past, this wide range of size, shape, and color led to the creation of several species of chimpanzees from what represented no more than individual differences within the normal range of variation.

Although the differences of opinion are still far from being settled, many authorities suspect that there are only two species of chimpanzee, a full-sized one ranging from Gambia at the very westernmost tip of Africa throughout the forested areas of West Africa and the Congo drainage basin, and a pygmy chimpanzee just south of the great bend of the Congo river itself. It is not yet certain, however, whether the pygmy chimpanzee is a genuine separate species, or whether it is simply the small end of a line of normal chimpanzee variation. If the latter is found to be the case, there would be but one species of chimpanzee throughout the

FIGURE 32. Chimpanzee
(*Pan troglodytes*). (Courtesy of the New York Zoological Society.)

whole range, an area larger in extent than the area inhabited by any other anthropoid ape.

In contrast with the Asiatic anthropoid apes which are exclusively arboreal in habitat and specialization, the African apes are predominantly terrestrial. This is particularly true of the gorilla which, because of its size, is almost completely terrestrial, but even the smaller chimpanzee spends some two-thirds of its life on the ground. In arm, shoulder, and trunk structure, both apes are classed as brachiators despite the predominance of terrestrial quadrupedalism as a means of locomotion. In their arboreal activities, the chimpanzees (and the gorillas when young) behave as their structure would indicate and brachiate as expected. While the immediate fossil precursors of gorillas and chimpanzees are not known, it is believed by most investigators that they must have been more thoroughly arboreal than either is today, and that they utilized brachiation as their mode of progression, otherwise the development of the brachiating build in the modern representatives could not be explained.

The chimpanzee possesses a particular fascination for layman and scientist alike, representing a form more nearly resembling man's probable prehuman ancestor than any other living Primate. Although it is less highly specialized either for arboreal living, as are the Asiatic anthropoids, or secondarily for terrestrial quadrupedalism, as are the gorillas, yet the chimpanzee may have gone just a little farther in the brachiating direction than man's prehuman ancestors. The chimpanzee hand is long and strong, but the thumb is short, opposition to the fingers is awkward, and the muscular definition which would allow fine finger movements is sacrificed in favor of the ability to flex the fingers all together as a powerful weight-supporting hook.

The chimpanzee, however, should not be regarded as a creature doomed by limiting specializations. Though it possesses less manual dexterity than many monkeys, its manipulative ability is nevertheless greater than that of any other ape and its ingenuity exceeds that of any Primate with the exception of man. Recent prolonged field observation by Miss Jane Goodall in Tanganyika has greatly increased our knowledge of chimpanzees behavior in their natural habitat. Miss Goodall has recorded that they use an astonishing variety of food sources, even indulging in a little hunting when the opportunity arises.

Most remarkable of all is the fact that chimpanzees actually modify natural objects to be used as tools. A slender twig or stalk of grass is carefully stripped of projections, moistened with the lips, carefully inserted into the middle of a termite's nest, then withdrawn; the attached termites are licked off and eaten with relish, providing a good source of protein for the chimpanzee. Knowledge of this procedure obviously is not gained through in-

FIGURE 33. Lowland young gorillas (*Gorilla gorilla gorilla*). Male (left), female (right). (Courtesy of the Zoological Society of Philadelphia.)

herited instinct, but must be learned by imitation. Here, then, is an activity which must have been discovered in some previous generation and which has become part of a transmitted tradition. Such behavior is cultural behavior, and it follows that chimpanzees possess the rudiments of culture. In contrast to man, however, culture is not the *primary* adaptation of the chimpanzee. Man deprived of his culture is totally helpless, while the cultureless chimpanzee would still have a better than even chance for survival.

GORILLA. It may appear somewhat surprising, but the very existence of the gorilla was not suspected until almost the midpoint of the nineteenth century. Africa was among the last of the world's great land masses to be explored; hence, despite the gorilla's great bulk, its habitat in the more remote and inaccessible parts of the continent guaranteed a seclusion from all but the relentless push of twentieth-century *Homo sapiens*.

The appearance of the gorilla—large and black and hairy— presented a perfect image upon which the Victorians could project and thus "substantiate" the alleged inherent beastliness of man himself, in which they so perfervidly believed. As such, the poor gorilla was invested with the attributes of ferocity which were assumed to belong to this repressed animal nature, and all kinds of bizarre and frequently unsavory legends were created to fit the gorilloid image. Recent detailed and excellent field study has shown that the actual facts of gorilla behavior are about as far removed from the lurid fancies of the popular accounts as it is possible to be. In reality, the gorilla is so involved in the process of acquiring enough of the low-nutritive-value food of its characteristic diet to nourish its vast bulk that it has little time for the varied and interesting activities which account for so much of the fascination of chimpanzee behavior. In fact, gorillas tend to be incurious, unimaginative, peaceful, and dull.

The gorillas of Africa are found in two regions separated by some 650 miles and are considered to belong to corresponding subspecies. The western or lowland gorilla, occurring in the forests of the Cameroons and Gabon in the north and westernmost parts of the Congo basin, was the first to be discovered. As the type species and subspecies of the Genus *Gorilla*, the full formal designation is *Gorilla gorilla gorilla*. Early in the twentieth century, the mountain gorilla was recognized as being distinct and has been named *Gorilla gorilla beringei*. This population inhabits a narrow area at an elevation of over ten thousand feet in the cold damp forests of the mountains at the very eastern edge of the Congo basin.

Gorillas, as the largest living Primates, are bulky creatures, although the real massiveness is predominantly a property of the males. Female gorillas tip the scales somewhere in the neighborhood of two hundred pounds, but males average twice that size. Normal male stature is somewhere between five and six feet with large males occasionally reaching well over six feet and a weight of over five hundred pounds. In captivity some gorillas have become quite obese and have weighed well over six hundred pounds.

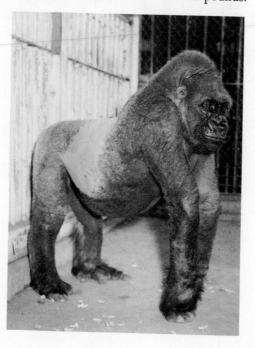

FIGURE 34. Adult male lowland gorilla (*Gorilla gorilla gorilla*). (Courtesy of the Zoological Society of Philadelphia.)

TABLE 1
CLASSIFICATION OF THE LIVING PRIMATES

Order	Suborder	Infraorder	Superfamily	Family	Subfamily	Genus	Common Name
Prosimii	Prosimii	Lemuriformes	Lemuroidea	Lemuridae	Lemurinae	Lemur	Common Lemur
						Hapalemur	Gentle Lemur
						Lepilemur	Sportive Lemur
					Cheirogaleinae	Cheirogaleus	Mouse Lemur
						Microcebus	Dwarf Lemur
						Phaner	Fork-Crowned Dwarf Lemur
				Indridae		Indri	Indris
						Lichanotus	Avahi
						Propithecus	Sifaka
			Daubentonioidea	Daubentoniidae		Daubentonia	Aye-Aye
		Lorisiformes	Lorisoidea	Lorisidae		Loris	Slender Loris
						Nycticebus	Slow Loris
						Arctocebus	Angwantibo
						Perodicticus	Potto
				Galagidae	Galaginae	Galago	Bush Baby
						Euoticus	Needle-Clawed Bush Baby
		Tarsiiformes	Tarsioidea	Tarsiidae		Tarsius	Tarsier
				Callithricidae	Callithricinae	Callithrix	Plumed Marmoset
						Leontocebus	Tamarin
						Cebuella	Pygmy Marmoset
						Mico	Naked-Eared Marmoset
						Marikina	Bald-Headed Tamarin
						Tamarin	Black-Faced Tamarin
						Oedipomidas	Pinché
					Callimiconinae	Callimico	Goeldi's Marmoset
					Aotinae	Aotes	Douroucouli
						Callicebus	Titi

Primates	Anthropoidea						
		Platyrrhini	Ceboidea	Cebidae	Pithecinae	*Pithecia*	Saki
						Chiropotes	Saki
						Cacajao	Uakari
					Alouattinae	*Alouatta*	Howler
					Cebinae	*Cebus*	Capuchin
						Saimiri	Squirrel Monkey
					Atelinae	*Ateles*	Spider Monkey
						Brachyteles	Woolly Spider Monkey
						Lagothrix	Woolly Monkey
		Catarrhini	Cercopithecoidea	Cercopithecidae	Cercopithecinae	*Macaca*	Macaque
						Cynopithecus	Black Ape
						Cercocebus	Mangabey
						Papio	Baboon, Drill
						Theropithecus	Gelada
						Cercopithecus	Guenon
						Erythrocebus	Patas Monkey
						Mandrillus	Mandrill, Drill
					Colobinae	*Presbytis*	Common Langur
						Pygathrix	Douc Langur
						Rhinopithecus	Snub-Nosed Langur
						Simias	Pagi Island Langur
						Nasalis	Proboscis Monkey
						Colobus	Guereza
			Hominoidea	Hylobatidae	Hylobatinae	*Hylobates*	Gibbon
						Symphalangus	Siamang
				Pongidae	Ponginae	*Pongo*	Orang-utan
						Pan	Chimpanzee
						Gorilla	Gorilla
				Hominidae		*Homo*	Man

While they are equipped with a strength to match their bulk, it is obvious that a quarter-ton of gorilla is going to think twice before attempting to brachiate carelessly from tree to tree. Simply finding branches or even trees to support so much weight requires careful selection. Young gorillas, and to a lesser extent grown females, do utilize trees and construct their nighttime sleeping nests in them, but the adult males generally remain on the ground, sleeping at the bases of the trees in the branches of which are the nests of the younger and smaller animals. As with the chimpanzee, the chief natural enemy, apart from parasites and infections, is the leopard. The size and strength of the male as well as the formidable canine teeth are useful in defending gorilla groups, since even these imposing animals are not immune from leopard predation.

In terrestrial Primates generally the male is much larger than the female and equipped with larger canine teeth, whereas in the more arboreal Primates the sexes tend to be much more equal in size. In the gibbon for instance, there is scarcely any size difference, although the size difference—sexual dimorphism—of the orang does not fit this generalization. This is just one more enigma clouded by our lack of knowledge concerning the life way of the orang in the wild.

As a terrestrial animal of respectable bulk, the problem of weight support has led to some interesting adaptations in the gorilla. Particularly in the mountain gorilla which is the less arboreal of the two subspecies, the foot has been modified to a remarkable extent in the human direction. The big toe has greatly reduced powers of opposition, the other toes are much reduced, there is something of a heel, and the sole is supported by dense fibrous tissue in a marked convergence toward the human condition. The mountain gorilla foot more closely resembles a human foot than it does the foot of any other Primate including the chimpanzee, which is more closely related to the gorilla than is any other Primate.

But the gorilla is a quadruped, and the hand, too, has been modified for weight support. The short forearm flexor tendons, remnants of the gorilla's brachiating past, prevent the hand from

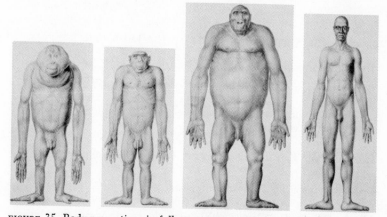

FIGURE 35. Body proportions in fully-grown apes and man. From left to right: orang-utan, chimpanzee, mountain gorilla, and man. (Courtesy of Dr. A. H. Schultz.)

being extended palm down on the ground. The weight-supporting part of this hand-hook, then, becomes the knuckles as is also the case in the chimpanzee. Strengthening for this weight-bearing role has necessarily had to proceed further in the gorilla than in the chimpanzee with the result that manipulative ability is still further reduced.

Impressive as the gorilla is, it is clear that man's precursors could not have descended from a line in which size had developed to such a degree. The gorilla's bulk is a key to its safety as a terrestrial vegetarian, but it has necessitated weight-supporting changes which effectively eliminate the possibility that the descendants of such a creature could ever become a man. We see, then, that the Primates constitute an Order characterized by great variability, the earliest members of which are of considerable antiquity. More than six hundred species of the Order have been described, and it is of more than passing interest to note that this speciation has occurred largely among the non-hominoid Primates, the prosimii and the New and Old World monkeys. The great apes have tended toward a comparative conservatism in virtually every way.

SUGGESTED READINGS

Buettner-Janusch, J. (editor). *Evolutionary and Genetic Biology of the Primates*, 2 vols. Academic Press, New York and London, 1963/64.
A valuable survey of contemporary research on the Primates written by specialists in each field.

Calman, W. T. *The Classification of Animals.* John Wiley, New York, 1949.
A brief introduction to zoological taxonomy.

Clark, W. E. Le Gros. *The Antecedents of Man.* Quadrangle Books, Chicago, 1960.
An introduction to the evolution of the Primates.

DeVore, I. (editor). *Primate Behavior.* Holt, Rinehart & Winston, New York, 1965.
An invaluable source-book reporting the field studies on the behavior of monkeys and apes.

Hooton, E. *Man's Poor Relations.* Doubleday, New York, 1942.
An informative account of the Primates.

Mayr, E., E. G. Linsley, and R. L. Usinger. *Methods and Principles of Systematic Zoology.* McGraw-Hill, New York, 1953.
A standard text on taxonomy.

Simpson, G. G. *Principles of Animal Taxonomy.* Columbia University Press, New York, 1961.
By a master of the subject.

Washburn, S. L. (editor). *Classification and Human Evolution.* Aldine Publishing Co., Chicago, 1963.
A most valuable series of contributions, by different specialists, relating to the classification of the *Hominoidea.*

The Fossil
Record

CHAPTER FOUR ❦ DATING
PROBLEMS AND THE CENOZOIC
GEOLOGICAL SEQUENCE

B EFORE WE CAN DEAL with ancient man himself and with his
precursors, some kind of perspective is necessary concerning
the dimensions of geological time and the age of life on earth.
During the height of the controversy which attended the advent
of evolutionary thought, the eminent British physicist Lord Kelvin
attempted to establish the age of the earth by mathematical
projections based on rates of heat loss. While Kelvin was not in-
sistent on a precision of more than within several tens of millions
of years, by the end of the nineteenth century he was confident
that the correct figure was probably nearer twenty than forty
million. Contrast this with our realization today that the detailed
history of life on earth as revealed in the fossil record is more
than twenty-five times as long, and with our suspicion that the
age of the earth itself may be on the order of 250 times as long as
Kelvin postulated.

Our present estimates, however, are based on time determinations made with the aid of a knowledge of the phenomena of
radioactivity and their significance. The existence of radioactivity

was not even suspected until very near the end of the nineteenth century, so for a period of about fifty years there was a considerable gap between earth age estimates made by geologists and those made by physicists. Within the time span allowed by Kelvin, Darwinian biologists could not construct a picture of organic evolution any more than could geologists picture the building of contemporary physiography by means of observed rates of erosion and deposition.

The twentieth century discovery that nuclear reaction produced the heat generated by the sun eliminated the whole theoretical basis for the time estimates made by Kelvin and his followers and showed that while his mathematics, which had caused so much despair among the Darwinians, were perfectly correct, the assumptions on which they were based were untenable. As it turned out, the geologists had been much more nearly correct in their appraisals, although the sedimentation rates on which their estimates were based could not be subjected to any degree of mathematical precision or elegance and were necessarily somewhat crude. While Kelvin's specific assumptions had been wrong, his realization that accurate age estimates could only be based on quantitative treatment of the properties of the basic materials of which the universe is constructed was quite correct. It is to the continuing efforts of physicists in attempting to refine the bases for such quantitative treatment that we owe our present knowledge of the age of the universe, of the duration of life on earth, and of the antiquity of man.

The investigation of the characteristics of radioactivity has had an explosive impact upon the life of the twentieth century. Rather paradoxically the technology which has given us a more or less accurate idea of how long we have been in existence also has moments when it threatens to put a term to that existence. At the moment we are concerned with those properties of matter which enable us to measure time.

In all creation, among the stablest things known are the various rates of decay of radioactive elements; while radioactive elements have been called "unstable," the *rate* of their instability is quite constant, and eventually this decay stops when the radioactive element is completely transformed into a stable element and all further change ceases. With decay proceeding at an unvarying rate, the stable end-product accumulates in proportion to the amount of the radioactive substance and the length of time during which the process has been going on. If nothing has artificially occurred to upset the quantities of substances present, the ratio between the remaining radioactive element and its stable end-product should be directly related to time. In practice there are several limitations, for instance, the half-life (the amount of time it takes any given quantity of a radioactive element to decay to half what it was) of various radioactive elements varies all the way from a few seconds up to billions of years. Too short or too long a half-life means that the accurate measurement of the ratio of unstable to stable elements built up during the period of interest to geologists and prehistorians will be difficult or impossible to compute. Furthermore, either one or both elements may be subject to removal or addition by the action of weathering or chemical reaction, aside from the fact that most radioactive elements are so rare as to be virtually useless for dating purposes.

Despite all these difficulties, there are a few radioactive elements that have been successfully used, and it is with the aid of these that our entire picture of the absolute age of the various strata of the earth has been constructed. Uranium 238, with a half-life of 4.51 billion years, is one of the most useful of these. One of the stable elements into which uranium is transformed is lead, and by measuring the uranium to lead proportion in an unweathered igneous rock, the geophysicist can arrive at an accurate figure for the amount of time which has elapsed since the uranium-containing mineral within the rock crystallized. The rate of decay of uranium is so slow, however, that not enough of it is transformed to yield accurate measurements for any time period of less than several million years. Therefore, however useful uranium and thorium determinations may be for determining the age of the various earlier epochs of the Cenozoic or the periods of the Paleozoic and Mesozoic, they are of no help at all in attempting to date events within the last two million years. For the student of human evolution this is rather a pity since it is within this time span that man's evolution has occurred.

For events within the last fifty or sixty thousand years, the use of radioactive carbon, C14, has proven most successful, but for anything much older, this is of no use since its half-life is so short (5,730 ± 40 years) that very little is left after this much time, and accurate measurements are not possible. But for determining the dates of the late Neanderthals and the development of modern man, C14 has been invaluable. At the moment, techniques involving the use of Potassium 40 have yielded some dates for the Middle and lower Pleistocene and further refinements are eagerly awaited since this is the time span during which many of the most crucial events in human evolution occurred. Many interpretations involving the known fossil record will stand or fall on the basis of the determinations being made at the present and to be made in the near future with the Potassium-Argon (K/A) technique.

With this brief discussion of the techniques of absolute time designations as a basis, Figure 36 shows the various accepted subdivisions of the stretch of geological time during which life has advanced from its invertebrate origins. The numbers indicate tentative dates for the onset of the division to which they correspond. Although the dating techniques are called "absolute," the figures must remain tentative since further refinements may alter them by several millions of years. Despite this uncertainty, it is generally felt that at least the right order of magnitude is being expressed—always bearing in mind that Kelvin said the same sort of thing more than a century ago when he proposed a radically different time scale for the entire age of the earth, not merely for the span of organic life in the fossil record. Our confidence in these more recent estimates is increased by the fact that physicists, geologists, and evolutionary biologists are now in mutual agreement in accepting dates of this magnitude, and the consensus is that the future will bring no really radical alterations.

While there is scattered evidence for the existence for some invertebrate forms in the Pre-Cambrian, the really reliable picture of the unbroken continuity of organic forms running right up to the present day does not begin until the Cambrian period early in the Paleozoic era, and even then there is no evidence for the presence of animals with backbones. Hints of the presence of primitive fishes occur in the Ordovician, but it is not until the

ERA	PERIOD	EPOCH	TIME	
Cenozoic	Quaternary	Recent	(10,000)	
		Pleistocene	2	
	Tertiary	Pliocene	12	M
		Miocene	25	I
		Oligocene	35	L
		Eocene	55	L
		Paleocene	60	I
				O
Mesozoic	Cretaceous		120	N S
	Jurassic		180	O F
	Triassic		200	Y E A
Paleozoic	Permian		285	R S
	Carboniferous		350	
	Devonian		400	
	Silurian		450	
	Ordovician		500	
	Cambrian		600	

Pre-Cambrian

FIGURE 36. Geological time table.

Silurian that we find the first complete fossil of a kind of jawless fish, the Ostracoderm. This appears to have developed in fresh water streams and it seems likely that some form of Silurian Ostracoderm was the ancestor to all subsequent vertebrate life, including man himself.

Widespread terrestrial uplifting during the Devonian so altered the environment in which the Ostracoderms had lived that these

FIGURE 37. Swift-moving ostracoderm from the Late Silurian of Norway (*Pterolepis nitidus*) (Courtesy of the American Museum of Natural History.)

FIGURE 38. Crossopterygian fish, the Coelocanth (*Latimeria chalumnae*), a living fossil from the Jurassic or earlier, thought to have been extinct since then, but discovered to have survived in 1954 when the first specimen was caught off the east coast of South Africa. Others have since been caught off the Comoro Islands (Madagascar). (Courtesy of the American Museum of Natural History.)

fish were forced to undergo a variety of adaptive changes in response to the requirements of the changing environment. The uplift and desiccation reduced the security of fresh water streams, and, as a response, some of the fishes underwent modifications enabling them to invade the oceans, where they underwent further changes which culminated in the oceanic fishes of today.

More important to our story, however, are the fishes which met the challenge of reduced water levels in the streams of their origin. Of these, the most significant are the Crossopterygians which developed muscular lobes at the bases of their fins which could serve as props for helping push the fish from one puddle to another in the beds of the drying streams. While these adaptive changes enabled these fish to remain in their watery niche, it also meant that more time was being spent on dry land, and what with the development of lungs and nostrils, the Crossopterygians actually became transformed into crude amphibians by the end of the Devonian.

The succeeding Carboniferous saw a return of the moist, damp, lowlands, and it was during this time that the amphibians enjoyed their heyday, undergoing adaptive radiation in the lush swampy environment which was to give rise to much of the coal used today. Terrestrial uplifting started at the end of the Carboniferous and uplifting inevitably produces desiccation. Amphibians—compromise land animals at best—cannot endure prolonged existence in a dry environment. Part of their respiration is carried on by the moist glandular skin and should they be too long in the dry air, they become completely dried up. Furthermore, amphibians require the presence of standing water for purposes of breeding. Their eggs must be laid in water and the larval tadpole stage of development must occur there before they have reached the point where temporary excursions can be made on land.

The hint of uplift at the end of the Carboniferous was a prelude of what was to come, but it was sufficient to produce an important adaptive response in some of the amphibians. A dry protective skin was developed so that the creature could remain indefinitely out of water, and protective coatings for the eggs were developed so that it was no longer necessary to return to water to reproduce.

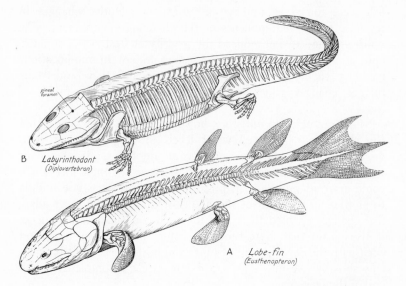

FIGURE 39. A crossopterygian lobe-finned fish (*Eusthenopteron*), of Devonian age, compared with a labyrinthodont amphibian (*Diplovertebron*) of Devonian age. It is from this kind of crossopt that the first labyrinthodont amphibia are believed to have evolved. (Courtesy of the American Museum of Natural History.)

Effectively, then, some of the amphibians had become primitive reptiles and the foundation was laid for the extensive development of terrestrial animals which was to come in the Permian and the following Mesozoic.

During the Permian, major geological changes occurred greatly altering the face of the earth. These are referred to collectively as the Appalachian revolution, and involved the upthrust of the entire Appalachian mountain chain from an area which for millions of years had been intermittently awash. As with the other great upthrusts of geological history, two major climatic changes occurred. First of all, the rise of extensive land masses and the interruption of air flow by high mountains created large areas with a dry climate. Reptiles, whose development enabled them to solve the problems of desiccation, took advantage of this developing ecological niche and commenced the adaptive radiation which was to produce the bizarre and spectacular forms of the Mesozoic, the Age of Dinosaurs.

The second consequence of uplift is often overlooked, but, in our picture of the forces shaping the development of terrestrial life, it is at least as important. This is the fact that extensive uplift necessarily produces large areas of land which are not only high but also cool. There is relatively extensive evidence for glaciation in the Permian nearly 230 million years before the great Pleistocene Ice Age was to have its impact on the development of man. The existence of a large Permian life-zone which was cool and moist provided the challenge to one branch of the developing Reptile class, which was successfully met by the Therapsids.

Successful survival in a cold climate requires that an organism maintain its body temperature above that of the surrounding environment. Generation of body heat in turn requires continued and regular fuel intake and this requires an efficiency of locomotion and the mechanics of capturing and eating food well above that generally thought of as being characteristic of reptiles. In their limb structure, tooth differentiation, and the separation of the breathing and eating passages, the Permian mammal-like reptiles, the Therapsids, clearly show that they were developing an elevated metabolism and had taken a long step in the direction of true mammals to which they eventually gave rise. So it was that the climatic developments of the Permian initiated a direction of organic evolution culminating in the mammals that were later to dominate the earth.

Following the Permian, however, worldwide climate improved and the ensuing Mesozoic saw the adaptive radiation of the reptiles that filled most of the available ecological niches. Herbivorous and carnivorous dinosaurs roamed the land, aquatic forms became adapted to the oceans, flying forms invaded the air, and the largest terrestrial animals that ever lived, the Sauropods, pursued a semi-amphibious life in the swamps where a part of their vast bulk was supported by water. The Mesozoic was the Age of Reptiles proper, and although the mammalian development triggered by the preceding Permian continued in the form of a number of small true

FIGURE 40. Mesozoic reptiles: dinosaurs. *Stegosaurus* in the foreground, *Tyrannosaurus* in the middleground, and *Brontosaurus* in the water. (Painting by R. Kane, courtesy of the American Museum of Natural History.)

mammals, these were relatively unimportant at the time and remained in the background.

At the end of the Mesozoic, for reasons which we can only guess, the large dominant reptiles all disappeared. Some have postulated that the cooling of the climate heralding the beginning of the Cenozoic was the crucial factor, but this leaves unexplained the fact that the large reptiles had vanished *before* the changes in climate occurred. Some have suggested that the origin and spread of modern seed plants in the middle of the Mesozoic may have accounted for the extinction of the characteristic Mesozoic vegetation on which the herbivorous reptiles were dependent, and that without their food supply, and failing to adapt to a new one, they became extinct. This would have caused the extinction also of the carnivorous dinosaurs that preyed upon them and the whole chain of reptilian existence could have been upset. Perhaps this was the cause or perhaps it was something else; in any event, the ruling reptiles vanished towards the end of the Mesozoic, leaving a world of unoccupied ecological niches into which the mammals would radiate in the ensuing Cenozoic.

The few inconspicuous mammals that had survived throughout

the Mesozoic provided the base for the adaptive radiation which started at the beginning of the Tertiary, and among the first orders to appear in the Paleocene was the order Primates. Today, of course, Primates include higher monkeys, apes, and man, but in the early Cenozoic they were a primitive lot that scarcely represented much of an advance beyond a late Cretaceous insectivore.

SUGGESTED READINGS

Brothwell, D., and E. Higgs, (editors). *Science in Archaeology*. Basic Books, New York, 1963.
A comprehensive survey of progress and research, especially good on dating methods.

Butzer, K. W. *Environment and Archaeology*. Aldine Publishing Co., Chicago, 1964.
An authoritative reconstruction of Pleistocene physical environments and man-land relationships at different stages of prehistory.

Heizer, R. F., and S. F. Cook, (editors). *The Application of Quantitative Methods in Archaeology*. Viking Fund Publications in Anthropology No. 28, New York, 1960.
With useful discussions of dating methods.

Hole, F., and R. F. Heizer. *An Introduction to Prehistoric Archeology*. Holt, Rinehart & Winston, New York, 1965.
A most useful systematic introduction to the history, method, and theory of archeology.

Oakley, K. P. *Frameworks for Dating Fossil Man*. Aldine Publishing Co., Chicago, 1964.
A comprehensive summary of data for relative and absolute dating, with an inventory of the dating of all fossil human remains.

Zuener, F. E. *Dating the Past*. 4th ed. Methuen, London, 1959.
The standard work.

CHAPTER FIVE ❦ PRE-
PLEISTOCENE PRIMATES

I N OUR CONSIDERATION of the development of life on earth we
have progressively narrowed down our concern, proceeding from
the simple recognition of "Life" in the Pre-Cambrian to Vertebrates in the Ordovician, through Amphibia, Reptilia, Mammalia
and now more specifically Primates. Until this present focusing,
our picture has tended to touch on the more dramatic aspects of
the organic world, but with the appearance of Primates at the
beginning of the Cenozoic, it is our task to limit our attention to
them rather than to continue chronicling the major events of
organic evolution. Actually, from our point of view, the appearance
and development of Primates could properly be regarded as a
major event, but, at the time, it was not particularly dramatic.

The discovery of fossil Primates played something of a role in
the development of evolutionary thought in the nineteenth century since the founder of the science of paleontology, Cuvier, in
his attempt to dispel the concept of evolution as an explanation
for sequence in the fossil record, had not only claimed that fossil

man did not exist but that fossil Primates of any kind were impossible. In 1836, just four years after Cuvier's death, the first fossil monkey had been found, and just a year later, one of Cuvier's own disciples, Edouard Lartet, found the fossil *Pliopithecus*, a possible precursor of modern apes.

Despite the interest which has been devoted to the unravelling of Primate evolution, there have been a number of obstacles in the way of complete success in this endeavor. In the first place, Primates are not comparable to the great herd animals and they have never been particularly numerous in any one spot. Furthermore, most of them have been relatively small creatures so that the probability of a Primate being preserved as a fossil has never been very good. Finally, Primates have tended to live in tropical forests where conditions for fossilization are poor. Because of these problems, the Primate fossil record is disjointed and incomplete, and if this were all we had to go on it would be difficult to chronicle Primate evolution prior to the appearance of man. As we shall see later, the fossil evidence for man, while not without its own problems, is much more satisfactory.

The one thing that makes it possible to venture tentative interpretation of the course of Primate evolution prior to the Pleistocene are the inferences that can be made from a thorough comparative study of the living Primates. Up to a point, we can regard the living Primates as a frozen picture of Primate evolution in the Cenozoic, with the various major taxonomic groupings representing the various stages of Primate evolution as they appeared. We must stress, however, that this approach can only be used with caution since there is no guarantee that our various representative groups of living Primates have not undergone significant modifications since they first appeared in the Tertiary. Man himself has continued to evolve and it is abundantly clear that the other Primates have not obligingly stood still to aid us in our interpretations. With this caution then, a combination of the direct evidence from the fossil record and inferential evidence from living Primates can provide us with a much better idea of the course of Primate evolution than could the exclusive use of either one of these approaches.

Among the living Primates there are representatives of four

grades in their adaptive radiation with the fourth grade being represented by man alone. As we shall see in Chapter 7, man himself has developed through a series of four stages since his first appearance, but since he has remained within the same ecological niche and since the stages succeed each other with the earlier ones becoming transformed into the later ones, never more than one being in existence at any one time, the series of stages in human evolution cannot themselves be called an adaptive radiation. For the Order Primates as a whole, their four grades, Prosimian, Monkey, Ape, and Man, do represent an adaptive radiation since they did develop to take advantage of differing ecological niches and while each appears at a different time during the Cenozoic and develops out of the preceding grade, all four continue to exist today. We shall treat them in order of their appearance.

1. The Prosimian Grade

The living Prosimians represent less of a change from the ancestral mammalian pattern than the higher Primates do, so it is not surprising that the earliest creatures that are recognizably Primates are effectively at the Prosimian grade of organization. The first Primates took to the trees with the sensory equipment of terrestrial animals. In terrestrial (ground-living) as opposed to arboreal (tree-living) creatures, the senses of smell and hearing are relatively more acute than is visual ability. The hindrance to vision which grass, brush, and other vegetation offers means that the ability to see acutely is less important to a small terrestrial creature than the ability to detect invisible danger. On the other hand, the small arboreal animal leaping from branch to branch of his forest home would be in difficulty if he were forced to locate the next branch by sniffing it out, or by cocking a sharp ear and listening for it.

However, even for a creature whose sensory abilities were primarily those of a terrestrial mammal, the trees did offer an ecological niche relatively free from predators, and it required only one development to utilize them. This was the development of prehensile appendages—grasping hands and feet. From the fossil record of the earliest Cenozoic Primates we can see that they possessed the elongated snout of animals with a well developed sense of smell. This is still reflected in most of the living Prosimians where the snout is capped by the naked and moist rhinarium which indicates olfactory acuity. Furthermore, the living Prosimians have sensory whiskers on the sides of the snout, the eyes have not rotated forward to give them the well developed binocular vision of the higher Primates and, in some, the ears can be moved to help localize sound. Using the living Prosimians as a guide, and comparing their skeletal structure to that preserved for the earliest Primates, we are certain that the Paleocene representatives possessed sensory equipment rather like that of a modern lemur. By noting further that they lived in forested areas, we can infer that they possessed the grasping ability which has characterized Primates ever since. For this we have no direct evidence since no hand or foot bones have been discovered—not too surprising when the chances against fossilization and discovery of such small and delicate pieces of anatomy are overwhelming. We do, however, have arm and leg bones which are consistent with the assumption that their possessors were climbing creatures rather than terrestrial running animals, and it is reasonable to suppose that prehensile appendages had been developed.

While this assumption is generally held and certainly cogent since the entire subsequent adaptive radiation of the Order Primates is based upon it, still it is apparent that the earliest Primates were not so restricted to the arboreal ecological niche as is true for most of their descendants up to the appearance of man. There was a proliferation of Eocene Prosimians that attained a wide distribution for a brief duration and lived the life of small scurrying, scampering animals in bush and grasslands. Many of these showed dental modifications toward the increase in gnawing ability. This perhaps accounts for the world-wide distribution of Primates by the middle Eocene by which time relatively similar Prosimians had spread throughout the tropics of the entire world connected by the grass and brush land of the more temperate zones. In the latter part of the Eocene and continuing into the Oligocene, the adaptive radiation of the rodents rather changed this picture. With more effective gnawing teeth, with the ability to withstand greater temperature fluctuations, and above all with the ability to produce little rodents in greater quantities in a shorter length of time, it was not long before the grassland ecological niche was the property of the rodents alone.

We do not know what the crucial factor was, but certainly the difference in rates of reproduction must have been important. An arboreal animal with eight or ten offspring is rather restricted in its movements, and with this background, Primates characteristically have a greatly restricted number of offspring per pregnancy—generally only one for the higher Primates. With the parental care concentrated on only one or two youngsters, the chances that any given individual may live to maturity are greatly increased, but in the competition for space in the Eocene grasslands, little Primates apparently were not produced at the same rate as little rodents.

While surprising numbers of different Eocene Prosimians have been found, their relations to each other, to their predecessors, and to their followers are not at all clear. This is a problem frequently encountered in trying to interpret the fossil record, and its solution requires either an extraordinarily complete sequence of fossils such as is known for the development of the horse, or some other clearly interpretable phenomenon such as the unbroken line of man's cultural adaptive mechanism which, as the archeological record reveals, ties together the otherwise diverse and isolated human fossils of the Pleistocene. Pre-Pleistocene Primates left no cultural remains, and there are not enough of them to indicate clear evolutionary lines, so our discussion is forced to focus on the general emergence of the various Grades of Primate adaptation.

2. The Monkey Grade

Today the dominant Primates in the arboreal ecological niche throughout the tropics of the entire world are various kinds of monkeys. This simple observation takes on added interest when it is realized that the Primates of the Old and New Worlds have been separated since the Eocene, some fifty million years ago. This separation occurred before the Monkey Grade had been attained in either hemisphere. Further, the monkeys of each area developed from different Prosimians, which makes the independent attainment of a similarly advanced grade of development a classic case of evolutionary parallelism.

The most evident difference that distinguishes the Monkey Grade from the Prosimian Grade is the conversion of the primitive mammalian dependence upon the olfactory means of orientation into one primarily dependent upon vision, along with an accompanying increase in brain size. This can be simply stated as a change from a smell brain to a sight brain with attendant cerebral increase.

The advantages to a tree-living creature are obvious, and a whole series of anatomical adjustments accompany this basic change. Full binocular stereoscopic vision is attained as the eye sockets swivel around toward the front. Not only are the visual parts of the brain developed at the expense of the olfactory parts, but the forward swivelling of the orbits (the eye sockets) greatly reduces the part of the face which can be devoted to the development of the nose. With the reduction in the importance of the sense of smell, and with it the development of the nose, the whole snout becomes shortened. This, along with the increase in brain size, is what contributes to the appeal which monkeys have to the human imagination since it makes them look more human than any other animal, and in our anthropocentric way, we tend to regard a human appearance as being, by definition, appealing.

The increase in brain size also requires some comment. Monkeys exceed the Prosimians in the relative size of their brains, but even the Prosimians are clearly distinguishable from the other early Cenozoic mammals by their relative cranial enlargement. Most likely this can be related to the conditions attendant upon an arboreal existence. Locomotion through the tree tops requires the continual making of choices—certainly to a much greater degree than would be the case for a terrestrial quadruped where there is virtual certainty that there will always be ground wherever one's feet are moved. In a tree, however, there is more space than support, and, in addition, locomotor decisions have to be made in three dimensions rather than in only two. Obviously an expanded choice-making mechanism, i.e. brain, is of relatively greater importance to an arboreal animal than it would be to an average terrestrial quadruped.

Fossils from a number of places in the Old World show that the Monkey Grade had been reached by the Miocene, and there are indications that this must have been attained during the Oligocene, but since the very few Oligocene fossils are confined to jaws and teeth the diagnostic characters of the Monkey Grade have not yet been discovered. The first fossil monkey recognized was a specimen from the upper Miocene of northern India. This was followed by relatively complete remains of an early Pliocene monkey in Greece in 1840, and, in the years that followed a slow trickle of finds attributable to the Monkey Grade has accumulated. These are scattered over an area ranging from Europe on the north to Africa in the south and extending as far east as Japan. Most of these are Pliocene and Pleistocene in date but a few are Miocene as are some of the very few fossil monkeys from South America. Evidently the Monkey Grade had been reached independently in both the Old and New Worlds by the Miocene.

3. The Ape Grade

The third Grade in the adaptive radiation of the Primates, like the first and the fourth, is characterized by a change in the characteristic means of locomotion. When a modern ape moves from one place to another in the trees, it does so by going hand-over-hand, hanging beneath the branches from which its weight is supported. This means of progression is called brachiation (arm-swinging), and as a primary means of locomotion, is used by the apes alone. Prosimians and monkeys, in contrast, are tree-going quadrupeds, scampering along the tops of branches and actually jumping from one to another.

Just as the grasping-manipulating development of the Prosimians and the expanded sight-brain of the monkeys were important preadaptations without which the later Human Grade could not have arisen, so the development of brachiation in the anthropoid ape was an important step in the direction of the upright posture which ultimately freed human hands from any involvement in locomotion. The role played by brachiation in directing an organism toward an habitually vertical position is obvious—it is rather hard to hang horizontally—and if it can be assumed that man's precursors developed by way of the Ape Grade, then the extensive similarities between the chest, shoulder, and arm structure of humans and the modern great apes would be explained as would be the initial adaptation to erect posture on the part of the early human precursors.

Brachiation as a mode of arboreal progression allows for two possibilities which are not initially obvious. For a brachiator of average monkey-like size, it extends the area which can be used for locomotor purposes. Staying within the same kind of supporting framework commonly used by monkeys, it also allows for a considerable increase in bodily size without appreciably affecting locomotor efficiency.

These two possibilities result from the fact that an arboreal quadruped needs relatively more stable support for its normal mode of locomotion. As an effective support for running and jumping, a monkey needs relatively unyielding branches. When the support is flexible, the problem of maintaining balance on top is increasingly difficult, and jumping becomes quite impossible. As Dr. Virginia Avis has pointed out, this is no problem for a creature that habitually hangs from branches. Small brachiators, then, can utilize parts of the trees normally avoided by monkeys, and, in the more stable parts of the arboreal environment, brachiators can become very much larger without the attendant loss of locomotor efficiency—hence the orang.

This may also be related to the re-invasion of a terrestrial ecological niche such as that exhibited by the gorilla and partially by the chimpanzee. A creature that has successfully become large in an arboreal environment will have fewer natural enemies on the ground simply because of its size, and there will be less reason to avoid the ground as does the gibbon in the wild. It might even be possible to speculate that this may have had something to do with the return to the ground by the pre-Pleistocene forerunners of man, but we lack the fossil evidence to support such a supposition.

Against the theory that man had a brachiating ancestor, it has been argued that man's more generalized hands and arms could not have developed from something like the comparable members of such an animal as a chimpanzee without reversing the evolutionary process. At bottom, this objection seems to be another manifestation of the difficulty which some have had in facing the possibility that man descended from something less man-like than man himself. This was further supported by the view formerly held that evolution was irreversible.

To counter these objections, the old idea of the irreversibility of evolution has been largely abandoned with the increase in understanding of the evolutionary process. To be sure, the *exact* reacquisition of a former stage of development is so unlikely as to be impossible, but a reversal of selective pressures or their suspension can result in reversals of adaptations or their reduction. The human pectoral appendage is not the exact replica of a former evolutionary stage, but it *is* just what one would expect of a limb which had formerly been adapted to brachiation, but which, as a result of the cessation of its function as a suspensory organ, had undergone reduction by means of the probable mutation effect. Finally one need not postulate that the human ancestor underwent such an extreme brachiating adaptation as that seen in the modern anthropoid apes where it has continued for some two million years after it had been abandoned by man.

In sum, we feel that the extensive anatomical similarities between the upper parts of modern men and modern apes indicates a community of descent of greater degree than that existing between any other two Grades in the Primate adaptive radiation. As a preadaptation to terrestrial bipedalism, it seems most likely that the precursors of man developed through the third or Ape Grade of Primate development.

While these statements all seem reasonable enough, there is an embarrassing lack of direct fossil evidence in their support—not that the fossils support any other view, but the problem is simply a lack of fossils. The deficiency is not total since there are some tantalizing fragments, but interpretation is difficult, and it is not possible to. say exactly when the brachiating grade was effectively attained.

An assessment of what we have in the form of better-preserved fragments will convey some idea of the nature of the problem. Within five years of the death of Cuvier, his follower Lartet unearthed a small incomplete mandible in southern France which was recognized as a possible precursor to the modern gibbons.

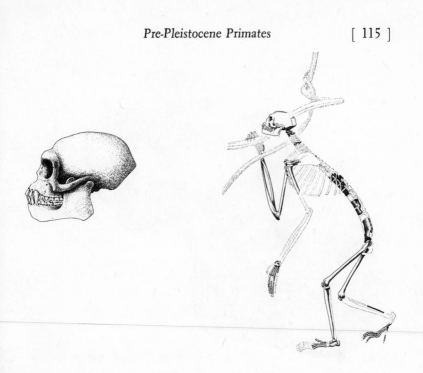

FIGURE 41. Reconstruction of the skull and skeleton of *Pliopithecus*. (Reprinted with permission. Copyright © 1964 by Scientific American, Inc. All rights reserved.)

This was named *Pliopithecus*, and subsequent finds in Europe and East Africa show that it must have been widespread in the Old World ranging in time from the lower Miocene up into the Pliocene. In the patterns evident in the crowns of the teeth, *Pliopithecus* showed that it was more closely allied to the modern anthropoid apes than to the Old World monkeys, but the only evidence discovered for the form of the arm indicates that it could not have been an habitual brachiator.

In 1856, Lartet described another fossil ape from southern France, *Dryopithecus*. Except for the fact that the incisors were smaller, the teeth were remarkably like those of a modern chimpanzee, and the pattern on the crowns of the lower molars was identical with those found on many well-developed modern human molars. While this was very interesting, indeed, almost dramatic,

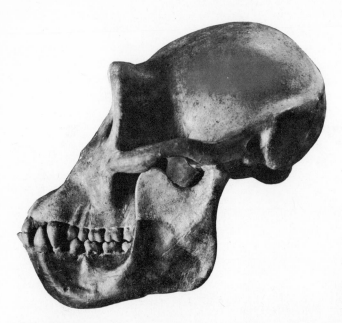

FIGURE 42. *Dryopithecus.* Reconstruction from portion of lower jaw (darker color) of a representative of the genus thought to have given rise to the great apes and man. Of Miocene Age. (Courtesy of the American Museum of Natural History.)

such a finding did not greatly assist in solving the dilemma which remains with us today concerning the placement of the third adaptation of the Primates, since, however ape-like the teeth of *Dryopithecus,* the evidence of its postcranial skeleton again showed that it was not a brachiator.

While there can be no doubt that the late Miocene saw Primates, especially *Dryopithecus* and other similar forms, which may well have been ancestral to living apes and perhaps men, yet it is equally clear that the brachiating adaptation had not yet occurred. Teeth of such a characteristic form could only indicate phylogenetic relationship, but it is ironic that, while the teeth are recognizable as ape teeth, their possessors had not yet reached the Ape Grade of development as we have considered it here.

Evidently the lines represented by monkeys and apes today diverged well before the grade of adaptation which we have called the Ape Grade was attained.

Extensive work in East Africa by Dr. L. S. B. Leakey and others has resulted in the discovery of a wealth of early Miocene Primates, notably the several species of the genus *Proconsul*, ranging in size from a modern pygmy chimpanzee to a stature larger than a gorilla. In the small size of the incisors and the somewhat elongated form of the premolars, *Proconsul* teeth look a little less like those of modern representatives of the Hominoidea than do the teeth of *Dryopithecus*, although there is no question that, dentally, *Proconsul* is ape rather than monkey. Relatively complete remains

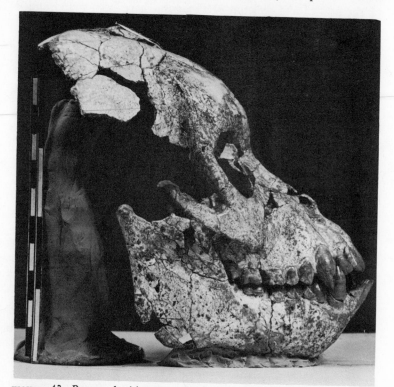

FIGURE 43. *Proconsul africanus*, a Lower Miocene ape. (Courtesy of Dr. L. S. B. Leakey.)

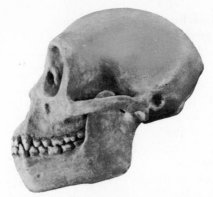

FIGURE 44. *Propliopithecus*. Reconstruction of representative of Oligocene Anthropoid Genus, possibly ancestral to the gibbons and the hominoids. (Courtesy of the American Museum of Natural History.)

of the post-cranial skeleton of *Proconsul* have been found and it has been claimed that *Proconsul* may have been a "semi-brachiator," that is, generally a quadruped but anatomically capable of utilizing brachiation as an alternate mode of progression.

The pattern of the molar teeth recognizable from *Proconsul* up to modern apes and men also extends back into the Oligocene. In the first decade of the twentieth century, two fossil jaws were found in lower Oligocene deposits in the Fayum depression just west of the Nile river in lower Egypt. One of them, *Parapithecus*, is so small and undistinguished that some authorities have questioned whether it was even a Primate and no one at present is willing to interpret it. The other, *Propliopithecus*—so named because it appeared to be a logical precursor to *Pliopithecus*—fulfills the requirements for serving as an ancestor to the Miocene forms with the hominoid dental pattern, but the form of the ascending ramus of the mandible suggests that it had a low and distally placed brain case and a projecting snout, possibly more like that of a Prosimian than even a monkey, let alone an ape.

While early workers, in their enthusiasm, felt that the presence of the characteristic pattern in the molar teeth indicated that their Oligocene and Miocene discoveries were ancient apes, it is now clear that if brachiation is a distinguishing criterion, these early forms had not yet passed out of the Monkey Grade. Phylogenetically they are more closely allied to the later apes than they are to what remains at the Monkey Grade today, but functionally they were still within the second Primate adaptation.

[118]

This brings us to the final irony. Recent discoveries in Italy show that an undoubted brachiator existed in the lower Pliocene, but a careful examination of the teeth shows that it could not have been in the anthropoid ape or ultimately the human line of development. This form, *Oreopithecus*, has been known since 1872 from jaws and teeth, and the exact classification has been a continuing source of minor dispute, but in 1959 an entire skeleton was discovered in a coal mine near the west coast of Italy and the minor dispute has expanded to a major professional row. The postcranial skeleton shows that it was a brachiator while the teeth show that it was not a pongid. Dentally it resembles the Cercopithecoidea to a greater extent than any of the other members of the Hominoidea, and has recently been granted the status of a separate family, Oreopithecidae.

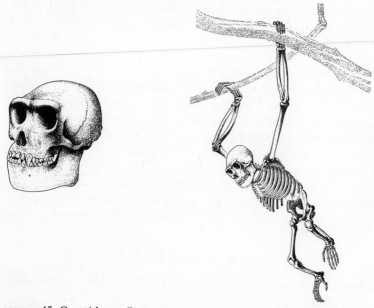

FIGURE 45. *Oreopithecus*. Reconstruction of representative of pliocene anthropoid genus which apparently represented an evolutionary dead-end. (Reprinted with permission. Copyright © 1964 by Scientific American, Inc. All rights reserved.)

Faced with a Primate which had reached the Ape Grade but which was not in the line of development of the modern apes, our explanation is that there is no reason why more than one family of Primates could not have made such an adaptation. The Monkey Grade was reached at about the same time by the Ceboidea in the New World, the Cercopithecoidea, and the Hominoidea (later to become apes and man) in the Old World. Furthermore the spider monkey today in the jungles of South America is the only monkey in the world that characteristically uses brachiation as an alternate mode of progression, and, were it not for its prehensile tail, would come close to being an example of the Ape Grade among the New World monkeys. With such a background, it is not impossible that members of more than one family made the adaptation to brachiation at about the same time that the ancestors of the modern great apes were also beginning to take advantage of that facet of the arboreal ecological niche. Evidently *Oreopithecus* was not successful in this venture for it is not represented by descendants.

As may be judged from what has been said above, the evidence for the third development in the adaptive radiation of the Primates is more inferential than direct. Somewhere within the ten million year blank of the Pliocene, brachiation must have developed among the Hominoidea. The living apes of today and the chest, shoulder, and arm structure of men back to the beginning of the Pleistocene indicate that this must have occurred, but we are uncomfortably lacking in direct evidence. The development of the fourth or Human Grade in Primate evolution is, of course, the primary concern of this work and will be treated at somewhat greater length in a subsequent chapter.

SUGGESTED READINGS

Clark, W. E. Le Gros. *The Antecedents of Man*. Quadrangle Books, Chicago, 1960.
An introduction to the evolution of Primates.

Simons, E. L. "A critical reappraisal of Tertiary primates," J. Buettner-Janusch (editor), *Evolutionary and Genetic Biology*

of the Primates, Academic Press, New York, vol. 1, pp. 65–129, 1963.
A stimulating discussion.
——— "The early relatives of man," *Scientific American*, vol. 211, 1964, pp. 50–62.
A most helpful discussion.

CHAPTER SIX ❧❧ HISTORY
OF THE DISCOVERY
OF THE FOSSILS

THE IMPACT CHARLES DARWIN made on the world, and indeed on the whole course of development of natural science, was tremendous. However, as we have noted in the first chapter the world was not wholly unprepared for Darwin. Even the most conservative scientists at that time (and earlier, as exemplified by Cuvier) were grudgingly admitting that changes of some sort had occurred in the past. Articles and books had been appearing regularly during the decades .preceding publication of "The Origin," presenting, albeit piecemeal, the ideas Darwin was to assemble into a single epoch-making volume.

Although interest in phenomena that might have a bearing on the question of the possibility of evolution was lively and enlarging, serious consideration of such matters was limited to a small segment of the reading public. Where it was a question of evidence for the prehistoric existence of man himself, there were few who were even willing to grant it a hearing. During the 1840's, the first clearcut proof was collected which established the existence of men in a prehistoric age.

FIGURE 46. Jacques Boucher de Crévecour de Perthes (1788–1868), father of prehistoric archeology.

M. Boucher de Perthes, a customs inspector at Abbéville in northwest France and the son of a distinguished botanist, had been an enthusiastic amateur archeologist for some years. In the late 1830's he propounded his views on the archeological antiquity of man at a meeting of the Société d'Emulation at Abbéville, and in 1839 before the Institut at Paris, describing quantities of shaped flints which he had discovered in the gravels deposited by the Somme river in ages past. In 1847 he put his views into print, though they were not actually published till 1849. These flints, Boucher recognized, could only have been shaped by human agency, and, since they occurred in deposits with animals now long extinct, he believed that they indicated the prehistoric existence of man in northern France. They were the tools of prehistoric man.

This, however, was France, and the intellectual tone in the natural sciences, especially those concerned with prehistoric events, had been set by the late Georges Cuvier. "L'homme fossile n'éxiste pas." If this were true, then it was clear that M. de Perthes must be deluded. This seemed so self-evident to the official representatives of French science that they denounced his conclusions without ever taking the trouble to examine the finds on which they were based. This is not quite the complete story of the reception of Boucher de Perthes in his own country since one of his countrymen, M. Rigollot, was sufficiently aroused to visit Boucher's sites in an effort to discredit his claims. The evidence, however, was so convincing that, far from continuing in his attempts to discredit de Perthes, Rigollot became an ardent convert and proceeded to conduct his own investigations nearby. In 1855 Rigollot published an historic communication, *Mémoir sur des instruments en silex trouvé à St. Acheul près Amiens.*

By and large, however, scientific men continued to turn a deaf ear to accounts of prehistoric man. It was not until 1859, the year after Darwin and Wallace had read their papers at the meeting of the Linnaean Society, foreshadowing the appearance of the *Origin*—that a committee of British savants, Charles Lyell, Joseph Prestwich, John Evans, Hugh Falconer, and William Flower, visited Abbéville to satisfy their curiosity at first hand. One of them, Hugh Falconer, had visited Abbéville the year before and been convinced of Boucher's claims. Boucher de Perthes conducted them to the terraces of the Somme Valley where they witnessed the uncovering of stone tools in prehistoric strata that had clearly remained undisturbed since the time of deposition. Indeed, the first to discover a flint implement in situ was Arthur, the younger son of John Evans. Now thoroughly convinced, the committee returned to England and presented its findings before the Royal Society. Later on, in the autumn of the same year (No-

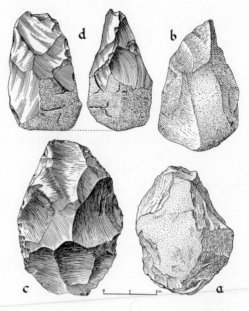

FIGURE 47. Abbevillian tools. *a.* Lava hand-axe, Bed II, Olduvai Gorge, Tanganyika. *b.* Quartzite hand-axe, raised beach, Morocco. *After Neuville and Ruhlmann. c.* Hand-axe, derived, Chelles-sur-Marne. *After Breuil. d.* Hand-axe, 150 ft. terrace of Thames, near Caversham, Berks. *By courtesy of Oxford University Museum.* (From K. P. Oakley, *Man the Tool-Maker.* Courtesy of the British Museum, Natural History.)

vember 24, 1859), Darwin's epoch-making "Essay," as he called it, appeared *On the Origin of Species By Means of Natural Selection or the Preservation of Favoured Races in the Struggle for Life.* Man's thinking concerning the antiquity of the life on earth and the forces shaping its development has never been the same since.

Stone artifacts, unlike fossil organic remains, are imperishable, with the fortunate result that quantities of them have been found. With the interest aroused by the events of 1859, a great deal of new archeological evidence was uncovered and the skepticism with which such discoveries were formerly greeted was now replaced by a growing enthusiasm. There still remain many unsolved problems in archeology, but this is simply a reflection of the healthy state of affairs of contemporary research and by no means the residue of the earlier disrepute which attached to claims made for human antiquity.

It has been otherwise with the actual remains of prehistoric men themselves. Bones and teeth, the most durable parts of the human body, are much more fragile than stone artifacts and far less likely to be preserved, in addition to which, man has been a decidedly rare animal for most of his existence on earth. The result is that relatively little human fossil material has come to light, especially from those earlier periods when man less closely resembled his modern descendants. With human fossil material so rare, it is not surprising that many of prehistoric man's fragmentary remains have been interpreted in the atmosphere of the intellectual climate prevailing at the time of discovery. In many cases, some residue of these former interpretations still remains.

Two representatives of a stage in human evolution earlier than that of modern man had already been found by the time Darwin changed the orientation of the intellectual world. The earliest find of such a fossil occurred in a quarry on the north face of the Rock of Gibraltar in 1848. This was during the years when Boucher de Perthes was experiencing the frustration of having his work ignored by his contemporaries, and the same indifference befell the Gibraltar skull.

The Gibraltar skull was sent to England in 1862 where, following a brief appearance at the 1864 meetings of the British Association, it was turned over to the Museum of the Royal College of Surgeons in London in 1868. At that time, Hugh Falconer, the paleontologist who in 1858, and again in 1859, did most to help the cause of Boucher, referred to it as ". . . a very low type of humanity—very low and savage and of extreme antiquity—but still man . . ." Falconer was fully alive to the fact that here was a new form of man, and proposed the name *Homo calpicus*, after the ancient name for Gibraltar. Little further notice was taken of the Gibraltar find until the turn of the century. By the time it finally attracted the attention it deserved, the exact location and deposit in which it had been discovered could no longer be determined. This, together with the fact that there is no record of any archeological associations, means there is no way of determining its actual antiquity.

The Gibraltar skull, a face and part of a cranial vault, minus the jaw and all of the postcranial skeleton, is recognized as belonging to an earlier stage of human evolution. We are forced to make this judgment on the unsatisfactory basis of anatomical features

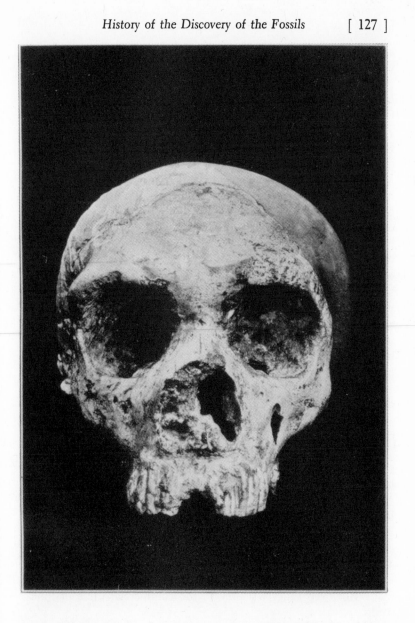

FIGURE 48. The Gibraltar skull. (Courtesy of the American Museum of Natural History.)

alone and this implies familiarity with trends in human evolution which could not have been available to mid-nineteenth-century students. It is not too surprising, then, that Gibraltar received so little notice even in a world alive to the implications of Darwin's *Origin*.

More dramatic and more important was the finding in 1856 of fossil human remains in a little German valley which has given its name to a whole stage of human evolution—Neanderthal. With the growth of archeological and paleontological knowledge in the preceding decade and with the first published description of the gorilla in 1847, general interest in the possibility of human evolution was much keener in 1856 than at any previous time. It is a great pity that the remains could not have waited a few more years to be found, for had they been discovered after the publication of the *Origin*, their reception would almost certainly have been more sympathetic. It is useless, however, to speculate, and we can only be grateful to the Industrial Revolution for the material comforts it has given us, for the revolution in scientific thinking which it has supported, and for the fact that in the constructions it has engendered, roads, bridges, buildings, a great many pieces of evidence relating to the human past have turned up (although unknown numbers have been destroyed) that would otherwise have remained buried.

The small stream, the Düssel, flows from Elberfeld to Düsseldorf where it joins the Rhine just north of one of the most famous wine-producing regions in the world. Just east of Düsseldorf the stream passes through a narrow valley which was named after the seventeenth century organist and poet, Joachim Neumann. This gentle scholar had used a pen name, Neander, which was a translation of his own name (new man) into Greek, and the Düsseldorf townsfolk named the valley Neanderthal in his honor. The steep sides of the valley, however, were formed of Devonian limestone and with the industrial expansion and the attendant building boom in the nineteenth century, the quiet charm of Neumann's beloved valley fell prey to the commercial value of limestone.

In August, 1856, workmen at a quarry in the Neander valley were cleaning out a cave locally known as the Feldhofer Grotto. In

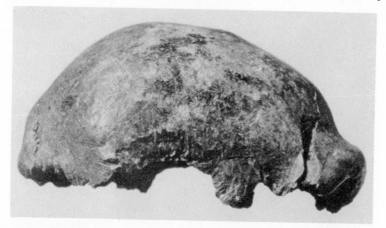

FIGURE 49. The Neanderthal skull-cap. (Courtesy of the American Museum of Natural History.)

the course of their work they came across some old bones, and not realizing their significance, threw them out. These were brought to the attention of Dr. Johann Carl Fuhlrott, a teacher at the Realschule in Elberfeld who had been collecting geological and paleontological specimens from the area for many years. Fuhlrott immediately recognized their importance, and, realizing that a proper professional appraisal was beyond his competence, he communicated with his friend Dr. Hermann Schaaffhausen, Professor of Anatomy at the University of Bonn.

Schaaffhausen and Fuhlrott exhibited the discovery at the meetings of a number of scientific societies where they discussed the implications and presented their interpretations. The remains included thigh bones, some arm bones, fragments of ribs, clavicle, scapula, and pelvis, and a complete skull cap, although unfortunately this latter lacked the basal parts and face. Fuhlrott's investigations showed that the skeleton had most probably been complete, indicating that it had been a deliberate burial. In spite of his efforts it proved impossible to associate the skeletal material with any layer of earth. No artifacts and no associated fauna could be found, and therefore the Neanderthal remains were fated to become the subject of argument and controversy continuing well into the twentieth century. Some of the repercussions of that controversy are still being felt today.

Although they had no inkling of the vast vistas of time which twentieth century science was to open up for human evolution, both Schaaffhausen and Fuhlrott felt that the Neanderthal relies represented a form of humanity more ancient than man of today. They felt that the thickness of the low skull vault, the heaviness of the bony brows over the eye sockets, and the curved heavy thigh bones were simply the normal attributes of earlier forms of men. When these characteristics were compared with those of the newly-described gorilla, it was recognized that the Neanderthal man had a hint of the gorilloid in some of his features. It was but a short step for the popular mind to invest the "cave man" with many other supposedly gorilloid traits. Thus he was said to have long "ape-like" arms, although we know today that, if anything, the Neanderthal arm was short in relation to stature and body bulk. He was fancied to be stooped in posture although there was no evidence to support this figment of the imagination, and it has recently been thoroughly discredited. Finally, Neanderthal behavior was pictured as being bestial and ferocious—again on the assumed model of the gorilla. In this instance, not only was there no evidence to support such a claim for the Neanderthal, but it involved the matter of being grossly unfair to the gorilla! The popular imagination would change that peaceful vegetarian into an embodiment of the principles of ruthless competition applauded by the economists and social theorists associated with the industrial developments of the eighteenth and early nineteenth centuries in Europe.

Such was the interpretation placed on the Neanderthal find even by the minority of people who *did* believe that he was a genuine representative of a former stage in man's evolution. More than just residues of this libel remain today in casual conversation, in the standard newspaper cartoon portrayal, in numerous popular books on science, and even in professional circles where it should have long since disappeared.

If such was the treatment accorded the find by people inclined to believe that this really *was* a fossil man, then one could expect even less charitable behavior from those who were not prepared to admit that modern man had evolved from anything less than modern man. Opinion ranged from one extreme to the other. To some, the Neanderthaler was to be regarded as merely a crude specimen of modern man—extreme perhaps, but still modern man. One eminent anatomist referred to it as an "old Dutchman." Rudolf Virchow declared it to be pathological; another authority, Dr. Pruner Bey, thought it was the skull of a powerfully built Celt, "somewhat resembling the skull of a modern Irishman with low mental organization." Another authority believed it to have been an idiot, and another suggested that it may have been ". . . one of those wild men, half-crazed, half-idiotic, cruel and strong . . ." who occasionally lurk at the outskirts of civilization and often come to a violent end.

One of the most imaginative appraisals was delivered by the anatomist Mayer, a colleague of Schaaffhausen's at Bonn. The Neanderthaler's left elbow had apparently been broken early in life, and this, claimed Mayer along with the pain caused by the rickets which the individual was said to have suffered since childhood, had caused him to pucker his brow in a permanent frown which was eventually ossified in the skull's heavy brow ridge. Mayer continued with his free-wheeling deductions by pointing to the bowed femora (thigh bones). These, he claimed, were the result of having spent long years in the saddle. He also believed that the skull had a Mongolian appearance although in fact it would be hard to find a skull bearing less resemblance to the Neanderthaler than the skull of a typical modern Mongolian. It is rather like comparing a coffin to a billiard ball. Putting these fuzzy ideas together, he emerged with the unique conclusion that the Neanderthal skeleton had belonged to a rickety Mongolian Cossack, a residue of the Russian forces which had chased Napoleon back to France in 1814!

It need scarcely be said that few scientists since have shared Mayer's views. However, this piece of history does serve to illustrate the extent and nature of the controversy stirred up by the discovery in the Neanderthal. While there was no lack of interest in the remains, clearly no fully considered appraisal of these undatable remains could be made on the basis of existing evidence alone. It is interesting to note that in the book which Darwin

eventually did write devoted specifically to human evolution, *The Descent of Man*, published more than fifteen years (1871) after Neanderthal became known, only very brief and cautious reference is made to the Neanderthal remains. With one exception the soundest students generally adopted a wait-and-see attitude.

The one exception was the eminent German physician, pathologist, anthropologist, and politician Rudolf Virchow (1821–1902). Virchow's influence during the late nineteenth century was enormous, his impact in the scientific, social and also political worlds being analogous to that of Cuvier a half century previously. Perhaps it is unfair to compare him with Cuvier since that immediately implies that his scientific contributions merely balance his scientific obstructions, which in Virchow's case is something of an injustice. His contributions to medical and anthropological research are of permanent value, and the value of his insistence upon accumulating documented proofs before accepting likely theories far outweighs the slight inhibiting effect such an attitude has upon the initial formulation of said theories—in most instances.

It so happened that, in the field of fossil man, the likely theories arose long before there was adequate evidence with which to test them. Neither the Gibraltar nor the Neanderthal finds could serve as evidence for human antiquity since their ages were completely unknown. Virchow, then, was in the position of casting legitimate scientific doubt on what we now know to be perfectly genuine human fossils. He did, however, go beyond the bounds of proper scientific caution in the case of the Neanderthal skeleton, and attempted to explain all of its anatomical peculiarities by viewing them as pathological. Since Virchow was the founder of cellular pathology, and accepted as the world's leading authority on the subject, no one dared contradict him.

T. H. Huxley's cautious dismissal of the Neanderthal find as merely an extreme variant of the modern type of man, was shared by most other contemporary anatomists. An exception was William King, Professor of Anatomy at Queen's College, Galway, Ireland. King classified the Neanderthal find on the basis of the skull as a new species of man, *Homo neanderthalensis*—a classification generally recognized as valid. But in the 1860's the most reasonable position to take seemed that of Huxley. Furthermore, as a result of the excavations of a rising generation of archeologists stimulated by the reception of Boucher de Perthes' work, the increasing discoveries of fossil men which were generally recognized and accepted as such in the 1860's were not markedly different in form from modern man. In 1868 descriptions were published of the human skeletal remains from the famous rock shelter of Cro-Magnon in the town of Les Eyzies in southwestern France. The Cro-Magnon remains were associated with Paleolithic (old stone) tools and with remains of extinct animals, and, although there was some debate about the significance of the fact that they represented burials, most authorities accepted these finds as clear evidence of the antiquity of man.

More finds of a similar nature were to be made in the years that followed, but, for the moment, we shall consider the impact made by the discovery of the Cro-Magnon remains. As with so many of the crucial finds, discovery was purely accidental, coming as a result of work connected with putting a railroad line through Les Eyzies. There could be no question of fraud, and, because of the great interest surrounding such matters, the work was carried out under the closest public scrutiny and supervised by people with archeological training. The fragmentary remains of five skeletons were uncovered which were clearly contemporary with the extinct

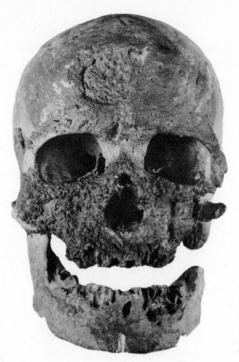

FIGURE 51. Cro-Magnon Skull from Cro-Magnon, Les Eyzies, Mentone, France. (Courtesy of the Musée de l'Homme, Paris.)

fauna and very probably the manufacturers of the Paleolithic cultural debris.

After the authenticity of Cro-Magnon had been established, some scientists recalled that similar finds had been made in earlier years. In the University Museum at Oxford lay the bones of a headless skeleton which had been found in a cave at Paviland on the coast of southern Wales in 1823 where it had been recovered with the bones of mammoths, woolly rhinoceros, reindeer, cave bear, hyena, and other animals long since gone from the British Isles. Paleolithic tools were found as well, but because of the climate of opinion at the time of discovery, no claim had been made for the antiquity of the human remains. Similarly in Belgium, Dr. P. C. Schmerling had excavated the cave of Engis in the province of Liège in 1829 and discovered human bones associated with stone tools and extinct animals. Although he had clearly stated that the human remains must date from the time of the extinct animals he was not taken seriously. Following the revolution in thinking which came with the acceptance of Boucher de Perthes, the publication of Darwin's *Origin*, and the discovery at Cro-Magnon, the importance of these earlier finds was eventually recognized. The "Red Lady" of Paviland turned out to be a man not markedly different from the Cro-Magnon remains, and the Engis finds apparently included cultural and skeletal materials belonging to similar as well as even earlier populations. Fossil man was accepted.

Now that fossil man had been discovered and he was found to be not markedly different from the inhabitants of modern Europe, it seemed to many that this confirmed Virchow's appraisal of the Neanderthal skeleton, which clearly did not look like modern man. What was not realized was that there are all sorts and degrees of antiquity. Even the best practicing archeologists were lumping strata belonging to fifty thousand years into single "ages" without any real awareness of the immense amounts of time involved, while individuals unconnected with the actual process of prehistoric research simply had no inkling of the antiquity of life on earth and of the various already-discovered fossil men.

Part of the problem stemmed from the fact that much of the cultural and osteological evidence for human antiquity emanated from continental Europe. This meant that those doing the interpreting had been brought up and educated in an atmosphere dominated by the catastrophism of Cuvier. They had been trained in the view that the animals of the modern world, including man, dated from the last of a series of deluges—the Biblical flood or "diluvium." The extinct animals found in cave deposits and river terraces were regarded as having been drowned by the flood, hence they were called "diluvial," a term which survives in German learned publications to this day. It was in reference to the possibility of human existence with a "diluvial" or "antediluvial" fauna that Cuvier made his pronouncement that fossil man did not exist. To the discoverers of the cultural and physical remains of undeniable fossil men, the fact that their discoveries were all "diluvial" implied that they all belonged to the same time level.

Research which was to correct this confusion was already in process. As a consequence of the great expansion of prehistoric research at this time, geologists and paleontologists became aware that the conditions of life just prior to the supposed deluge must have been decidedly colder than at present, since the "diluvial" animals were of notably arctic species—reindeer, musk-ox, arctic fox, lemming, and the like. In addition, many topographic features could best be explained by the action of ancient glaciers. Before long, geological chronologies based on the supposed flood made way for those based on an "Ice Age." At first this was not much better than the flood theories, since it appeared that all fossil men and cultures dated from Ice Age times and were therefore contemporaries. A really sound basis for judging the relative placement of human fossils in the estimated two million years of their existence did not begin to assume a substantial form until well into the twentieth century, when it slowly became evident that man has lived through four major ice advances (in the northern hemisphere) and innumerable minor oscillations.

This knowledge belonged to the future, however, and during the late 1850's and 1860's, when the controversy over the interpretation of the Neanderthal skeleton was at its height, judgment had to be delivered in terms of the information available at that time. Two sets of facts dictated the form of this judgment:

1. All known fossil men came from the Ice Age and were not markedly different from modern man.

2. The Neanderthal remains, while of unknown date, were clearly different from modern man and the differences had been declared to be due to pathology by the greatest living pathologist and one of the founders of German anthropology. Although the grounds for interpretation have shifted many times since that period as information has accumulated, the conclusions reached during the decade following discovery are largely the same as those held by the great majority of anthropologists today. Neanderthal is *not* regarded as a representative of a former stage of evolution and is *not* regarded as a precursor of modern man.

While this is the view of the majority of modern anthropologists, although the genuine antiquity of the population to which the Neanderthaler belonged is unquestioned, it is *not* the view which is presented in this book. It seems clear to us that the Neanderthaler *did* belong to one of a series of populations which do represent a former stage in human evolution and did evolve into modern man. We should mention that this idea is far from being original with us since it has had highly respected proponents for nearly half a century (Gustav Schwalbe, 1844–1916; Aleš Hrdlička, 1869–1943; Franz Weidenreich, 1873–1948) although, besides ourselves, it finds few outspoken defenders at the present time. The reasons for the common interpretation of the significance of the Neanderthal remains have been set out above. As our survey of the history of the discovery of fossil men proceeds, we shall see how the new material which came to light with the passing years was utilized to support the basic tenets of the judgment of the 1860's and 70's, and we shall set forth the reasons for our own interpretation.

During the 1870's and early 1880's, skeletal remains of more than a dozen fossil men were discovered in Europe. None of these resembled the Neanderthal skeleton and seemed to offer support to the legitimately skeptical views of Virchow and to the beliefs of the great number of continental students who did not want to accept evolutionary ideas—especially when applied to man. During this time also, bits and pieces of what we now know to be Neanderthal-like skeletal remains were found. It happened that these fragments were all mandibles (lower jaws) or pieces of mandibles, and since the original Neanderthal find had been lacking a mandible, there was no basis for making a comparison. Only a couple of these finds can be given a relative age. They are rather robust fragments, but not really complete enough to call much attention to them. One of them, the La Naulette mandible, found in 1866 with an extinct fauna in a large cave not far from Dinant in the Belgian province of Namur, consisted of about three-quarters of the tooth-bearing part, but all of the teeth were missing. Despite this, the heaviness of the jaw and the size of the tooth sockets impressed many and somehow the rumor got under way that it was "primitive" and even had projecting "ape-like" canine teeth which, of course, was ridiculous since it did not have any teeth at all. One other datable jaw, found in the Moravian (Czechoslovakian) cave of Šipka in 1880, proved to be a juvenile mandibular fragment, as could be seen from the unerupted state of some of the teeth. It is a rugged piece of jaw nevertheless, but it had the misfortune to get into the hands of

Virchow who promptly labelled it—as one might have expected—pathological.

Nevertheless, the ferment of evolutionary thinking had been at work during these years and many people were now alert to recognize the faintest traces of "primitive" characteristics in excavated fossil remains. The proponents of a theory of human evolution were anxious to find "primitive" features which would support their theoretical position, and the opponents of evolutionary views were equally sensitive to anything "primitive" so that they could be ready with their denials. As a result, the few fragmentary pieces of non-modern human fossils to turn up were recognized, at least for their anatomical peculiarities, as soon as they were found.

During these years also, especially as a result of the growing field of prehistoric research in France, cultural subdivisions of the assumed Ice Age were made, and it was gradually realized that an Ice Age date was no assurance that different fossil men were anywhere near each other in time. Then in 1886, just thirty years after the discovery in the Neanderthal, two Neanderthal-like skeletons were discovered in a known archeological deposit at the mouth of a cave in the district of Spy (pronounced Spee) in the Belgian province of Namur. The bones were associated with flint tools of an industry called Mousterian, after the site of Le Moustier not far from Cro-Magnon in southern France where they had first been recognized. Because of this it was now realized that the Spy remains must be older than the Cro-Magnon remains which were associated with the subsequent Aurignacian tool-making tradition.

The two Spy skeletons were represented by two skulls, fragments of both faces and jaws, teeth, arm bones from both individuals and leg bones from both skeletons. The postcranial fragments, while yielding more information than those of Neanderthal, evidently belonged to individuals of the same sort as the Neanderthaler. The skulls, more complete than the Neanderthal skull cap, are most interesting and illustrate the truth of Virchow's observation that one fossil does not make a population. One skull has the low vault and heavy brow ridge noted in the Neanderthaler, while the other skull, belonging to the robust male, has a

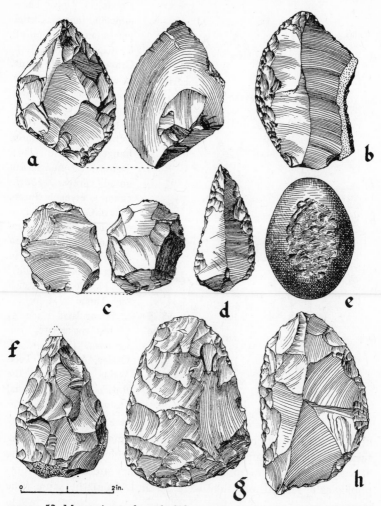

FIGURE 52. Mousterian tools. *a, b*. Side-scrapers (*racloirs*), *c*, disc-core, and *d*, point, from rock-shelter at Le Moustier near Peyzac (Dordogne). *e*. Small anvil- or hammerstone (pebble of ferruginous grit), Gibraltar caves. *f*. Hand-axe from Le Moustier. *g*. Hand-axe (chert), and *h*, oval flake-tool (flint), from Kent's Cavern, Torquay. *a–d*. Typical Mousterian; *f*. Mousterian of Acheulian tradition; *g, h*, of Acheulo-Levalloisian tradition. (From K. P. Oakley, *Man the Tool-Maker*. Courtesy of the British Museum, Natural History.)

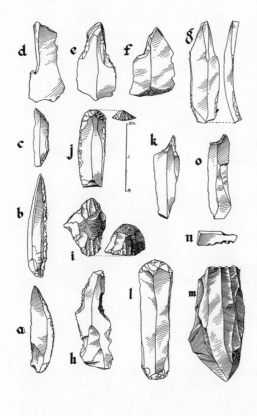

FIGURE 53. Upper Paleolithic flint tools. *a.* Chatelperronian knife-point, Châtelperron (Allier). *b.* Gravettian knife-point, Laussel (Dordogne). *c.* Trapezoid blade, Creswellian, Kent's Cavern, Torquay. *d.* Perigordian (Gravettian) graver or *burin*, Laugerie Haute (Dordogne). *e.* Aurignacian nosed graver (*burin busqué*), Ffynnon Bueno, Vale of Clwyd. *f.* Aurignacian *burin busqué*, Cro-Magnon, Les Eyzies (Dordogne). *g.* Magdalenian graver (*burin bec-de-flûte*), La Madeleine rock-shelter, Tursac (Dordogne). *h.* Strangulated blade, or double "spokeshave," Aurignacian. (From K. P. Oakley, *Man the Tool-Maker.* Courtesy of the British Museum, Natural History.)

much higher vault and a brow ridge intermediate in form between the heavy Neanderthal brow and the ridge of a particularly heavy browed skull of modern man. Yet they are obviously morphologically related and they were certainly from the same time layer.

The Spy finds should have taught prehistorians that, individuals being what they are, whenever more than one member of a population is discovered, one should expect to find differences illustrating the normal range of morphological variation. Furthermore, Spy No. 2 should have indicated that there is no unbridgeable gap between members of Mousterian and members of more

[140]

recent populations. Both these points have been overlooked and they have both caused no end of trouble from that day to this.

The resemblance which the Spy remains had to the earlier Neanderthal discovery was noted soon after they had been found. In 1893 the American paleontologist E. D. Cope proposed that they be called by the species name *Homo neanderthalensis* which the Irish anatomist William King had given in 1864 to the skeleton from the Feldhofer Grotto in the Neander Valley. Ever since, fossil men of similar anatomical features have been called by English-speaking scholars "Neanderthal men," "Neanderthalers," or "Neanderthals." In 1897, a German anatomist proposed the specific name *Homo primigenius* which has enjoyed wide popularity in Germany ever since. Not to be outdone, the French have used the name *Homo mousteriensis* after the French site Le Moustier where the tools of the Neanderthalers were first recog-

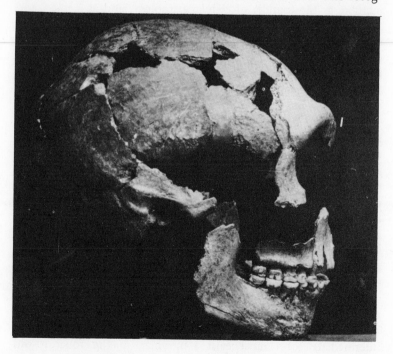

FIGURE 54. One of the Spy Skulls. (Courtesy of the Musée de l'Homme, Paris.)

nized. This usage was strengthened by the find in 1908 of a complete Neanderthal skeleton at Le Moustier.

Despite these various attempts at labelling, there is general agreement among even the most conservative of zoologists, anatomists, and anthropologists of the English-speaking world that the differences between Neanderthals and modern men are not great enough to warrant separate specific designation. Both are included within *Homo sapiens.*

Two things conspired to limit the influence of the Spy discoveries. First, anything with a Neanderthal-like morphology tended to be regarded as abnormal or peculiar because of the position held by Virchow. Admittedly the cry of "pathological" began to grow a little thin as a total explanation for non-modern morphology, as find after find was made in early strata, but such was the immense influence of Virchow as a champion of the scientific method, as the founder of cellular pathology, and as a social and political leader that the true significance of the Spy remains was not appreciated till well into the twentieth century. Virchow's influence is felt today in the writings of modern anthropologists who make the vague claim that the Neanderthals were too "extreme" or "specialized" to have served as the ancestors of subsequent men.

The second consideration that served to keep the Spy remains from occupying the center of the stage was the discovery during the early nineties of a representative of a far earlier stage in human evolution. Even the most ardent defenders of the antiquity and prior evolutionary status of the known Neanderthalers granted that they were fully human and that there was a far greater gap between Neanderthal and non-human than between Neanderthal and modern man.

Despite the cautions of Darwin that the non-human Primate which preceded the human stage of evolution probably looked nothing like an ape of today, the popular and even the scientific world looked with fascination at the living Primates, picking the most manlike as a model for the precursors of man. The flamboyant German evolutionist Ernst Haeckel predicted that an intermediate form must exist somewhere in the fossil record which stood on the borderline between ape and man, and he even went so far as to give it a name—*Pithecanthropus alalus*, or "ape-man without speech." These speculations, criticized by Virchow as being without factual basis, were the source of talk about the mythical "missing link" which survives even today in twentieth century folklore.

Beginning in 1890, some fossil fragments came to light in Java which appeared to correspond to the popular conception of the "missing link," and these soon became the center of a lively controversy. The circumstances surrounding the finds seem so unlikely that it is worth recounting them here. This is one of the very few cases where a competent and scientifically trained individual deliberately set out to find a human fossil. The fact that he actually found what he was looking for constitutes one of the most remarkable stories in the history of human paleontology. In one of the only other instances in which an explorer set forth to find the origins of man he returned with a clutch of dinosaur eggs, but even that is no less improbable than was the finding of the remains of that rarest of all fossils, man himself.

The discoverer of this "missing link" was a young Dutch physician and anatomist Eugene Dubois who had been greatly stirred by the evolutionary ferment in German and British scientific circles. Darwin, writing in *The Descent of Man* (1871), had noted that man, being a hairless animal, probably arose in the tropics, and that the most likely place to look for early human fossils should be Africa where there is a wide variety of non-human Primates, including the two apes, gorilla and chimpanzee, which show the greatest structural and behavioral similarities to modern man. Discoveries within the last few decades have fully substantiated Darwin's prediction and so it may seem a little peculiar to us that Dubois went to Java to make his find, although there actually were a number of good theoretical and practical reasons for doing so. In the first place, Indonesia is in the tropics and it is the home of a wide variety of non-human Primates including the two remaining members of the Superfamily Hominoidea found outside of Africa, the orang and the gibbon. Furthermore, Haeckel, whose writings had much influenced Dubois, had stressed those parts of the anatomy of the gibbon which bore a particular resemblance to human characteristics. Reasoning that the circumstances which gave rise to human-like characteristics in a non-human might also have influenced the development of a related line which eventually did become human, Dubois' choice of a southeast Asian field for research can be seen to have intellectual justification. The final reason, however, was a purely practical one. After years of rivalry with England in the acquisition of as much as possible of the African colonial grab-bag, Holland had finally lost out. This meant that even had Dubois wanted to search for fossil man in Africa, he would have had to finance his research himself in territories under foreign control—not very tempting circumstances for a young scientist without much money. In Indonesia, however, the Dutch still had a booming colonial empire, and, with his medical training, Dubois had no trouble getting himself assigned there as a health officer in the colonial armed forces.

In 1887, his first assignment was in Sumatra where he spent some time searching cave deposits and where he became familiar with the published works on Indonesian paleontology which dated back a considerable time before his arrival. This plus the interesting prehistoric material that had been sent to him from Java, convinced him that Java was a more likely place in which to pursue his search. He succeeded in getting himself transferred in 1889, and from 1890 until 1895 he was supported in his paleontological researches by the colonial government. The result was that the government gained information concerning geological deposits of potential economic value to mining interests and science acquired its first "ape-man."

The first find came late in 1890 and was a small fragment of a jaw which Dubois recognized as being definitely human but with even less chin than the La Naulette and Šipka mandibles. Then late in 1891, at the village of Trinil on the banks of the Solo river in central Java, he made the discovery that made him famous. In September, he found an upper right third molar of what he at first believed was a chimpanzee, and a month later he found what was to become one of the most celebrated skull-caps ever discovered. The next year, August of 1892, he found a complete femur approximately forty feet from the place where the skull cap had been found. Another molar, an upper left sec-

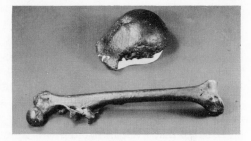

FIGURE 55. Skull-Cap and femur of Pithecanthropus (*Homo erectus*). (Courtesy of the American Museum of Natural History.)

ond, was found a short distance away. All of these finds were at first attributed by Dubois to an extinct creature which he labelled *Anthropopithecus erectus*, or erect-walking man-ape which he believed to be an extinct species of chimpanzee.

The results of his findings were originally published in an obscure mining journal, but since their significance became increasingly evident to him, he published a pamphlet in 1894 which had wide circulation and was the cause of heated controversy in the intellectual centers of Europe. He recorded in detail measurements which he had made on the skull and compared them with those published by other investigators on the skulls of chimpanzees. His gross skull measurements are recorded in Table 2, together with his estimate of cranial capacity, while the chimpanzee measurements are averages calculated from the figures he quotes.

TABLE 2

	Pithecanthropus	Chimpanzee
Skull length	185 mm.	135 mm.
Skull breadth	130 mm.	95 mm.
Cranial capacity	1000 cc.	400 cc. (Hooton 1942)
	(Hrdlička 1930:39)	

As he realized, the gross measurements of his find greatly exceeded those of the chimpanzee and fell within the lower limits of the modern range of variation. Cranial capacity, which various authorities have since estimated to be between 900 and 1000 cubic centimeters, was more than double that of an average chimpanzee and, as we now know, half again as large as the largest recorded gorilla, yet markedly smaller than the approximately 1400 cc. which is normal for modern man. To be sure, modern men do exist with skulls of 1000 cc. or less and some of these

[145]

have been men of recognized genius, but the small size of the Java skull *plus* the heavy brow ridge projecting some 2 cm. beyond the forward extension of the brain cavity clearly showed Dubois that he was dealing with a creature that possessed more morphological resemblances to the great apes than to any men living today.

He noted that while in size the skull approached that of man, in some ways it resembled that of a chimpanzee or of a gibbon. His solution was to create a new genus for his find indicating that it was to be a transitional form which leaned toward the human side. Hence, he called it *Pithecanthropus erectus*, the erect-walking ape-man, which he believed to be the precursor of modern man himself.

From the vantage-point of more than half a century of added experience and a much greater number of human fossils, we are able to see that while Dubois went somewhat too far in creating such a special category for his fossil, in the light of the state of knowledge at the time of discovery, one cannot but sympathize with him. Today, most anthropologists interested in fossil man prefer to include Java man, or Pithecanthropus as many still call him, in a non-technical sense, in the genus *Homo*. Some anthropologists have gone so far as to see no specific differences between the Java finds and *Homo sapiens*, but we prefer a designation which was suggested in 1950 by Ernst Mayr and which has been gaining increasing support, that is, *Homo erectus*.

In 1895, Dubois returned to Holland, carrying his fossils with him. In Holland he demonstrated them before several groups of the most eminent anthropologists, anatomists, and zoologists in the world. Interest was intense and virtually all the scientists involved published their opinions almost simultaneously. It was immediately obvious that opinion was very far from unanimous. One group of savants felt that the remains were clearly human, although of a crude sort, another group of the less eminent, chiefly noted for the fact that they were headed by the renowned Virchow, claimed they were not human at all, and a third group led by Dubois himself was of the opinion that they were intermediate, which was perhaps the wisest stand to have taken in view of the meager amount of evidence available at the time.

Virchow took the extreme position that the Pithecanthropus remains belonged to an extinct species of giant gibbon, although as time went on fewer and fewer authorities were inclined to agree with him. He was, however, greatly interested in the finds which he regarded as extremely important, and he invited Dubois to Berlin to lecture on his discoveries, which may not be without significance in explaining Dubois' final views on the fossils.

For the next few years arguments and opinions multiplied, ranging all the way from regarding Pithecanthropus as a man to viewing him as an idiot, a freak, an ape, a transitional form, or an illusion. Dubois, originally at the center of the controversy, gradually withdrew into silence and for the next quarter of a century made almost no contribution to the subject. During this withdrawal, he also withdrew the controversial bones from public view; in fact, he pried up the boards of his dining room floor and buried the boxes of fossils in the earth beneath, apparently under the impression that the world was intent on stealing them. This may be contrasted with the relaxed behavior of Dubois when he had just returned from Java and was so eager to discuss and demonstrate his finds that he carried them from place to place in a satchel. This satchel and its precious contents were almost lost when Dubois left them in a Paris restaurant when he and the professor whom he was visiting became so engrossed in their conversation that they walked away without them.

The bones were not to be seen again until 1923, when, quite inexplicably, Dubois allowed the American anthropologist Aleš Hrdlička and a number of other scientists to see and handle them. Dubois had just published on two other fossil skulls in his collection from Java, but which did not belong to the Pithecanthropus (*Homo erectus*) stage, being of apparently more recent origin but nevertheless remarkable in their own right. No one knows why Dubois waited nearly thirty years to reveal these finds. Equally puzzling was the revelation made in the late 1920's that four more fossil thigh bones were in the collection. Strangest of all, however, was the view of Dubois himself when he once again began to publish on his discoveries. His revised opinion was that Pithecanthropus had been a giant gibbon and quite unrelated to the line of human development. Despite the discovery of more Pithe-

canthropus material from Java during the 1930's and quite extensive remains from a related form of fossil man in China, Dubois maintained this view until his death in 1940—alone in a scientific world which had at last come to accept his discoveries as truly representative of an early but fully human stage in the evolution of man.

As the furor over Java man began to subside during the first decade of the twentieth century—partially at least because no one was allowed to see the original fossils and expeditions to Java failed to produce any more—the spotlight of public attention was focused on fossil finds of a more familiar sort, Neanderthals. In the breathing spell between the excitement over the Java finds and the discovery of the new Neanderthals, one eminent anatomist, Gustav Schwalbe (1844–1916) of Strasbourg, synthesized the knowledge of fossil man that had been collected so far. In his publications, he proposed two possible schemes for human evolution which arranged the known fossils in relation to each other (see Figure 57). Schwalbe placed Java man, Neanderthal man, and modern man in their respective time periods and drew lines indicating their possible lines of relationship. He postulated that a Pithecanthropus stage was the direct ancestor of both modern man and the Neanderthal, but that the Neanderthals had separated from the main line of evolution well back in time, proceeded on its separate way for a while, and eventually had become extinct. In Figure 57b he postulated a direct line of evolution from a Pithecanthropus stage through a Neanderthal phase to man as we know him today. This latter scheme, in its simplicity, he regarded as the most likely picture of what had actually occurred.

Now, some sixty years later, it is our belief that Schwalbe's appraisal was correct, as we shall attempt to demonstrate in Chapter 7. But since most anthropologists now use some modification of Figure 57a we shall have to explain how this situation came about. Part of this can to some extent be appreciated from the discussion of the manner in which Neanderthal man came to be regarded as "peculiar" or somehow not normal even before he was sufficiently well known for such a judgment to have an adequate basis. The remainder can be understood from the subsequent history of fossil discovery.

For two decades following the turn of the century, scarcely a year elapsed without another fragment of fossil man being discovered in Europe. Between 1899 and 1905 fragments of fourteen or perhaps fifteen individuals of Neanderthal morphology were

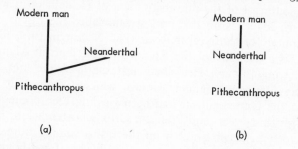

(a)   (b)

FIGURE 57. Two possible courses of human evolution discussed by Schwalbe.

discovered at Krapina in Croatia, now one of the republics of Yugoslavia. All ages from birth to adulthood were represented, but because the pieces were so badly broken and because the describer was a relatively unknown professor of paleontology at Zagreb, capital of Croatia, the Krapina remains have suffered from the same fate which overtook the Spy discoveries. Despite excellent descriptive monographs, both finds have received far less attention than they deserved. In some respects, the Spy remains showed fewer differences from recent man than has often been assumed to be "typical" for Neanderthals, and the Krapina remains amply confirm these tendencies. It transpires that every prehistoric site yielding the bones of more than one individual of a population, also produces anatomical variations that many earlier authorities found hard to account for. It is now recognized that individual variability is no exclusive prerogative of modern man and is really what one should expect when evidence appears in quantity.

Although the range of variation of the Krapina population was well-documented in the publication of the Croatian professor, Gorjanović-Kramberger, in 1906—the year Schwalbe's extensive attempt to synthesize existing knowledge concerning the evidence for human evolution ranging from Pithecanthropus, Neanderthal, Gibraltar and Spy to modern man—these excellent works had relatively little influence on the reading public, whether learned or lay. One cause for the neglect of these worthy efforts was the discovery in 1907 of the famous Heidelberg mandible by workmen in the Grafenrain sand pit at the little village of Mauer, just 10 kilometers southeast of the university town of Heidelberg in western Germany. Mauer is situated on a stream called the Elsenz, which is a tributary of the Neckar River. The Neckar in turn, like the Düssel, is a tributary of the Rhine which it joins at Mannheim after flowing through Heidelberg just south of the area which produces Germany's famous vintage wines. Commercial operations at the Grafenrain pit had been yielding Pleistocene animal fossils for thirty years and Professor Otto Schoetensack of Heidelberg had been keeping watch on the fossils coming from Mauer with the patient hope that eventually a human fossil might turn up. His patience was rewarded on 21 October 1907, when the

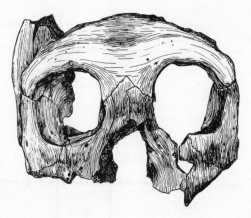

FIGURE 58. One of the fragmentary skulls of the Neanderthal population found at Krapina, Yugoslavia. (Drawing by Mary L. Brace.)

owner of the pits informed him of the epoch-making discovery. Schoetensack immediately commenced his study of the mandible and the clear stratigraphic circumstances surrounding the find, and shortly (1908) produced an admirable and detailed monograph on his findings.

Two outstanding sets of facts guarantee the permanent position of the Mauer jaw or *Homo heidelbergensis* as Schoetensack tried to christen it, among the most important human fossils ever discovered. Most striking is the enormous size of the jaw. As a heavy, bony, chinless, mandible it far exceeded the known Neanderthal jaws (La Naulette, Šipka, Spy, Krapina) although its teeth were remarkably similar to the latter. The molars, in fact, are not distinguishable from those of a robust big-toothed modern man, although the incisors, in spite of being heavily worn, were apparently beyond the upper limits of the modern range of variation, although decidedly human in form. The canine teeth did not project above the chewing surface and it was quite clear from the morphology of the dentition as a whole that the jaw belonged to an early form of man.

The second important set of facts involves the dating. The stratigraphic sequence in the Mauer sand pits was well known from the quantities of fossil animals discovered. Among these animals were a straight-tusked elephant and a browsing rhinoceros, an extinct form of horse, a giant beaver, a hippopotamus, a sabre-

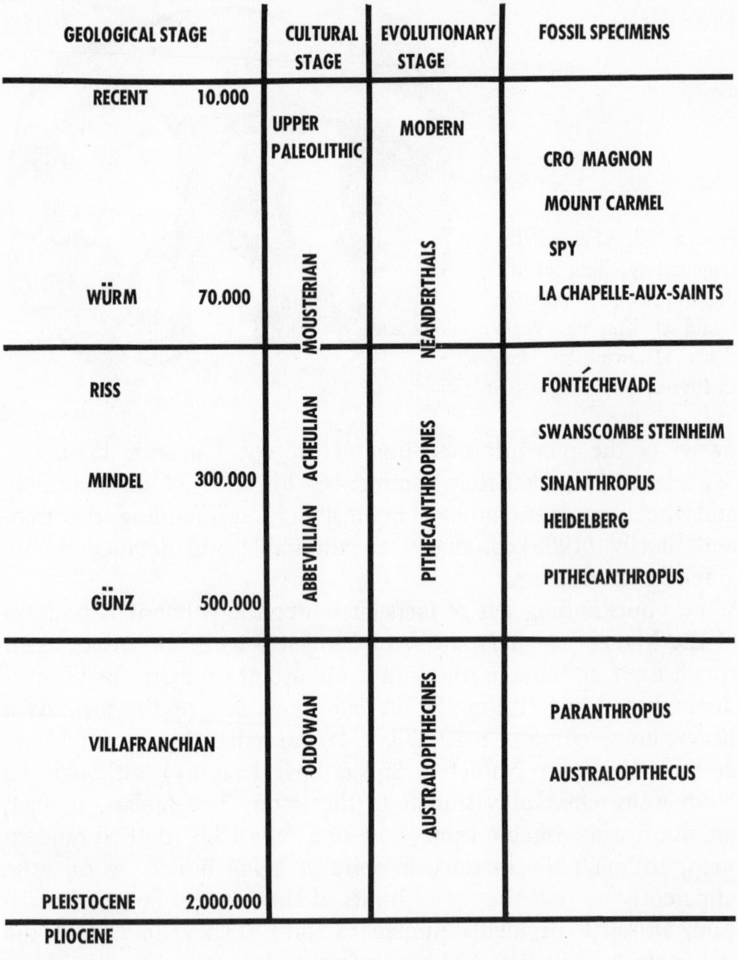

GEOLOGICAL STAGE		CULTURAL STAGE	EVOLUTIONARY STAGE	FOSSIL SPECIMENS
RECENT	10,000	UPPER PALEOLITHIC	MODERN	
				CRO MAGNON
				MOUNT CARMEL
				SPY
WÜRM	70,000	MOUSTERIAN	NEANDERTHALS	LA CHAPELLE-AUX-SAINTS
RISS				FONTÉCHEVADE
		ACHEULIAN		SWANSCOMBE STEINHEIM
MINDEL	300,000		PITHECANTHROPINES	SINANTHROPUS
				HEIDELBERG
		ABBEVILLIAN		PITHECANTHROPUS
GÜNZ	500,000			
VILLAFRANCHIAN		OLDOWAN	AUSTRALOPITHECINES	PARANTHROPUS
				AUSTRALOPITHECUS
PLEISTOCENE	2,000,000			
PLIOCENE				

FIGURE 59. The Pleistocene. The glacial periods, cultural stages, and fossil specimens.

tooth tiger, and others, indicating an antiquity far greater than the last (fourth) glacial stage to which the Neanderthals belonged. Schoetensack believed that his find belonged to the warm period between the first two glacial stages of the Pleistocene chronology which the geologists Penck and Brückner were at that time working out. Other authorities revised his estimate to place Heidelberg man between the second and third glacial stages, while today, as a result of detailed reappraisal by Clark Howell of the University of Chicago, the date has been fixed as a climatic amelioration (interstadial) *within* the latter part of the second glacial stage (see Figure 59). Despite the slight uncertainty of the exact date, the early estimates were quite close and there could be no doubt that the Heidelberg jaw was by far the oldest human fossil to have been discovered in western Europe, a circumstance which remains true to this day. The date and the morphology of the mandible make Heidelberg man a probable contemporary of Pithecanthropus. This we recognize by placing him in the same precise taxonomic category, *Homo erectus*. Unfortunately no tools were found with the Heidelberg mandible, although they exist at a comparable time level elsewhere. Similar human remains have been unearthed neither in the Mauer pits nor elsewhere in Europe, so it remains as an isolated, fortunate, and extremely significant find.

The significance was appreciated and the interest and excitement surrounding the discovery were intense. Now that the twentieth century was well under way and a greatly extended antiquity for man's ancestry was being documented and appreciated, national scientific prestige was, in some circles, being measured by the number of striking sites yielding the remains of early man. Kudos went with the oldest finds. Germany, with its Nean-

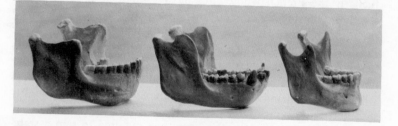

FIGURE 60. The Heidelberg jaw, compared with the jaw of a chimpanzee and that of a modern man. (Courtesy of the American Museum of Natural History.)

derthal and now with its Heidelberg man, enjoyed the highest prestige.

England, grasping at straws, claimed great antiquity for a number of fragments, the most important being the Galley Hill skeleton discovered in 1888 on a terrace of the Thames in Kent, southeast England. Such was the desire for pre-eminence in the field of prehistory that one Englishman was even led to forge a fossil discovery—the famous Piltdown fraud—but the further significance of these events will be considered in due course.

Germany's period of pre-eminence was short-lived, for in 1908 the scene shifted to France where a decade was ushered in which assured France of first rank status in the realm of human fossil discoveries. Two complete Neanderthal skeletons were discovered in southern France, and the years which followed saw several more complete and a quantity of fragmentary Neanderthals brought to light. On 7 March 1908, Otto Hauser, a Swiss "dealer" in antiquities, uncovered the complete skeleton of a Neanderthal youth in a rock shelter at Le Moustier—the village of the Vézère river in southern France which had given its name to a whole stage of human cultural evolution, the Mousterian.

Several unfortunate coincidences have combined to prevent the Le Moustier skeleton from receiving the attention which it deserved. First of all, Hauser was a difficult and unpopular personality who had acquired a deservedly unsavory reputation for systematically looting prehistoric sites and selling the proceeds to foreign museums at inflated prices. The scientific world, and particularly the French whose sites he was plundering, were understandably unsympathetic to his efforts to be accepted as a prehistorian. Since Hauser was well aware that proof of any genuine find he should happen to make would have to be iron-clad, he made certain that several groups of persons witnessed the discovery of the Le Moustier skeleton. After the initial discovery, which had been made by his field foreman, Hauser ordered the find buried. A month later he uncovered it again in the presence of several French officials who were then required to sign a statement testifying to its authenticity. It was then reburied to be "discovered" once more in the presence of a group of Germans in June. Once more Hauser had the skeleton buried, and the

FIGURE 61. An Otto Hauser digging party: Left to right, Drs. Haake (holding shovel), Wirtz, Hahne, Kossina, Mrs. Paul Virchow and her husband, Drs. Klaatsch and von den Steinen, Counselor Rehlen, von Baelz. (Courtesy of the American Museum of Natural History.)

performance was repeated for some Americans in July. Excavation was finally carried out on 10 August 1908, in the presence of several eminent German scholars (Figure 61). Significantly, the skeleton was finally sold to the Museum für Völkerkunde in Berlin in 1910 for what amounted to a small fortune.

Unrest continued to plague the skeleton of the Le Moustier youth, since it was the subject of four reconstructions during the next fifteen years. The first two were by Dr. Hermann Klaatsch, the anthropologist from Breslau. Klaatsch unfortunately died before a detailed report could be written, and, since the reconstructions he had made were still regarded as unsatisfactory, a third attempt was made by the preparateur at the Berlin Museum. This effort was made with plaster of Paris, colored to match the bones, and the shading was so skillful that no one could tell what was reconstruction and what was actual fossil without actually cutting

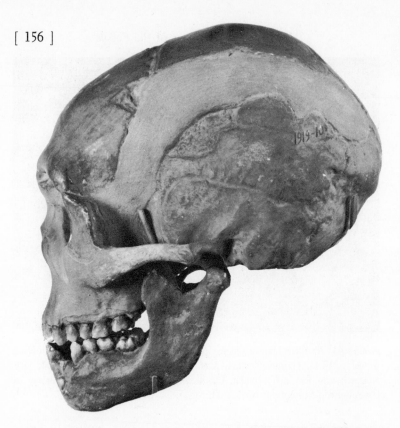

FIGURE 62. The Le Moustier Skull. (Courtesy of the Musée de l'Homme, Paris.)

into it. This resulted in the loss of many of the important small fragments and details when the fourth and final reconstruction was made by Professor Hans Weinert, the anthropologist at the University of Kiel. Weinert's descriptive monograph was finally published in 1925, more than seventeen years after the find had been made and more than a dozen years after the publication of the exhaustive description of the La Chapelle-aux-Saints skeleton which had been discovered in the same year as Le Moustier. For the few individuals who were still interested in the features shown by Le Moustier after this long and difficult history, the differences in form between it and the La Chapelle skeleton—which has served as a "type specimen" from that day to this—were attributed to the youth and immaturity of the Le Moustier remains. The fact, however, is that, at age sixteen, the Le Moustier youth had relatively little growing left to do, and that in those few remaining years, interrupted by his early death, he could never have acquired the formidable supraorbital torus or browridge so markedly developed in the remains from Neanderthal, La Chapelle-aux-Saints and one—not both—of the Spy skeletons.

Because of this variety of circumstances the differences between Le Moustier and the assumed "typical" Neanderthaler have been generally ignored. As a further and final distressing development in the troubled career of the Le Moustier Neanderthaler, the Museum was the unfortunate target of a bomb during the Second

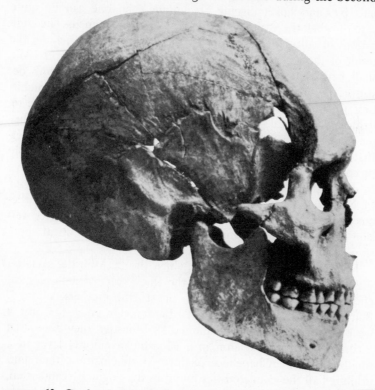

FIGURE 63. Combe Capelle Skull. (Courtesy of the Musée de l'Homme, Paris.)

World War and the skeleton is no more. Blown up at the same time was another crucial skeleton which had been so unfortunate as to have been discovered by Hauser on August 26, 1909, just a year after Le Moustier and in the same (Dordogne) region of southern France. This was the Combe Capelle skeleton which possessed some of the features one would expect of a population intermediate in form between Neanderthal and modern. Furthermore, the skeleton represents a burial from a time and cultural level somewhere on what has been regarded as the borderline between the Mousterian and the Upper Paleolithic. The skeleton was a burial, however, and so it is impossible to be precise about the level from which it was buried. In addition, because of Hauser's pick-and-shovel digging "technique," no one can be quite sure of what the various surrounding layers contained. The indications of cultural transition may be genuine or they may be the result of the actual mixing of what had been distinct layers. We shall never know. In any event, that World War II bomb destroyed two of the most important skeletons in European prehistory. One of these ought to have indicated that the caricature regarded as "typical" Neanderthal was unsound, and the other may have indicated the transition from a previous Neanderthal phase in human evolution to a stage which recognizably precedes modern man. Other material does exist which can serve to demonstrate these points, but we have mentioned the fate of Le Moustier and Combe Capelle before considering La Chapelle-aux-Saints in order to make clear why the generally accepted version of the "typical" Neanderthal met with so little critical opposition in those early years.

To return to the year 1908, in which the Le Moustier skeleton was discovered, success crowned the three years of archeological effort by a small group of French priests, the brothers A. and J. Bouyssonie and their colleague L. Bardon. On August 3, just a week before Hauser finally exhumed Le Moustier, they discovered a complete human skeleton in a Mousterian cultural layer in a small cave at La Chapelle-aux-Saints. Morphologically their find exhibited all the characteristics found in the original Neanderthal, and furthermore it was far more complete. Disregarding the fact that all but two of the teeth had been missing for years before

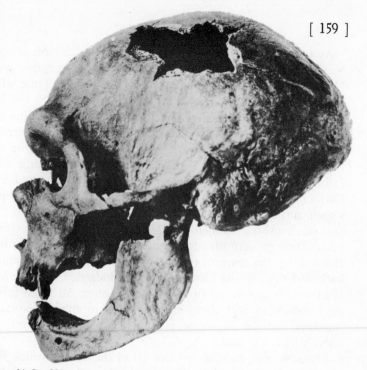

FIGURE 64. La Chapelle-aux-Saints Skull. (Courtesy of the Musée de l'Homme, Paris.)

death, this was the first Neanderthal to be discovered with the whole brain-case, including a complete face.

The excavators immediately informed their friend l'Abbé Henri Breuil of their good fortune, and Breuil (1877–1961), well on his way to becoming the most renowned archeologist in the world, gave them what appeared to be the best of advice. He urged them to turn their find over to the famous paleontologist Marcellin Boule for proper study. Boule (1861–1942), a professor at the National Museum of Natural History in Paris, who later founded the Institute of Human Paleontology, was one of the outstanding natural scientists of his day, and, on the face of it, he would seem to have been the obvious man to undertake the description. He immediately got to work and his exhaustive results were soon published in three weighty installments appearing in years 1911, 1912, and 1913.

As a result of this imposing publication, the cartoon image of Neanderthal man was foisted upon an all-too-receptive world. Neanderthal man was pictured as a coarse-featured brute with a brain which, though large, was qualitatively inferior to the brain of modern man. He was endowed with a heavy, lumbering body which could not quite maintain an erect posture. Together with this it was claimed that he characteristically walked on the outer edge of his foot since his big toe was supposed to diverge widely from the axis of the other toes in a way that was semi-prehensile. Furthermore, he was pictured as proceeding in a permanent slouch, unable to straighten his knees and restricted by the fact that his backbone formed a single arch, lacking the convexities which allow modern man to stand erectly. As a final touch, Boule claimed that the shape of the spines of the neck vertebrae and the backward slope to the foramen magnum indicated that the heavy head was slung forward in a gorilloid manner. All these features were recounted with frequent references to modern apes and monkeys and the aggregate picture was of an individual that scarcely looked human.

Recent studies have shown that *all* of these traits which Boule attributed to his La Chapelle Neanderthal are without substance in fact. Of all these characteristics, only perhaps the one claiming coarse facial features may have any validity to it and even this is highly questionable, since facial expression is determined by the soft parts which have no representation in the skeleton. That there might be some slight justification in suspecting coarse features in a Neanderthal is suggested by the fact that the one area of anatomy where Neanderthals clearly differ from modern man is in the face. The Neanderthal face was large, and if one counts largeness as "coarseness," then it must have been coarse. This, however, is a value judgment and not really subject to measurement, and we shall simply note that the Neanderthal face and everything related to it was large—jaws, teeth, eye and nose openings, and brow ridges.

It is legitimate to ask why Boule painted such a biased portrait. Of course, it is impossible to answer such a question with absolute certainty but a number of things suggest themselves. Boule was a paleontologist and had acquired his training in Toulouse and

Paris during the 1880's. Paleontology had been founded in France by Georges Cuvier during the first third of the nineteenth century and virtually all of France's paleontologists in the nineteenth century had been rigorously grounded in Cuvier's ideas. Boule's thinking, then, was thoroughly conditioned by the ideas of catastrophism and was at bottom opposed to an evolutionary point of view.

By the twentieth century one could no longer deny, as Cuvier had done, the existence of fossil man, but one could claim that the fossils discovered were not the ancestors of subsequent forms of men if they looked noticeably different from them. Boule, then, denied that either Pithecanthropus or Neanderthal were precursors of modern men. He allowed that they might be considered as primitive cousins—extinct side lines—but not in the direct line of human evolution. With the overemphasis of the non-modern features of the La Chapelle-aux-Saints skeleton it became a much less likely candidate for the forefather of the succeeding Upper Paleolithic forms. The fully modern features of the Cro-Magnon were also overemphasized to demonstrate the gap between the Mousterian and Upper Paleolithic populations. This was easy enough to do since the Cro-Magnon male was without teeth and possessed of a somewhat eroded face, which allowed rather a broad latitude in reconstruction.

The supposed sudden break between the Mousterian culture and the Upper Paleolithic tools which overlie it in the same European sites was also stressed. To Boule and to many European archeologists, this meant that the Upper Paleolithic had developed elsewhere—somewhere outside Europe, perhaps in "The East"— and swept in as an invasion. This, of course, was simply the kind of thinking represented in the theory of catastrophism and was here reapplied to explain the sequence of fossil men and their cultures as an alternative to an evolutionary explanation. Clearly Boule and his followers have done their best to discredit evolutionary explanations where they have been applied to man's prehistory, and the accident of historical events during the first two decades of the twentieth century has allowed this antievolutionary view to persist in many quarters right up to the present time.

Boule's influential position and extensive, if biased, publications

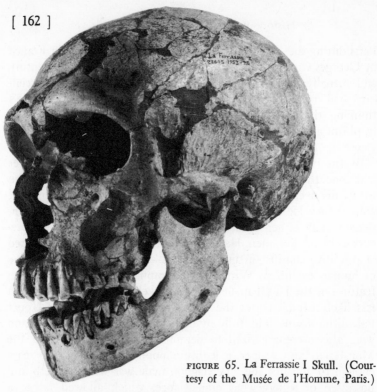

FIGURE 65. La Ferrassie I Skull. (Courtesy of the Musée de l'Homme, Paris.)

on the well-preserved La Chapelle-aux-Saints skeleton gave great weight to the views of hominid catastrophism which he advocated. Apparent support for his position was given, not only by the ill-fated Le Moustier find, but by the fact that the next few years produced more well-preserved Neanderthal skeletal material from nearby parts of southern France. In 1909 and 1910 undoubted Neanderthal skeletons were found at the site of La Ferrassie not far from Le Moustier and Cro-Magnon and more juvenile fragments were to follow in 1912. In addition, the site of La Quina not far away yielded a Neanderthal skeleton in 1911 and many more fragments in the immediately succeeding years. The La Quina skeleton was the subject of sound descriptive publications by the discoverer, Dr. Henri Martin, but these did not appear for another decade and contained no interpretations or comparisons, and it was generally assumed that this simply supported Boule's well-known assertions. The La Ferrassie material was turned over to Boule himself for description, but, either because he was so busy with the La Chapelle-aux-Saints material or because a careful consideration of the variation indicated by the two adult skeletons from La Ferrassie would have contradicted the views for which he stood, he never published anything on them. As a matter of fact much of the La Ferrassie material remains unpublished to this day, although from the few pieces of information in print it is evident that they differ as much from each other as each one does from La Chapelle-aux-Saints. It seems likely that a full appraisal of the French Neanderthals found between 1908 and 1912 will show that the picture of the curious and supposedly

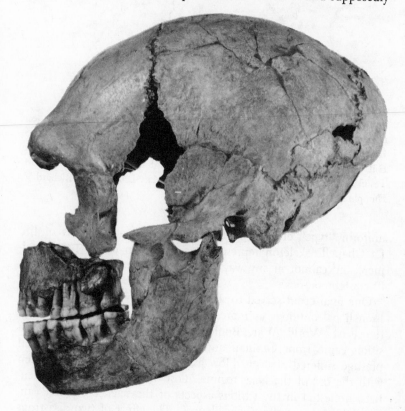

FIGURE 66. La Quina Skull. (Courtesy of the Musée de l'Homme, Paris.)

FIGURE 67. Location of sites where major Neanderthal discoveries have been made. 1. Neanderthal. 2. Spy. 3. La Chapelle-aux-Saints. 4. Le Moustier. 5. La Ferrassie. 6. La Quina. 7. Gibraltar. 8. Krapina. 9. Saccopastore. 10. Broken Hill (Rhodesian Man). 11. Saldanha. 12. Mount Carmel. 13. Shanidar. 14. Teshik Tash. 15. Solo. 16. Ma-Pa. (Drawing by Mary L. Brace and Richard V. Humphrey.)

uniform "type" created by Boule primarily on the basis of the La Chapelle skeleton represented a distortion of his type specimen, and cannot in any way be supported by the evidence from its contemporaries.

One final event served to solidify the anti-evolutionary views of French paleontology as represented by Marcellin Boule, namely, the First World War. Boule's only systematic critical opposition came from German anthropologists. German intellectual prestige suffered a severe blow as a result of the war, and then with the rise of the Nazi regime, most of the independent scientists interested in the various aspects of the science of man (anthropology) were effectively silenced. The effect of two disastrous wars and an intervening era of vicious intellectual repression can be seen in the fact that little survives of pre-World War I German anthropological thinking. As far as paleoanthropology is concerned, most modern German students avowedly trace the source of their thinking back to the position of Marcellin Boule, especially as it was expounded in the monograph on La Chapelle-aux-Saints and in Boule's compendious volume, *Les Hommes Fossiles* (*Fossil Men*), which appeared respectively immediately before and just after the First World War.

A brief history of the discovery of the major fossil finds, such as this, must necessarily omit many minor and fragmentary ones as well as some major and relatively important ones. During the last several decades finds have been made in such quantity that there is not space enough to describe the circumstances surrounding the discovery of each one. We shall, therefore, limit our concern to the treatment of those major discoveries which have important implications in the construction of a coherent scheme for understanding human evolution.

With all the excitement revolving around the Neanderthal discoveries and interpretations in France, one Englishman apparently resolved that England, too, could have its fossil man and he proceded literally to create it—both the excitement and the fossil man. This is the story of one of the most elaborate and successful scientific hoaxes ever perpetrated, and, while there is no need to discuss fraudulent material in any kind of detail, it is introduced here since it seriously clouded issues and colored the thinking of serious students for nearly half a century afterward.

In 1911, a Sussex solicitor and amateur prehistorian, Charles Dawson, claimed to have found a fragment of a fossilized human skull in a gravel pit at Piltdown in southern England. This he took to Dr. (later Sir) Arthur Smith Woodward of the British Museum (Natural History) who was greatly excited by the discovery. During the next year Dawson and Smith Woodward worked over the deposits in the gravel pit and discovered some more fragments, presumably of the same skull, as well as pieces of a variety of extinct animals which purportedly demonstrated the great age of the deposit. A few more finds were made during the next three years, apparently confirming the 1911 and 1912 discoveries.

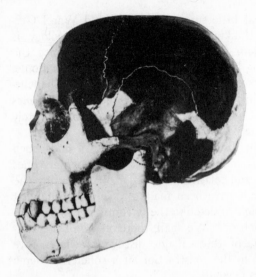

The remarkable thing about the supposed Piltdown man is that it coupled a brain-case of essentially modern form—steep smooth-browed forehead—with an entirely ape-like jaw, undeveloped chin, and with a projecting canine. After a few years of discussion, British anatomical authorities resolved their differences and agreed that the form of the skull was not different from that of modern man, and that the form of the jaw was not different from that of a modern anthropoid ape, which latter is not surprising since eventually it was demonstrated that this is precisely what it was.

While many non-British scientists balked at accepting such a bizarre association of apparently incompatible pieces, all doubts concerning the accuracy of the reconstruction were removed in a demonstration of anatomical virtuosity by Professor (later Sir) Arthur Keith of the Royal College of Surgeons in London, who for the next forty years was looked up to as the most distinguished and respected of British physical anthropologists. Critics of Keith's reconstruction of Piltdown challenged him to a test and he willingly complied. They took a skull of known shape and size from the collections, broke it into fragments resembling those of the Piltdown skull and asked Keith to reconstruct the original. With astonishing skill, Keith came within 20 cc. of the true cranial capacity. Considering that the original measured capacity was in the neighborhood of 1400 cc., an error of only 20 cc. can be regarded as totally insignificant. The result was an enormous boost to Keith's prestige and the removal of all doubts concerning the accuracy of the Piltdown restoration.

While many anthropologists continued to doubt the association of skull and jaw in a single individual, the fact that no other anthropoid ape fragments had been found in early Ice Age strata in England tended to increase the apparent probability that the Piltdown pieces belonged together. With the prestige and authority of such eminent scientists standing behind the discoveries, it

FIGURE 69. The Piltdown Committee. Personalities concerned with the Piltdown "discovery": *back row*: Mr. F. O. Barlow, maker of the casts; Prof. G. Elliot Smith, anatomist; Mr. C. Dawson, the "discoverer"; Dr. A. S. Woodward, zoologist; *front row*: Dr. A. S. Underwood, teeth expert; Prof. Arthur Keith, anatomist; Mr. W. P. Pycraft, zoologist; Sir Ray Lankester, zoologist. (From the painting by John Cooke, R.A., exhibited at the Royal Academy, 1915.)

never occurred to anyone—even the most critical scientists—that the finds might be forgeries and that they might not be genuinely ancient, although in retrospect it is clear that the published accounts of the actual findings were anything but satisfactory. To prove such great antiquity for a human fossil, especially one which so profoundly affected all interpretations of the course of human evolution, much more accurate documentation should have been demanded than the "Several years ago I was walking along. . . ." sort of account which was offered. More than one amateur archeologist acquainted with Dawson, and who had examined his artifacts was convinced that they were fraudulent, but put nothing into print to that effect.

Apparently the desire to believe in Piltdown was great enough to overcome any doubts. Among other things, it demonstrated to the satisfaction of the English that humanity had its origins on British soil; furthermore this most ancient man had the smooth and lofty brow of modern *Homo sapiens*, and this was taken as proof that the heavy-browed Neanderthals of continental Europe and the small-brained and bestial fossil from Java were not the direct ancestors of modern man. Interesting evidence for unsuccessful parallel evolutionary developments perhaps, but it was generally felt that Boule was correct in regarding them as having become extinct without issue. Thus by chance, the concepts of hominid catastrophism became established among the very people who were raised in an atmosphere of Darwinian evolution.

The evidence which Piltdown presumably offered for the great antiquity of the modern form of braincase was regarded as reinforced by the claimed antiquity of another skeleton which had been discovered in a gravel pit at Galley Hill on the banks of the Thames in 1888. The skull and skeleton were well preserved and relatively complete, unlike the highly fragmentary Piltdown remains, and were perfectly modern in form, although allegedly possessing some hints of the "primitive." The date was claimed to be mid-Pleistocene but the documentation again was more in the form of verbal assertion than demonstrable fact. Nevertheless, Galley Hill was accepted by British scientists as further evidence for the remote antiquity of modern forms of man. They did, however, admit that certain doubts could be entertained concerning the precise dating of their finds, which only produced further intensified efforts to discover unquestionable evidence of ancient *sapiens*.

The solution of the problems surrounding both Galley Hill and Piltdown came about as a result of a combination of events. Research by Dr. Kenneth P. Oakley of the British Museum (Natural History), in the late 1940's led him to reinvestigate some of the late nineteenth century attempts to determine how old things were by various forms of chemical analysis. Specifically it was shown that the amount of fluorine contained in bone increases in proportion to the length of time during which the bone has remained buried in the ground. It also depends on the amount of fluorine present in the particular area where the bone in question is buried. Hence, high content of fluorine determined for a bone from one area does not necessarily mean that it is older than a fragment with a lesser amount of fluorine but from another area. On the other hand, high fluorine content for a particular piece of bone *does* mean that it is older than another fragment from the same area but with a lower F content.

In 1948 Ashley Montagu made a thorough study of the Galley Hill remains, the result of which was to convince him that none of the alleged "primitive" traits which were supposed to characterize it were in fact present. The skull was that of a modern man in every way, shape, and form. Meeting Oakley shortly afterward, Montagu communicated his findings to him. A study of the Galley Hill site had brought Oakley to the same conclusion. Subsequent fluorine analysis of the Galley Hill bones confirmed the suspicion that the skeleton could not be of Middle Pleistocene age. This supported the view of those who had long pointed to the fact that the discovery of a complete and well-preserved human skeleton was exceedingly unlikely to have occurred *in situ* in a deposit which was completely devoid of the fossil remains of other animals. The downward percolation of carbonic acid-laden waters through the gravels was so pronounced at the site that all bones would have been decalcified in much less time than the age attributed to this skeleton. Additional evidence indicated an artificial burial and a post-Pleistocene age.

Dr. Oakley next applied the fluorine test to the Piltdown fragments, and his preliminary conclusion was that they were more recent than the early Pleistocene or late Pliocene dates originally claimed, but he still did not suggest anything irregular.

The suspicion that the whole thing might be a fake was first seriously entertained in 1953 by Dr. J. S. Weiner of Oxford University. Among other things it was known that Charles Dawson had treated the fragments he claimed to have found in 1911 with potassium bichromate according to the widespread nineteenth century belief that this hardened fragile bones. When Dawson showed the fragments to Smith Woodward at the British Museum in 1912, the latter commented that such a procedure was worthless, yet, later that same year when the mandible was found by Dawson in the presence of Smith Woodward, it was already stained with potassium bichromate and it clearly must have been a "plant."

There were other discrepancies which reinforced Dr. Weiner's suspicions and led him to institute a thorough reappraisal of the Piltdown remains with the collaboration of Dr. Oakley and Professor Sir Wilfrid E. Le Gros Clark of Oxford. Microscopic examination showed that the separate canine tooth had been ground down artifically so that it would not seem so large as to be unquestionably anthropoid. To produce a color appropriate for an iron oxide stain, the tooth was given a coat of paint. New drillings to get larger samples for chemical analysis produced the expected powder from the skull, but from the jaw came tiny white shavings of fresh bone accompanied by an odor like that of "burning horn." Only recent bone gives off such a burnt horn odor, fossil bone does not. Obviously this was not a fossil.

Exhaustive analysis showed that the skull fragments came from a recent human being and the jaw was that of a recent female orang-utan. Furthermore the Pleistocene mammalian remains discovered at the same time were shown to have come from other parts of the world far removed from England, and the crude stone and bone tools were likewise shown to be forgeries.

Drs. Weiner, Le Gros Clark, and Oakley made their sensational findings known to the world late in 1953 ending a hoax which had perplexed the anthropological world for more than forty years. The whole story was written up and published in 1955 by Dr.

J. S. Weiner in a fascinating book entitled *The Piltdown Forgery*, which reads like a detective story, which in fact it is.

There remains only to identify the forger. Only two people who had figured prominently in the history of the Piltdown discovery remained alive in 1953. One was the French Jesuit and eminent paleontologist Père Teilhard de Chardin, who had actually found the canine in 1913, but who was relatively dissociated from the wrangles over Piltdown interpretations. The other was Sir Arthur Keith who had played a prominent role in the establishment of the Piltdown remains as an authentic fossil. Sir Arthur's whole approach to human evolution—as was that of his numerous followers—was colored by the attempt to explain the existence of such a bizarre combination of traits at such an early time level. Teilhard could only register baffled astonishment without any suspicion of who had perpetrated the fraud or what the motivation had been. But Sir Arthur Keith when queried by a former student (Ashley Montagu), for a possible explanation of the forger's motivation, replied (September 19, 1954), "If you knew the wonderful fame won by Schoentensack in 1907 by the discovery of the Heidelberg jaw you would realise the fame waiting for the discoverer of the skull of that early date." It was as simple as that: the forger sought to win fame by his forgery.

Sir Arthur Smith Woodward had passed on many years previously, but the evidence of the years of fruitless toil which he had expended in the hope of discovering more material relating to Piltdown clearly declares his innocence. There remains only Charles Dawson who had died in 1916 before the issues surrounding Piltdown had fully gained momentum. Circumstantial evidence all points to Dawson as the forger, but Dr. Weiner is careful to make it clear that this does not constitute proof, and that we may never be certain of the forger's real identity or of all the reasons for his conduct.

Following the important Neanderthal finds of the first two decades of this century and the beginnings of the excitement over Piltdown, the scene of actual discovery was due to shift away from Europe. The first hint of what was to come was announced from South Africa in 1924 in the form of a small fossilized skull found during quarrying operations at Tuang, Bechuanaland. This

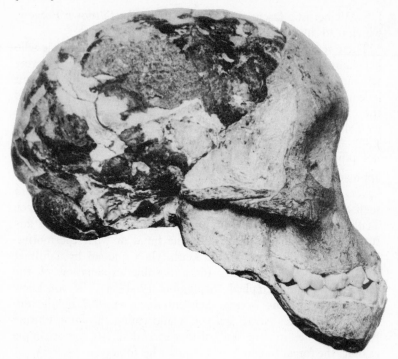

FIGURE 70. *Australopithecus africanus*. (Courtesy of the American Museum of Natural History.)

was given to a young professor of anatomy at the University of Witwatersrand Medical School in Johannesburg. Professor Raymond A. Dart studied it for several months, and then early in 1925 he published a relatively complete preliminary description in the British scientific weekly *Nature*. In this he noted that despite the juvenile age of his fossil—equivalent to that of a six year old child in the human growth cycle—it appeared to be closer to the human line of development than any other living or fossil ape. His cautious conclusion was that this little fossil was an advanced ape, and he christened it *Australopithecus africanus* (southern ape of Africa).

Dart's conservative description of the find and statement of his conclusions stirred up a storm in British scientific circles, which continues to reverberate to the present day. The most distinguished and influential men in anatomy and anthropology, some of whom had been Dart's former teachers, read his paper before it was printed, and then wrote disparaging comments which were published just after the article itself appeared. Dart, of course, had not seen these comments and was given no chance to discuss or reply to them. Criticism continued, becoming increasingly harsh. The impression thus created was that Dart was rash and hasty in publishing without the assistance of some established

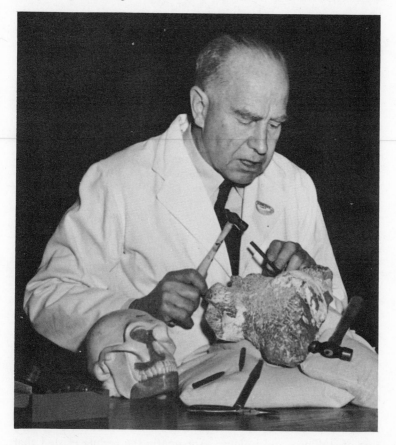

FIGURE 71. Raymond Dart. (Photo courtesy of Professor Raymond Dart.)

FIGURE 72. Australopithecine sites. 1. Taung. 2. Sterkfontein. 3. Swartkrans. 4. Kromdraai. 5. Makapansgat. 6. Olduvai Gorge. 7. Koro Toro. 8. Megan-thropus. (Drawing by Mary L. Brace and Richard V. Humphrey.)

"authority"—and so soon after discovery. Furthermore, it was claimed that he had exaggerated the man-like features of his fossil, and finally he was ridiculed for displaying his ignorance of the classics in his "barbarous" combination of Latin- and Greek-based terms in the word Australopithecus. Of all the criticisms levelled against his work, only this last has any truth to it, and, since it is totally irrelevant to the appreciation of the significance of Australopithecus, it should be ignored.

Time and further discoveries have shown that not only were Dart's critics badly in error, as they had previously been about the Piltdown remains, but that Dart's own interpretation was a conservative underestimate of the status of the population to which Australopithecus belonged. In retrospect, it seems as though the source of the criticism could be attributed to a mix-ture of stuffiness and jealousy. Apparently the feeling existed that Dart should properly have turned the fossil over to the established authorities in England for description and eventual publication, and there was evident annoyance that he had gone ahead on his own.

The prestige of his critics was such that an unbiased appraisal of his account could not be given, and it was more than ten years before further finds from South Africa reopened the issue and raised the possibility that Dart might have been right. Meanwhile, however, the spotlight had turned to other parts of the world, and in a sense the discoveries of the late 1920's and 1930's further reinforced the feeling that Dart had been ill-advised when he had intimated the possibility that Australopithecus might have been remotely ancestral to later fully human forms.

As a holdover from the economic and political practices of the nineteenth century, European influence continued to be directly felt in many parts of the world until the Second World War, while much of the budding nationalism and antiwestern sentiment

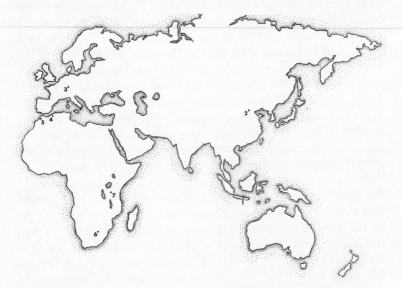

FIGURE 73. Location of Pithecanthropine sites. 1. Pithecanthropus (Java). 2. Sinanthropus (Choukoutien). 3. Heidelberg. 4. Ternefine. 5. Rabat. 6. Telanthropus. 7. Olduvai Gorge. (Drawing by Mary L. Brace and Richard V. Humphrey.)

prevalent in the world today can be traced to this, it is also true that scientific advances occurred which would otherwise have been long delayed. In the search for exploitable mineral deposits, the colonially oriented governments employed trained geologists, and inevitably these men made discoveries of general scientific significance as well as performing their commercial functions. We have seen how such activities led to the discovery of Pithecanthropus in Java, and it has been mentioned that Australopithecus in southern Africa was discovered in the same way.

During the early 1920's European-trained geologists were active in China, and as a consequence of their efforts evidence began to accumulate pointing to the existence of prehistoric man in the town of Choukoutien somewhat less than thirty miles south-west of Peiping (formerly Peking) in northern China. The first traces of the presence of man were in the form of quartz fragments in the fill of what had formerly been large limestone caves. Quartz could only get into such a place by human agency, and before long the presence of man himself was revealed by the discovery of a small number of human teeth. In 1927, on the basis of the study of a single tooth, Dr. Davidson Black (1884–1934), the Canadian born anatomist at the Peking Union Medical College, announced to a skeptical world that Choukoutien contained a new genus and species of fossil man, *Sinanthropus pekinensis*.

Modern experts in taxonomy deplore the tendency that formerly resulted in each new discovery being given a new taxonomic designation, but despite the fact that from the vantage point of our greater perspective, Dr. Black appears to have been overly enthusiastic in creating new names, nevertheless his appreciation of the significance of the fragments discovered led to a systematic investigation of the sites of Choukoutien and the recovery of one of the largest and most important collections of early human fossils ever made. Excavations in 1928 yielded skull and jaw fragments, and during the last day of the excavating season in December 1929, Dr. W. C. Pei, the paleontologist in charge of the excavation, himself found a complete skull minus only the face. This fully vindicated the predictions made by Black and served to usher in the 1930's on an appropriately dramatic note, for this decade was to produce a greater variety of remains from more

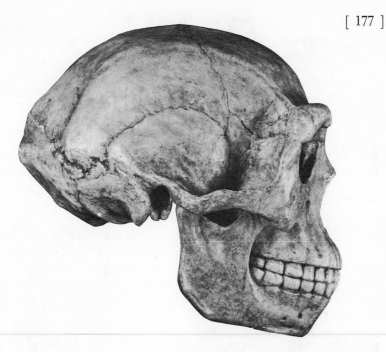

FIGURE 74. Reconstruction of Sinanthropus (*Homo erectus pekinensis*) by Franz Weidenreich. (Courtesy of the American Museum of Natural History.)

corners of the world illustrating all the various phases of human evolution than any other comparable period of time before or since.

Operations at Choukoutien during the next ten years produced abundant remains of a population at the same stage of evolution as Pithecanthropus. Furthermore, stone tools and the remains of hearths and butchered and roasted animals amply confirmed the first opinion of Dubois offered as long ago as the mid-1890's. Ironically, now that the world was finally convinced by the finds of Peking man that Dubois had been right, the only dissenting voice to be heard was that of the aging Dubois himself who refused to recognize any relationship between the Chinese fossils, which he regarded as fully human, and his precious Pithecanthropus which he alone, like Virchow so many years before, claimed to be a giant gibbon.

The excavations in China were momentarily halted in 1934 by

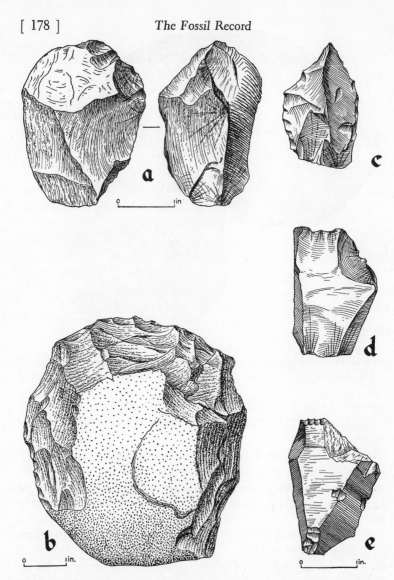

FIGURE 75. Stone tools of Pekin Man (*Homo erectus pekinensis*). *a*. Quartz chopper-tool. *b*. Boulder of greenstone flaked into chopper form. *c*. Pointed flake of quartz. *d*. Bi-polar flake of quartz. *e*. Bi-pyramidal crystal of quartz utilized as tool. *After Pei and Black*. (From K. P. Oakley, *Man the Tool-Maker*. Courtesy of the British Museum, Natural History.)

the untimely death of Dr. Black. At first it seemed as though this might present a serious hindrance to the work at Choukoutien, but the almost calamitous effect of the death of Black was alleviated by the appointment of the redoubtable Dr. Franz Weidenreich (1873–1947) to fill his position (see Figure 77). Weidenreich, a former student of Gustav Schwalbe before the turn of the century, together with his late teacher, was one of the very few scientists to defend a view of human evolution which in overall grasp is substantially similar to that being presented in the present volume. After a stormy but successful two-phased academic career (the phases being before and after World War I) and another career in politics, Dr. Weidenreich was forced to become an exile from Hitler's Germany, and at a time in life when most men are beginning to think of retirement he began the work which was to make him one of the immortals of physical anthropology. He continued his predecessor's work, and, although his life was again to be changed by war, he produced a series of outstanding monographs in the best tradition of German thoroughness. As a result, Peking man constitutes one of the best known of the early characters in the story of human evolution.

Among the various lands in which significant fossils were found during the 1930's the greatest variety came from Java. As the decaded wore on, older and older fossils were discovered, so that by the time the war in the Pacific put a halt to research, remnants of three distinct stages in human evolution had been accumulated.

The first finds were made in the years 1931–1932 at Ngandong on the banks of the Solo River, immediately downstream from

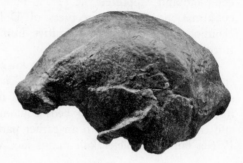

FIGURE 76. Solo Skull V, typical of all the Solo Skulls. (Courtesy of the American Museum of Natural History.)

Trinil, where Dubois had opened up the study of Javanese pre-history. All told, eleven Solo skulls were unearthed—each minus the skull base and the facial skeleton, facts which have been taken to indicate that their owners were probably victims of cannibalism. The important thing to note, however, is that in age and morphological development the Solo men are the far eastern equivalent of the Neanderthals of Europe. It has been claimed that in some respects they show affinities to the pithe-canthropines, and Weidenreich has noted that this is just what one would expect if they were the Upper Pleistocene descendants of this early Pleistocene stage.

In the mid-1930's, the Dutch paleontologist G. H. R. von Koenigswald, who had participated in the discovery of the Solo remains, exploited a number of successful methods of obtaining fossil material. In addition to his own collecting efforts, he trained Javanese villagers to spot fossils that might be discovered after the rains. He paid a flat price per fragment, a practice that almost led to his undoing in 1937. At Sangiran just upstream from Trinil in Central Java, his collectors had come across a skull in the same layer in which Dubois' 1891 find had occurred. His assistants, being practical-minded, proceeded to multiply the number of pieces he had to pay for by the simple expedient of breaking the skull into some forty small fragments. They were all accounted for, however, and, since the breaks were clean and fresh, it was a simple matter to fit the pieces together. The resulting skull was so similar to Dubois' original Pithecanthropus that Weidenreich remarked that they "resemble each other as much as do two eggs." Furthermore von Koenigswald's skull was somewhat more complete and supported the Peking finds in providing additional confirmation of the correctness of Dubois' original judgment claiming the ancient and primitive human status for Pithecan-thropus.

The Javanese fossils mentioned so far have all come from beds containing the so-called "Trinil fauna" indicating a Middle Plei-stocene age. Von Koenigswald's efforts, however, also turned up fossil human material from beds containing the "Djetis fauna" and therefore belonging to an earlier part of the Pleistocene. In 1936 a fairly complete skull minus face was discovered at Mod-

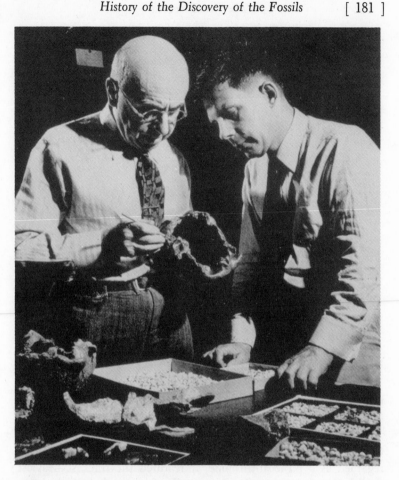

FIGURE 77. Franz Weidenreich (1873–1948) and Dr. G. H. R. von Koenigswald. (Courtesy of the American Museum of Natural History.)

jokerto which apparently belonged to an infant scarcely a year
old. Had it lived to maturity it probably would have developed
into an adult of the Pithecanthropus variety, although this is
mostly speculation, and it is evident that an infant fossil cannot
tell us a great deal about the characteristics of the population to
which it belonged. In 1939, however, Dr. von Koenigswald unearthed the back of the skull and part of the face of an adult

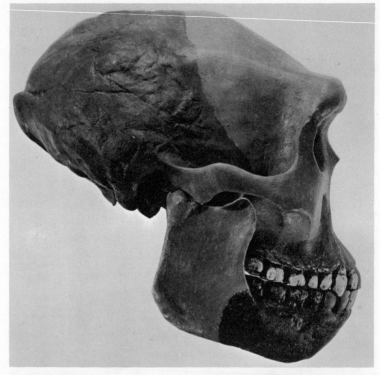

FIGURE 78. *Homo erectus robustus* (*modjokertensis*) (*Pithecanthropus robustus IV*). (Courtesy of the American Museum of Natural History.)

from the Djetis stratum at Sangiran. Although this could still be regarded as a pithecanthropine, it featured the thickest heaviest skull bones and the most robust teeth of any such fossil hitherto found.

The final treasure which this period in human paleontology was to produce from Java was found by von Koenigswald in 1941 in the Djetis layers of the same Sangiran area that had yielded the 1937 and 1939 Pithecanthropus skulls. This was a relatively small fragment of lower jaw, and from the form of the teeth there could be no doubt that it was human. What, however, makes it remarkable, is its enormous size. It is so large that it makes the massive dental apparatus of the 1939 Pithecanthropus look like a dwarf, and in fact it is twice as thick as the biggest known jaw of an adult male gorilla. Clearly this was not just another pithecanthropine, and von Koenigswald felt justified in christening it *Meganthropus palaeojavanicus.* Another similar mandible was found in the same area of Java in 1952 which supported the impression created by the earlier discovery. It has become apparent, however, that von Koenigswald was premature in applying his jaw-breaking name to the new find since, as we shall shortly see, similar finds had already been made and officially named elsewhere.

Suffice it to say that von Koenigswald's activities in Java during the 1930's were instrumental in yielding solid evidence for the existence of three former stages of human evolution: the Solo skulls as Oriental counterparts to the Neanderthals in the West, the Pithecanthropus remains, and finally the incorrectly designated *Meganthropus* which belonged to a still older stage.

While all these remarkable finds were being made in the Orient, the Middle East was not lagging far behind. Isolated material of importance had been found before the decade under consideration, but this was simply a prelude to what was to come. The real prize came as a result of the efforts of a joint expedition by the

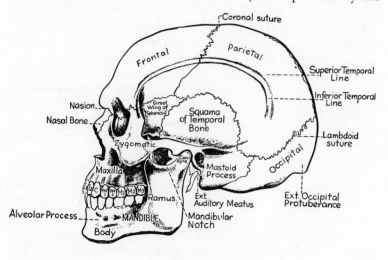

FIGURE 79. Human skull.

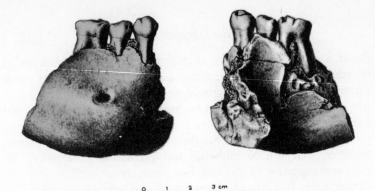

American School of Prehistoric Research and the British School of Archaeology in Jerusalem. Little more than a mile from the Mediterranean shore some fifteen miles south of Haifa in Palestine, the expedition excavated the contents of two caves on the western slopes of Mount Carmel. There in the years 1931 and 1932 the fossil remains of more than a dozen individuals were found, ranging from a few teeth to complete skeletons—all associated with stone tools belonging to a Middle Eastern version of the Mousterian, the industry of Neanderthal man in Europe.

In the cave of Mugharet et-Tabūn (Cave of the Oven) there was found the complete skeleton of a woman who was morphologically identical to the Neanderthals of Europe, which was not too surprising, but in the cave of Mugharet es Skhūl (Cave of the Kids), ten skeletons were found showing every possible combination of the features of Neanderthal with those of modern man. The anthropological arguments which the Mount Carmel finds stirred up continue unabated to the present day and revolve chiefly about two problems.

First, the dating of Mount Carmel has been a source of controversy from the outset, but in a sense the solution to this problem preferred by many authors has been largely influenced by their perception of the second problem which involves assumptions concerning the course of human evolution. Most practicing students of human paleontology were operating under the belief that the Neanderthals suddenly became extinct during the fourth and last glaciation, being replaced by men of modern form who had evolved elsewhere and whose ancestry, as indicated by Galley Hill and Piltdown, extended far back into the early Pleistocene. Here, however, in the very area where ancient *sapiens* was postulated to be most ancient, there was this curious melange of modern and

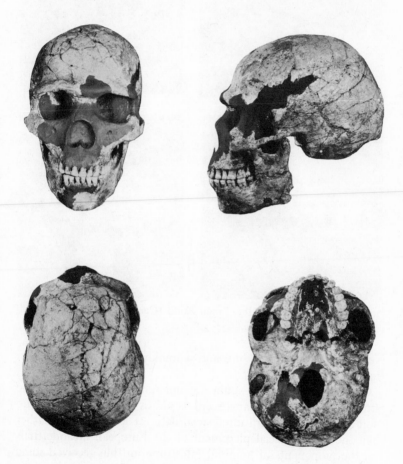

FIGURE 81. Four views of Skhūl V. (Courtesy Prof. Charles Snow, and the Peabody Museum, Harvard University.)

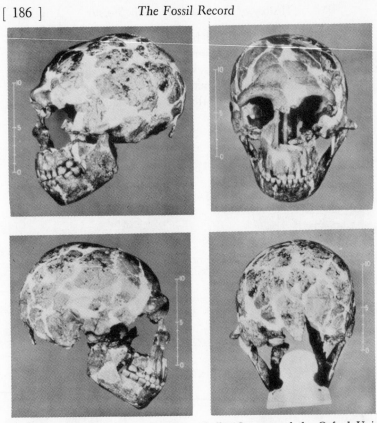

FIGURE 82. Four Views of the Tabūn Skull. (Courtesy of the Oxford University Press.)

Neanderthal traits at Skhūl, and a frankly Neanderthal skeleton from Tabūn.

Clearly the age of the strata was not early Pleistocene, and the efforts to make the remains seem as old as possible could do no more than claim a third interglacial date. At least this was earlier than the fourth glacial placement of the European Neanderthals and the proponents of hominid catastrophism thus received some consolation, although this was not the sort of evidence for early moderns which they had hoped to find. One solution to the puzzle was suggested which still left the door open for the as yet unfound ancient modern who was assumed to exist—still farther east perhaps?—and that was to regard the Mount Carmel remains as evidence for the hybridization of a local Neanderthal group, represented by the Tabūn female, and a population of the undiscovered *sapiens*.

The problem was dumped squarely in the lap of Sir Arthur Keith who was primarily responsible for the description and interpretation of the Mount Carmel remains. The uncertainties of the situation were the cause of a good deal of mental agonizing on the part of Keith, but he finally came up with the tentative suggestion that the Mount Carmel fossils presented a picture of a population in the throes of evolutionary change which presumably accounted for the amount of variability present. Precisely why an unusual rate of evolution should be going on here in the Middle East Keith did not even venture to guess, and why the Neanderthals of Europe presumably lagged behind was not a question which appeared to concern anyone.

Some authorities offered an alternative solution to the Mount Carmel population by pointing out that Tabūn and Skhūl were actually different in age and hence not really part of the same population. Tabūn had to be regarded as Neanderthal in any case, but Skhūl could then be treated as the long sought for *sapiens*, a little crude and "primitive" perhaps, but still "pure." While it was conceded that Tabūn and Skhūl may be of separate ages, most experts could not evade the realization that Skhūl was clearly neanderthaloid, i.e., morphologically half way between Neanderthal and *sapiens*. Then of course the plaguing problem of the third interglacial date would arise again, and there seemed no way to decide whether this was actually a picture of evolution in process or simply a case of hybridization.

Since the evolutionists could think of no particular reason why the observed changes should occur, and the would-be hybridizers could only produce a representative of one of the supposed parent populations, it seemed like a stalemate. Recently, however, the problem has been greatly simplified by the growing realization that the Skhūl remains occurred not in the third interglacial before the European Neanderthals, but only about thirty-five thousand years ago and hence substantially later than the Neanderthals. Not only are they half way in between Neanderthal and modern in form, but they are also half way in between in time. Tabūn (dated at 41,000 B.P.) would then be a contemporary of the European Neanderthals which, on the basis of form alone, is just what one would expect. Mount Carmel, then, does present a picture of the evolution of modern man out of a Neanderthal precursor just as Schwalbe predicted more than a half-century ago, and as we shall see in Chapters 7 and 8, we now think we can understand the reason why it occurred and why it should have happened at exactly this time.

While the Far Eastern finds were providing confirmation for the late nineteenth century views of Dubois and his followers, and Palestine was proving to be a troublesome thorn in the side of the hominid catastrophists, England finally acquired its only really ancient fossil man. This was found in 1935 at Swanscombe on the lower Thames in a gravel pit whose strata are composed of sediments laid down in the latter part of the second interglacial. Abundant evidence for the presence of prehistoric man had been accumulating for many years in the form of the Acheulean hand axes of the Lower Paleolithic but it was only after years of vigilance on the part of a London dentist, Mr. A. T. Marston, that a human occipital bone (the back and bottom of the skull) was discovered in 1935. Mr. Marston continued his interest and early the next year a left parietal bone (top and side) was found which articulated with the previously discovered occipital. This meant that the whole rear half of the skull could be reconstructed. It is interesting to note that by virtue of continued diligent search the right parietal was discovered in 1955, just 20 years after the other pieces, and confirmed the reconstruction.

Naturally, interest was intense, and, as a result, every conceivable method has been employed to check the reliability of the apparent Middle Pleistocene age of the Swanscombe skull. There can be no question that the skull is genuine, but from this point on certainty ends. Perhaps partly because of their intellectual committment to the existence of modern forms of man in the early Pleistocene, such as the now-discredited Galley Hill and Piltdown forms, British writers have been disposed best to prove that Swanscombe was modern. This of course has been most diffi-

FIGURE 83. The Swanscombe Skull, top and back views. (Courtesy of the British Museum, Natural History.)

cult to accomplish since, during the latter part of the Pleistocene, human evolutionary changes have largely occurred in the region of the face, and the face of Swanscombe was totally lacking.

Nevertheless, the analysts have done the best they could with what they had. They have discovered every possible measurement wherein Swanscombe did not differ from modern man, and they played down the one obvious dimension where Swanscombe clearly exceeds more than 90 per cent of modern men. Furthermore a recent reappraisal by Dr. T. D. Stewart, has shown that they have totally neglected to mention that the para-mastoid area is of a form found only in the known Neanderthal skulls and not in modern man at all. It certainly seems that the claim that Swanscombe is clear evidence for modern man in the second interglacial has yet to be substantiated, and it may yet be shown that the earliest Englishman was an early Neanderthal.

An accurate appraisal of Swanscombe is especially important because it is one of the very few pieces of evidence for the shape of mankind between Heidelberg and the pithecanthropines and the Neanderthals of the fourth glaciation. Two years before the discovery of Swanscombe, in strata of approximately the same age, a more complete skull was uncovered in a gravel pit at Steinheim, not far from Marbach, the birthplace of the German poet Schiller.

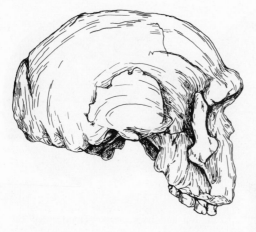

FIGURE 84. The Steinheim
Skull. (Drawing by Mary
L. Brace.)

The Steinheim skull had been partially crushed and warped by
its long interrment, but the frontal part of the skull is present
and all but the incisor-bearing part of the face is preserved. As in
the case of Swanscombe, the attempt was made to demonstrate
that here, too, was ancient *sapiens*, but again this was primarily
based on the non-diagnostic parts of the back of the skull and,
because of the degree of deformation, proves relatively little. The
heavy, projecting brow ridge or supraorbital torus, however, while
not quite up to that of a pithecanthropine, clearly exceeds that of
all the known Neanderthals of the fourth glaciation, as one would
expect in a population halfway in time between the pithecanthropines and the Neanderthals.

Steinheim and Swanscombe, discovered within two years of
each other during the mid-thirties, are the only pieces of fossil
evidence which fit in that blank part of the record between the
pithecanthropines and the Neanderthals. While they do not constitute evidence for the evolution of the pithecanthropines into
the Neanderthals, neither do they provide support for the presence of an elusive Middle Pleistocene population of "yet-to-be-
discovered" *sapiens*.

By and large, the anthropological world regarded the finds made
in the 1930's as valuable confirmation of the views which had become accepted on much less extensive evidence earlier in this

[190]

century. Pithecanthropus supported by Sinanthropus was considered the crudest possible form of man, Neanderthal was perceived as a gross and clumsy caricature, and *sapiens* was assumed to be of an antiquity which extended back to the beginning of the Pleistocene and was believed to have blossomed, unaccountably, late in the Pleistocene while engaged in the business of exterminating his primitive cousins.

To be sure the Mount Carmel problems had not been solved to the satisfaction of all concerned, von Koenigswald's Meganthropus and some finds of isolated teeth of enormous size had not been satisfactorily explained, and, most vexing of all, really solid evidence for ancient *sapiens* continued to elude discovery despite the confidence that this would be rectified by further exploration. However the most disquieting development from the point of view of anthropological orthodoxy came once again from South Africa.

Just when it seemed as though the accumulation of newly found fossil material coming from all over the Old World was effacing all memory of the brief stir caused by Dart's Australopithecus, the activities of the indomitable Dr. Robert Broom (1866–1951) resulted in the discovery of another australopithecine. This time no one could claim that the hominid features were a product of its relative youth because this time the skull was that of an adult. It had been blasted out of the face of a lime works quarry at Sterkfontein in the Transvaal area of South Africa, west of Johannesburg.

Broom, born in Scotland, had been an internationally famous paleontologist since the turn of the century. He supported his field work by practicing medicine in his spare time, or, if one prefers, he was a practicing physician who devoted his spare time to paleontology. Perhaps the first is the better way of considering it since the real interest of his life was fossil hunting, an interest which has contributed to the enrichment of all mankind. Broom's discoveries in the Karoo beds of South Africa have done much toward clarifying the story of the origin of mammals two hundred million years ago, and he was regarded as one of the world's leading authorities on fossil mammal-like reptiles. As was true for Franz Weidenreich, Robert Broom was in his sixties when he

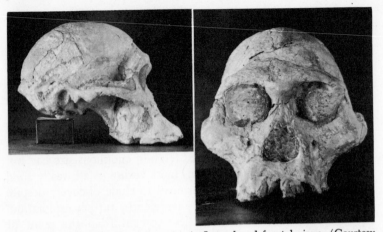

FIGURE 85. *Plesianthropus transvaalensis.* Lateral and frontal views. (Courtesy Drs. R. Broom and J. T. Robinson.)

became involved in discoveries of importance to the construction of a picture of human evolution. Like Weidenreich, Broom's astonishing energy and industry resulted in an immense output during the course of his fifteen years in paleoanthropology. He also followed the practice of giving each new find a different official name, but this was later simplified as we shall subsequently have occasion to observe.

The Sterkfontein find of 1936 was christened *Plesianthropus transvaalensis* by Broom. This was a relatively complete skull with a capacity of only 560 cc. which is right within the upper limits of the possible range of variation of a large gorilla, but about 200 cc. smaller than that of the smallest Pithecanthropus and not much more than a third of the size of an average modern man. The teeth, while large, are not nearly as large as they are in a chimpanzee at the forward end of the dental arch, and they are of human rather than anthropoid ape pattern. Finally the spinal cord entered the bottom instead of the back of the skull, and the upright carriage of the head thus indicated was strong evidence that *Plesianthropus* (almost man) was an erect walking biped, and therefore must have led a very different sort of life from that of any known nonhuman primate. This received confirmation from the fragment of femur (thigh bone) which was found at the same time.

Some years before, a piece of local publicity had advertised "Come to Sterkfontein and find the missing link." While Broom had not been attracted to the spot by this piece of publicity, there was a growing suspicion that he might have fulfilled the prophecy. At least it was now much less easy to ignore the South African "man-apes" as they began to be called, although there was still no suspicion even on the part of their most enthusiastic proponents that they might actually be very primitive man. After all it had only been a few years since the Peking discoveries had convinced a skeptical world that the pithecanthropines were human, and regarded as standing on the lowermost rung of the human ladder. The australopithecines, with cranial capacities little more than half those of the pithecanthropines, seemed much too bestial to warrant even the most incipient claim to the status of humanity. Anthropological opinion was summed up by the American anthropologist Earnest Hooton, a devoted follower of Keith's, in verse thusly:

> Cried an angry she-ape from Transvaal
> Though old Doctor Broom had the gall
> To christen me Plesi-
> anthropus, it's easy
> To see I'm not human at all.
> —Hooton 1946:288

It must be remembered that the general view was that more advanced types of man existed in the earliest Pleistocene which, if true, would have meant that the australopithecines were their contemporaries and could at most have been only crude cousins, doomed to eventual extinction. While this was hominid catastrophism again and could only be contradicted by inferences concerning the adaptations of the australopithecines based on an analysis of the significance of certain anatomical traits, yet direct evidence for an informed appraisal was not to come for more than a decade.

Two years later Broom's vigilance led to the recognition of another australopithecine at the Kromdraai farm, some two miles away from Sterkfontein. The molar teeth were substantially larger

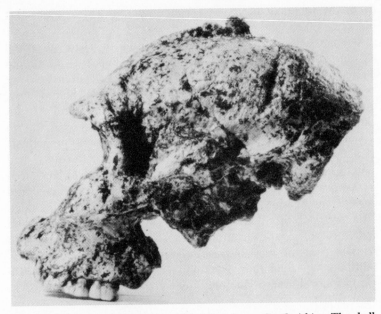

FIGURE 86. *Paranthropus crassidens*, from Swartkrans, South Africa. The skull is somewhat deformed and the lower face forced outward.

than those from Sterkfontein and Broom felt justified in creating yet another genus and species, *Paranthropus robustus*. Time has shown that this new name in its full taxonomic sense is not justified, but time and more fossils have also shown that Broom's *Paranthropus* has great importance for the understanding of the so-called *Meganthropus* which von Koenigswald was to discover three years later in Java.

The thirties were coming to a close, and the pursuit of fossil man, however fascinating and however significant for the understanding of the manner in which man has reached his present estate, was destined to be suspended for a while. The best illustration of the difficulties which beset paleoanthropology can be gained by tracing the fate of the Sinanthropus remains.

Because of political instability in China, working conditions had been somewhat precarious from the beginning. Choukoutien was sometimes isolated from Peking for weeks at a time by roving bands of "soldiers." Late in the 1930's, the Japanese moved into northern China and the future for paleontological research became increasingly uncertain. Working conditions become even more difficult, and finally, in 1941, Weidenreich was persuaded to take refuge in the American Museum of Natural History in New York. He brought with him an excellent set of casts, his notes, photographs, and drawings, which enabled him to complete his masterly works on Sinanthropus, but he left the originals in China where they properly belonged as the property of the Geological Survey of China.

Late in 1941, however, Dr. W. H. Wong, the director of the Geological Survey, became convinced with good reason that the originals were not safe in China, and, should they remain there much longer, were likely to become Japanese souvenirs. As conditions grew more tense and the American Embassy in Peking prepared to withdraw, Dr. Wong arranged to have the Sinanthropus fossils taken along in the hope that they would eventually reach the safety of the American Museum of Natural History. They were packed together with secret documents in the personal luggage of the colonel in charge of the American Marine detachment from the Embassy. Fossils and Marines left Peking by train headed for Chin Wang Tao, the port of embarkation, but by the kind of coincidence that only fate can arrange, they reached the coast on December 7, 1941, just as the bombs on Pearl Harbor ushered in a general state of war in the Pacific.

The Marines spent the war in a concentration camp, the liner on which they were to have sailed was sunk by an American submarine, some of the luggage from the captured train was seen in the possession of the Japanese, but no trace has ever been found of the priceless human fossils. Many theories have been offered to explain their disappearance, but the fact remains that they are gone and no one has any idea what became of them. In their brief resurrection after half a million years in the earth, the Sinanthropus population made a substantial contribution to the understanding we are beginning to have concerning our own evolution, and having thus assured their place in our memories they have passed into what we can only hope is a temporary physical oblivion.

So ended the 1930's, having produced a variety of types of human fossil with enough evidence for geographic distribution to provide us with the basis for an appreciation of the spread of hominid occupation during each of the major stages in human evolution. To be sure, the preconceptions of the majority of scientists prevented them from perceiving this, and it is only possible to make such a statement in retrospect. To those actually concerned with making sense of the fossil record, the thirties seemed to have raised more problems than they had solved.

As the fossil evidence accumulated, two problems became increasingly pressing. First, and most practically important, was the placement of each in the correct time relationship with the others. Fluorine analysis and allied techniques introduced in the late 1940's served to establish such gross relative differences within localized areas. The use of Carbon 14 further helped to sort out the ages of finds within given stratigraphic sequences, and, in addition, enabled the comparison of widely separated areas, since it made possible the establishment of the exact absolute age (up to approximately fifty thousand years) of the objects so dated. Yet further vistas of antiquity have been opened up by the refinement of the Potassium-Argon technique, now being used to give some idea of the placement of the earliest Pleistocene strata.

The second of the problems mentioned above was the growing need to make some sort of evolutionary sense out of the remains discovered. Adequate interpretations could not be offered until some definite picture of the relative stratigraphic ages involved was established. However, it still should have been possible to consider the kind of adaptation made by these early populations from the anatomical features exhibited by the fossil remains which resulted in the development of their characteristic appearance. With respect to interpretations of the australopithecines, it might be argued that there simply was not enough anatomical evidence to consider. In retrospect we can see that there was. This, however, will be the concern of our next chapter.

The postwar period, ranging from the late 1940's up to the present, has seen the gradual accumulation of evidence for the characteristics and distribution of the various stages of hominid evolution, with the most spectacular finds again coming from Africa and associated with the australopithecine group. After the war, Dr. Broom resumed operations literally with a bang. Although 80 years old, he was as dynamic as ever, as may be gathered from his use of dynamite in excavating. Petty bureaucracy in the form of the new Historical Monuments Commission, temporarily prevented Broom from continuing with his explosive approach. The technical objection offered was that dynamite might destroy valuable evidence for stratigraphy. Not only was this an insult to Broom, but it was also a declaration of ignorance on the part of the officials on the Commission. One scarcely needs Broom's more than fifty years of experience in geology and paleontology to realize that one cannot excavate anything from solid rock by the use of the approved whisk broom and trowel, let alone discover anything relating to stratigraphy. By now, however, Broom, with quantities of new australopithecines from Sterkfontein, was an international figure in the public mind as well as to the rarified little fraternity of vertebrate paleontologists, and was able to gain the support of an official who outranked the Historical Monuments Commission, namely the Prime Minister of the Union of South Africa. Field Marshal Jan Christian Smuts personally saw to it that Broom could continue unhampered.

Broom's efforts were promptly rewarded with the most important addition to the hominid fossil record since the discovery of "Dart's child," the original Australopithecus, almost a quarter-century before. In the summer of 1947 Broom recovered a complete half pelvis of his Plesianthropus at Sterkfontein. Of all the pieces of human anatomy, nothing is more distinctive than the pelvis. The dentition is no less distinctive, and it had been recognized for some time that the australopithecine dentition was far closer in form to being fully human than it was to resembling the dentition of an ape. Now, in addition, the first australopithecine pelvis had been discovered and it was radically different from that of a non-human primate, and in most important respects practically indistinguishable from that of a human being. Here without question was the pelvis of an erect-walking biped—an organism which was thoroughly terrestrial and which had ceased to be a tree-climber in the very remote past.

Some skeptics still refused to accept the growing evidence for the hominid status of the australopithecines, claiming that the pelvic and other postcranial fragments were the long-sought remains of modern man which simply happened to occur in the same strata as the australopithecine skulls. During the coming years when abundant evidence for hunting practices and a quantity of stone tools began to appear in deposits of the same time levels containing australopithecine remains, the cry of "ancient moderns" was raised again, and it was suggested that it was not the australopithecines who were responsible for these signs of intelligent activity, but rather that some as yet unfound true man had been their author and had furthermore been hunting the australopithecines themselves. There are still adherents of this position but their number is diminishing.

The year 1947, marking the resumption of australopithecine discoveries, also saw the return of Professor Dart to an active concern with paleoanthropology. In the dump of an abandoned limeworks at Makapansgat, two hundred miles northeast of the Sterkfontein area, his assistants found hominid fossil material for which he promptly created yet another species. He recognized that it belonged to the same genus as his 1924 skull, but because of the traces of carbon in the layers he assumed that fire was the cause, and he therefore credited his new australopithecine with the control of fire. Hence *Australopithecus prometheus*, in honor of the fire-bringer in Greek mythology. It transpired, however, that the amount of carbon present was so minute that it was in all likelihood only the residue of the organic constituent of the bones and was quite unrelated to any fire, whether deliberate or accidental. Also, in 1947, Sir Arthur Keith, long the most outspoken skeptic on the importance of the australopithecines, publicly acknowledged that he regarded the views he had held earlier were in error, and graciously credited Dart with having been correct from the outset. But 1947 was simply the beginning. In 1948 Broom initiated work at another site, Swartkrans about a mile from Sterkfontein, where, not to be outdone by Dart, he, too, found what he claimed to be another species of the genus he had first identified at Kromdraai. This new find he christened *Paranthropus crassidens*. The reader should not be discouraged by proliferation of the genera and species of australopithecines. A greatly-simplified picture will be presented in the next chapter.

Dart, by now, was just getting up steam. In 1948 Makapansgat produced pelvic fragments which, like the Sterkfontein and later Swartkrans pelves, were thoroughly human. Now that he had lived to see his anatomical judgment of the australopithecines vindicated, he embarked upon another and more tenuous path—he determined to prove that the australopithecines were toolmakers, hence culture-bearing creatures, and therefore true, if primitive, human beings.

Makapansgat has yielded an enormous accumulation of battered and fragmentary animal bones belonging to animals of the latter part of the Lower Pleistocene ranging from saber-toothed tigers down to hares and turtles, although the vast majority (over 90 per cent) were from antelope of more than a dozen kinds. These constitute clear evidence for the activities of a successful hunter which Dart claims was his *Australopithecus prometheus*. After painstaking analysis, Dart came to the conclusion that the fragments of animal bones at the Makapansgat limeworks constituted a selected sample since the various parts of the animal skeleton were not equally represented. Dart's theory was that the accumulated fragments represented those pieces of the animals' skeletons that the australopithecines were using for tools and weapons, and he went to great trouble to try and demonstrate deliberate shaping of the bone fragments in some cases.

These fragments Dart offered as the evidence for the culture of the australopithecines. His claims, however, until recently have received little support from professional archeologists, most of them inclining to the view that these so-called "tools" are the residue of australopithecine meals—indirect rather than direct evidence of their cultural capacities. But let us bear in mind Dart's uncanny capacity for proving right in the face of all the skeptics. It appears as though Dr. Dart will live to see his contentions for the human status of the australopithecines vindicated, but not altogether for the reasons he has proposed. We will discuss this in our next chapter.

In 1949 and again in 1950, during excavations at Swartkrans, where *Paranthropus crassidens* had been discovered, there was found a complete jaw and other fragments of the dental apparatus of an individual whose teeth were more like those of a pithecanthropine than an australopithecine. Dr. J. T. Robinson, Broom's assistant and successor and the discoverer of the new fragments, created yet another genus and species, *Telanthropus capensis*, which he now regards as identical with the pithecanthropines. He also assumes that the population represented was a contemporary of the Paranthropus material, but with the poor control over the relative (and even the absolute) dating, this would seem to be a risky supposition to make, particularly in view of the complexity which it introduces into interpretations of the australopithecine material.

If Paranthropus was contemporary with a pithecanthropine population, then we are faced with the difficulty of having to explain in terms of population isolation and differential selective pressures how they ever came to diverge in their evolutionary history. Robinson makes such an attempt, and this we shall consider later. At the moment, suffice it to say that this seems to us to be another application of the catastrophist view which we reject in principle.

Before completing our discussion of the fossil finds which concern australopithecines and Africa, we shall digress for a moment and mention some material which has been slightly overshadowed by the voluminous, spectacular, and extremely early finds south of the Sahara. In the Far East, the Chinese resumed work at Choukoutien in 1949 and a scattering of finds has resulted, adding to the Sinanthropus material. More important was the find, some distance north of Canton in southern China, of a skull cap including most of the right eye socket of what appears to be a genuine Neanderthal. This discovery at Ma-pa in 1958 marks the first appearance of a Neanderthal on the soil of continental eastern Asia, and, except for some teeth, this is the only fossil to fill the gap between the earlier Sinanthropus material and historic China.

Had it not been for the wealth of material coming out of Africa, the most spectacular finds to follow the war would have been the skeletal material excavated by Dr. Ralph Solecki of Columbia University at Shanidar cave in the Zagros Mountains of northern

FIGURE 87. The Ma-pa Skull. Front and right lateral views. [After Woo, *Vertebrata Palasiatica* 3, No. 4, plate I (1959).]

Iraq. Despite the various hardships which inevitably beset the archeologist who digs in the various corners of the world—like running out of money at the crucial moment, or getting caught in local revolutions—Dr. Solecki has been digging intermittently at Shanidar cave since 1951. The first skeleton was found in 1953, and although it was an infant, it already showed signs that it would have grown up to be a Neanderthal. Since then there has been ample proof of this supposition. To date Dr. Solecki has discovered seven Neanderthal skeletons, and as this was written there was the possibility that an eighth one remains in the excavation wall yet to be dug out.

Perhaps the most important aspect of Dr. Solecki's work is the light it throws on the sequence of human evolutionary stages in the Middle East. If, as was once claimed, southwestern Asia was the cradle of the development of the elusive modern *sapiens* form, then one should expect some sign of it in the upper parts of the Pleistocene. Mount Carmel, when it was believed to be third interglacial, was taken to be a possibility of such an occurrence. But as has been seen, Skhūl is estimated as being around 35,000 B.C. and coincident with the climatic amelioration between the two maxima of the last glacial stage. Tabūn then would be at least five thousand years older, and the distinct possibility is opened up that the population of which the Tabūn female was a member could be ancestral to the Skhūl population. Shanidar does

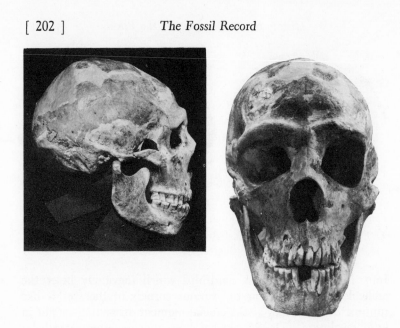

FIGURE 88. Skull of Shanidar I. Lateral and frontal views. (Courtesy of the Iraq Museum, Baghdad.)

not prove that such a development must have occurred, but it does prove that the Tabūn female was not a lone out-of-place Neanderthal. A C14 determination shows that the Neanderthals of northern Iraq lived about fifty thousand years ago with the temporal extent of their occupation from perhaps a few thousand years more recent than that date back to somewhere in the neighborhood of seventy thousand years. Only a fraction of the Shanidar cave has been excavated, and we confidently look forward to the discovery of many more Neanderthals from this the richest site of its time period.

The final series of discoveries which we shall cover in this survey are those which have been made in Tanganyika, East Africa, during the last several years. These finds have been made as a result of the determination and persistence of the British archeologist Dr. L. S. B. Leakey. Dr. Leakey is another one of that rare and astonishing breed of dedicated men who has devoted a lifetime to a subject which has demanded tedious and frequently thankless labor without offering much prospect of worldly reward. He had been working at the systematic study of East African pre-history since the mid-1920's, and since 1931 he had been periodically making expeditions to a site rich in archeological remains as well as the fossilized bones of Pleistocene mammals. This site is Olduvai Gorge in northern Tanganyika where Leakey had uncovered one of the most important archeological sequences ever found, involving the transition from the crudest recognizable chipped stone tool (Figure 89) to the classic "hand-axe" (Figure 90) of the kind which Boucher de Perthes a century ago used to advance his claims for the prehistoric existence of man.

This discovery alone would have assured Leakey a permanent place among the most eminent contributors to our knowledge of human origins, since this clearly demonstrated that the oldest evidence of human culture comes from Africa. One of the generally stated reasons for the relegation of the australopithecines to a non-human status had been the fact that no stone tools had been found in the deposits which yielded the bones of the australopithecines themselves, although crude pebble tools did exist in the river valley deposits which were contemporaneous with the cave breccias containing the fossils. Then in 1957, a few unmistakable stone tools were found at Sterkfontein. While this somewhat shook the formerly confident claims concerning the

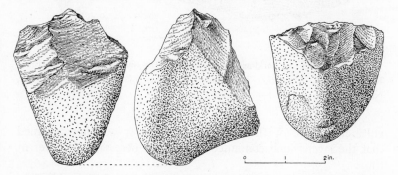

FIGURE 89. Oldowan pebble-tools (lava), Bed I, Olduvai Gorge, Tanganyika, East Africa. (From K. P. Oakley, *Man the Tool-Maker.* Courtesy of the British Museum, Natural History.)

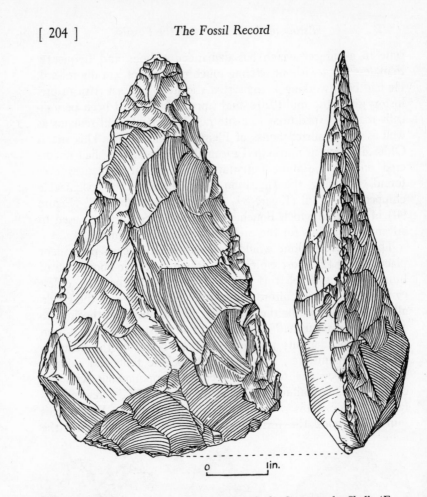

0   1in.

FIGURE 90. Acheulian hand-axe associated with the Swanscombe Skull. (From K. P. Oakley, *Man the Tool-Maker.* Courtesy of the British Museum, Natural History.)

cultureless state of the australopithecines, it was now claimed that the layer which contained them must necessarily be later in time.

Leakey not only found the most primitive of tools, he then proceeded to find remains of the "man" who had made them. On 17 July 1959 at Olduvai Gorge, Mrs. Leakey found a fragmentary but reconstructable skull in the midst of a working floor of early stone tools where, by the quantity of waste flakes, it was evident that the tools had been in process of manufacture. The skull, apparently, belonged to one of the manufacturers. When Dr. Leakey himself first looked at the skull, he was aware of the implications depending on a correct diagnosis of the stage of hominid evolution to which it should be assigned, but there was no problem in making this judgment. There could be no doubt that this was an australopithecine. To be sure, he followed the lamentable practice of African paleoanthropologists in assigning it a new generic and specific name, *Zinjanthropus boisei.* "Zinj" is the old Arabic word for East Africa, and *boisei* was in honor of Charles Boise whose financial backing had enabled the Leakeys to maintain their research over so many years. Nevertheless, the discovery of the skull and the context within which it was found constitute one of the most important—if not *the* most important —single contributions to the understanding of human origins ever made.

As a result of the work of the Leakeys, we now know that our highly-touted "Western Civilization" actually had its remote beginnings in Africa. This "Western Civilization" is an outgrowth of the first farming Neolithic way of life in eastern Europe and the Middle East, which in turn developed out of the hunting and gathering way of life of their Paleolithic precursors in the same regions. The Paleolithic itself extends far back into the Pleistocene, where we see its earliest and crudest form expressed in eastern and southern Africa. This must mean that man's physical origins are traceable to the same place. Culture without a creator is, of course, an impossibility, and the creator by definition is man. As the Leakeys have shown, this man at the earliest stages of the tangible evidence for culture was an australopithecine.

The deserved recognition which came to the Leakeys as a result of the Zinjanthropus discovery brought with it a vast increase in the amount of financial backing for renewed excavations at Olduvai Gorge. One of the severest problems which had beset Dr. Leakey's operations over the years had been transporting supplies over the non-existent roads. The nearest water, for instance, was thirty-five miles away, and survival itself required more than

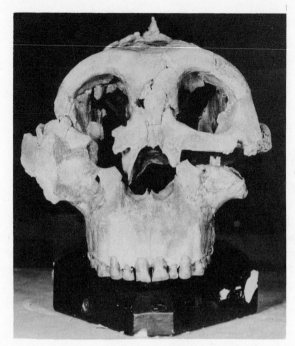

FIGURE 91. Skull of *Zinjanthropus*. Frontal, lateral and palatine view, compared with palatine view of modern man, above. (Courtesy of Des Bartlett, Armand Denis Productions, Nairobi.)

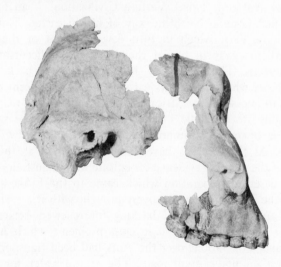

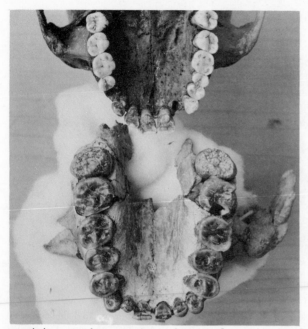

a minimum of precautions since such not insignificant inhabitants of the area as poisonous snakes, leopards, rhinoceroses, and lions regarded the place as their home. With the additional financial backing, the Leakeys were able to enlarge the extent of operations considerably, and during the following year it was possible for them to accomplish more than twice the work they had done in the preceding thirty.

The expanded activities paid off, and late in 1960 they discovered more australopithecine remains from an even earlier level in Olduvai Gorge. While the bones of Zinjanthropus had belonged to an individual of approximately eighteen years of age, this new find was that of an early adolescent. Although immature, the bones of the left foot provided confirmation, in addition to the evidence offered by the pelves of the South African australopithecines, for the erect bipedal mode of locomotion of these early hominids.

As if this were not enough, the final dramatic find of the season, made December 2, 1960, provided solid confirmation for the

FIGURE 92. Olduvai Gorge, Tanganyika, Dr. L. S. B. Leakey and his twelve-year-old son. The ravine slices through 300 feet of sediment covering the bed of a prehistoric lake. Faulting and erosion have brought to light numerous fossils and tools of early man. (Courtesy of The National Geographic Society.)

view that the australopithecines were the ancestors of the pithe-canthropines, for in Bed II, a level substantially younger than the Zinjanthropus level of Bed I, they discovered a fully pithe-canthropine skull (Figure 94) in association with evidences for a culture which had evolved without break from the pebble tools of Bed I.

The crowning touch to the work of Dr. and Mrs. Leakey was added when some perspective was given to the age of Zinjan-thropus as a result of a Potassium-Argon determination. On the basis of former estimates of an age bordering on one million years for the extent of the Pleistocene, they had estimated that Zinjanthropus must be in the neighborhood of six hundred thousand years old which would have made him roughly a con-temporary of Pithecanthropus in Java. The date that the Potas-sium-Argon determination indicates for their find is more than twice that figure, being a million seven hundred and fifty thousand years. As a result, it is not only possible but it becomes highly probable that Zinjanthropus is a representative of the ancestors of Pithecanthropus, a probability increased by findings subsequently made and reported in 1964. While the initial Potassium-Argon dates are somewhat crude and a certain amount of juggling will be necessary as techniques are refined, it has become apparent, nevertheless, that the early Pleistocene stretches back in time to a much greater extent than had been supposed by most geologists and paleontologists, and many authorities who have claimed that there simply was not enough time for the australopithecines to have evolved into later forms of man will be compelled to revise their thinking.

FIGURE 93. Dr. L. S. B. Leakey measuring *Zinjanthropus.* Under his right hand is the skull of a chimpanzee. (Courtesy of the National Geographic Society.)

FIGURE 94. The Bed II Pithecanthropine from Olduvai. (Courtesy of the National Geographic Society.)

As this book was being written, the indefatigable Leakeys were proceeding to extract yet more crucial fossil material from their East African treasure trove. Remnants of five more individuals were recovered from Bed II at Olduvai, and, some fifty miles northeast of Olduvai, on the shores of Lake Natron, the jaw of yet another individual was found. The Lake Natron jaw is clearly a large australopithecine and serves as a fine complement to the Zinjanthropus skull, but the Bed II fossils promise to be a source of some confusion. Dr. Leakey is trying to equate them with the Pre-Zinj. child of Bed I and create a new species for them—the whole being named *Homo habilis*. Jaws and teeth are preserved along with skull fragments including the better part of the back end of one cranium, but measurements are not yet available. From a study of the photographs and casts, however, it seems to us that the Bed II jaws and teeth, like the Bed II skull of 1960, belong in the pithecanthropine category, well removed from the Pre-Zinj. australopithecine.

It is as yet too early to comment adequately upon these finds. Whether *Homo habilis* is, indeed, a distinct species of the genus *Homo* or an australopithecine or a pithecanthropine, it will be possible to decide only when a sufficient number of independent comparative studies of these finds have been made. Until that has been done it would be wisest to suspend judgment.

One thing appears certain. Much yet remains to be learned as Olduvai Gorge continues to divulge its secrets, and it is more than likely that further major discoveries will be made before this book appears in print.

SUGGESTED READINGS

Andersson, J. G. *Children of the Yellow Earth.* Kegan Paul, London, 1934.

Studies in prehistoric China, containing the account of Andersson's discovery of quartz in the cave at Choukoutien which led to the discovery of Sinanthropus.

Bishop, W. W., and J. D. Clark (editors). *Background to Evolution in Africa.*

An invaluable survey of the paleontological, stratigraphical, and archeological findings and problems relating to man's evolution in Africa, by leading authorities from many lands.

Brace, C. L. "The fate of the 'classic' Neanderthals: a consideration of hominid catastrophism," *Current Anthropology*, vol. 5, 1964, pp. 3–43.

A re-examination of thinking on the Neanderthal question.

Broom, R. *Finding the Missing Link.* Watts, London, 1950.

Broom's own account of his australopithecine discoveries.

Daniel, G. *A Hundred Years of Archaeology.* Duckworth, London, 1950.

Giving an account of the most important archeological discoveries since 1840.

Dart, R. *Adventures with the Missing Link*. Harper & Row, New York, 1959.
Dart's own account of his steadfast and illuminating work on the australopithecines.

Day, M. H. *Guide to Fossil Man*. World Publishing Co., Cleveland & New York, 1966.
A most valuable handbook of human paleontology, providing the basic information for each of the sites which have yielded the bulk of significant hominid fossils.

Howell, F. C., and F. Bourlière, (editors). *African Ecology and Human Evolution*. Viking Fund Publications in Anthropology No. 36, 1963.
A major reference work on African prehistory, covering a wide variety of topics.

Hrdlička, A. *The Skeletal Remains of Early Man*. Smithsonian Miscellaneous Collections, vol. 83, 1940.
A fundamental work, and up to the date of publication the best of its kind.

Keith, A. *The Antiquity of Man*. 2 vols. Williams & Norgate, London, 1929.
Invaluable for the history and detail of the subject.

Koenigswald, G. H. R. von. *Meeting Prehistoric Man*. Thames & Hudson, London, 1956.
———. *The Evolution of Man*. University of Michigan Press, Ann Arbor, Michigan.
Two books, giving firsthand accounts of the discovery of a number of fossil hominids.

Leakey, L. S. B. "Finding the earliest man," *National Geographic*, vol. 118, 1960, pp. 420–435.
A beautifully illustrated account of the discovery of Zinjanthropus.
———. "Exploring, 1,750,000 years into man's past," *National Geographic*, vol. 120, 1961, pp. 564–589.
An account of additional finds including the Olduvai Pithecanthropine.
———. "Adventures in the search for man," *National Geographic*, vol. 123, 1963, pp. 132–152.
An account of further discoveries, including Kenyapithecus.

McCown, T. D., and A. Keith. *The Stone Age of Mount Carmel: The Fossil Human Remains from the Levalloiso-Mousterian.* The Clarendon Press, Oxford, 1939.
The account of the Skhūl and Tabūn finds.

Montagu, M. F. Ashley. *Darwin, Competition, and Cooperation.* Schuman, New York, 1952.
An examination of the background and sources of Darwinian thought.

Oakley, K. P., and M. F. Ashley Montagu. "A reconsideration of the Galley Hill skeleton," *Bulletin of the British Museum (Natural History),* vol. 1, 1949, pp. 27–46.
The demotion of Galley Hill man.

Tobias, P. V. "Early Man in East Africa," *Science,* vol. 149, 1966, pp. 22–33.
The fullest account of *Homo habilis* and its possible relationships.
———. "New Discoveries in Tanganyika: Their Bearing on Hominid Evolution," *Current Anthropology,* vol. 6, 1965, pp. 391-411.
The fullest description to date of the habiline *(Homo habilis)* remains, together with the discussion by various authorities of the finds and their interpretation.
———. *Olduvai Gorge 1951-1961,* vol. 2, *The Cranium of Australopithecus:* Zinjanthropus boisei. Cambridge University Press, London & New York, 1967
The definitive analysis and description.

Weidenreich, F. *Apes, Giants, and Man.* University of Chicago Press, Chicago, 1946.
———. *Anthropological Papers of Franz Weidenreich 1939–1948.* (Edited S. L. Washburn and D. Wolffson), The Viking Fund, New York, 1950.
Two books containing Weidenreich's always interesting views on the evolution of man.

Weiner, J. S. *The Piltdown Forgery.* Oxford University Press, London and New York, 1955.
The most fascinating of anthropological "whodunits" by the leading detective who uncovered the fraud.

CHAPTER SEVEN ❧❧❧ THE
STAGES OF HUMAN EVOLUTION

W
HILE A RECOUNTING of the history of the discovery of the major human fossil finds helps us to understand their importance as well as the genetic position assigned to them, it does not automatically produce a clear sequential picture of the crucial developments which have occurred in human evolution. Only by arranging the various fossils according to their relative geological ages can such a picture be constructed, and full understanding can be reached only when it is accompanied by a discussion of the major observable differences between the phases considered. Finally, the differences noted must correlate with major changes in selective factors of sufficient importance to have been able to produce such effects.

Before we apply these principles to the human fossil record, we should state the basis of our claim that the known fossils are most realistically placed in a linear evolutionary relationship. It has been argued, particularly by modern French paleoanthropologists, that the vast majority of the fossil plants and animals discovered to date represent lines which became extinct without descendants. These authorities have attempted to apply the same line of reasoning to hominid fossils, claiming that australopithecines, pithecanthropines, and Neanderthals were too specialized to evolve further and therefore eventually died without progeny. This, however, is an argument by analogy and fails to appreciate the real nature of human adaptation.

In spite of the vague claims for the "specialized" nature of various human fossils, the only discernible specialization which man has ever developed is culture, and this is only indirectly reflected by skeletal anatomy. Furthermore, as man's primary adaptive mechanism, it has done far more to prevent than to cause man's extinction (thus far). None of the earlier forms of man could have existed without the adaptation of culture, and it is significant to note that the evidence for human cultural traditions commences in the early Pleistocene and continues without break right up to the present time with subsequent traditions being clearly derived from earlier ones by cultural evolution: from the Oldowan to the hydrogen bomb without a break. Since the various hominid fossils can be associated with successive stages in the relatively more complete archeological record, it would be absurd to deny that these fossils represented previous stages in the evolution of modern man. Finally, if culture can be correctly regarded as man's principal adaptation, then major changes in this adaptation should be paralleled by major changes in the anatomy of the fossil men, and it is our intention to consider the cause and effect relationship between such correlated changes as we discuss the stages of human evolution.

The possibility has been advanced by some anthropologists that more than one primate developed culture as an adaptive mechanism in the early Pleistocene. These developments presumably occurred independently, and it has been suggested that the various australopithecines and pithecanthropines represent these separate lines as contemporaries occupying different ecological niches. We shall discuss this view further in our consideration of the australopithecines. At the moment, however, we should mention the two major objections that contradict such an interpretation.

The first objection is a theoretical one. Culture as a major means of adaptation is unique in the world of living organisms, and for all important purposes can be considered an ecological niche in itself—the cultural ecological niche. There is an evolutionary principle based on the logic of efficiency which states that, in the long run, no two organisms can occupy the same ecological niche. In the end, one will out-compete the other and retain sole possession of the niche in question. Applied to the primates, this should mean that no two forms could occupy the cultural ecological niche for any length of time. This objection has been countered with the claim that the various supposedly contemporary australopithecines and pithecanthropines were in the process of being eliminated in the competition for survival in the cultural ecological niche, but this raises the final and, we believe, conclusive objection.

All the evidence for the existence of culture, from the present day back to the early Pleistocene, appears to stem ultimately from a single tradition, and any claim that different kinds of primates simultaneously invented the same cultural adaptation puts a strain not only on our credulity, but also on the laws of probability. In addition, it adds unnecessary complexity to a situation that can be much more simply explained by a straightforward evolutionary approach.

To begin with, we recognize four stages or phases in human evolution: Australopithecine, Pithecanthropine, Neanderthal, and Modern. In reality these are merely points in what is in fact a continuum. The main justification for focusing our attention on these four phases of development is the simple fact that we have more fossil evidence for these four phases than for the periods in between. It seems highly probable that, as more material becomes available in the future, our scheme will have to be modified by the addition of stages or by the modification of some of the stages we posit. Basically our scheme is that of Gustav Schwalbe, with the addition of an australopithecine phase at the bottom, and already it appears that this added stage may be divisible into two sub-stages. Further discoveries may well show that these sub-stages warrant elevation to the rank of full phases equal in importance to the other three. For the time being, recognizing that our stages are arbitrary matters of convenience, we shall adhere to the four here discussed.

1. The Australopithecine Stage

No complete australopithecine is preserved although some hundreds of fragments have been collected and recognized. From these we can construct a fair picture of what the australopithecines looked like. That they were all bipedal is clearly evidenced by the form of the pelvis. The broad and expanded crest of the ilium indicates that the trunk muscles were so situated they could serve as adjustors which continually act to maintain the center of gravity in the trunk over the center of support in the legs and feet. The form of the upper pelvis is related to the body balancing which is so obviously important for a biped, and therefore the position of the pelvis differs little from that of modern man.

The lowermost part of the pelvis, the ischium, is relatively longer than that of modern man, although not so long as that of the anthropoid apes. This means that the attachments for the muscles which extend the leg in walking arise farther from the hip joint. While this indicates that any given contraction of these muscles produces a powerful extension of the limb, it also means that a relatively large amount of contraction produces a limited *amount* of extension, however powerful this may be.

The ischium in the pelvis of modern man is relatively short, so that while the extensor muscle mass loses some of its power, it also produces relatively more action for a given amount of contraction. Since ordinary walking does not require great power of extensor action, the production of sufficient movement with a minimum of contraction actually is desirably efficient. Since a maximum of movement is produced by a minimum of contraction, it is easy to see the advantages of such an arrangement where the action has to be repeated a great many times. The short human ischium constitutes a more efficient adaptation for a creature that survives by being able to move over large areas and walk long distances without fatigue. In this respect the lower part of the australopithecine pelvis, while clearly that of a biped, is not quite so well-adapted to continued effortless walking as is that of modern man. Apparently the selective advantage of a

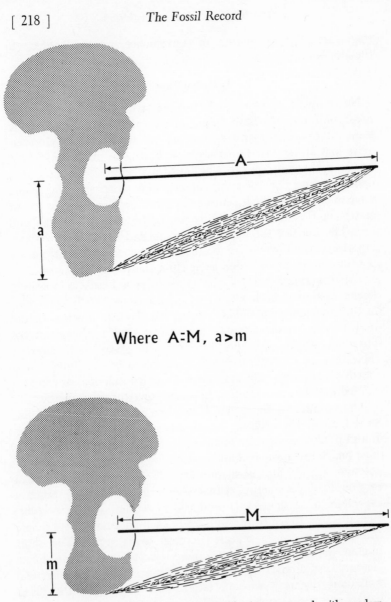

Where A=M, a>m

FIGURE 95. Relative efficiency of Australopithecine compared with modern pelvic function. A is taken to be the Australopithecine femur length, and M the modern femur length from the hip socket to the distal end. *a* is the

shortened ischium was great enough so that the australopithecine pelvis soon evolved into one of modern form which has remained relatively stable ever since.

A word on the adaptive significance of hominid bipedalism. If bipedalism were simply a means of locomotion and nothing more, there would never have been any advantage inherent in its development. As anyone who has ever tried to catch a frightened house cat is well aware, *Homo sapiens* pound for pound is one of the slowest and clumsiest of all terrestrial mammals. Evidently if man cannot outrun even the smallest of carnivores, his chances of relying on speed of foot to evade pursuit by a dangerous animal are lamentably small.

Nor is bipedalism any more efficient for hominid predatory activities. A man cannot even catch the smallest cottontail rabbit let alone run down an antelope in a flat race. In fact it is not certain that a man in full sprint can outrun a bipedally running chimpanzee or gorilla, and these primates are habitual quadrupeds which only occasionally use bipedalism as an alternate mode of progression. It seems probable, then, that speed of progression is not something which has ever had much significance for hominid survival.

If any mammal had to rely upon uncompensated bipedalism for its survival, it would quickly become extinct. In the hominid case, however, bipedalism is not uncompensated. The big advantage of a bipedal mode of progression is that it frees the hands from any involvement in locomotor duties. An organism with freed hands not only can manufacture tools, but can carry tools and weapons with him as a substitute for anatomical inadequacy. The regular manufacture of tools and the reliance upon them as a primary means of survival immediately implies the existence of

---

Australopithecine ischium length, and m the modern ischium length from hip socket to tuberosity. If A is set equal to M, then a will be longer than m. With the major extensors of the leg arising from the tuberosity of the ischium, a longer ischium in proportion to femur length should give a greater mechanical advantage and result in greater power of leg extension. In the modern situation, however, the same amount of muscle contraction will produce a greater although less powerful extension of the leg.

a complexity of learned behavior and traditions which we recognize under the name of culture. Even without any further evidence then, anatomical indications for bipedalism should lead us to suspect that culture was the primary means of adaptation, and since we define "man" as the organism whose primary means of adaptation is culture, then our biped must by definition be a man, however primitive. On these grounds alone, we should recognize the australopithecines as human beings, and, as we shall see shortly, an ever increasing volume of additional evidence of various kinds clinches our argument.

At this moment we should like to indulge in a bit of interpretation which borders on sheer speculation. There is a corollary that might be added to Washburn's observation that the development of the hominid pelvis indicates the adaptive advantage inherent in covering long distances bipedally with the expenditure of relatively little effort. It is true that a foraging animal can increase its food supply by extending its range, but there is another facet to hominid bipedalism which is often overlooked. Slow though they are, human bipeds do run down fleet and nimble quadrupeds by the simple though tedious method of continuing to plod after the animal until it drops from exhaustion. This method of hunting was utilized right into the present century by members of the few hunting and gathering populations that still inhabited a plains environment, for instance, the aborigines of the Australian bush, the Bushmen of the Kalahari desert in Africa, and the Indians in the American Great Basin. This rather exhausting but effective means of hunting depends on two factors. First, a large herbivorous quadruped has to spend a considerable portion of its time ingesting sufficient quantities of its fibrous and bulky food in order to get enough nourishment to survive. If it is kept constantly on the move for a day or two, even if it doesn't have to move very fast, it begins to run out of fuel.

More important, however, is the fact that large furry quadrupeds are less well provided with heat-dissipating mechanisms than is man with his hairless skin richly endowed with sweat glands. Man, as is true for the majority of primates, inherits excellent visual powers from his remote arboreal ancestors, but his ability to see is drastically curtailed as the intensity of illumination decreases. Unlike the great majority of terrestrial mammals, man's vision is quite poor in the dark, and, since his arboreal ancestry confers on him an indifferent sense of hearing and a very poor sense of smell, it is evident that man's activities are primarily confined to the daylight hours when his vision is effective. Of all the major predators in the world, man alone functions exclusively in broad daylight.

Until the advent of man as a serious menace, the large game quadrupeds had less to fear from predators during the heat of midday than at any other time. Hunting canines tend to perform their activities during the latter part of the afternoon while the big cats operate during dusk and early evening. Man, however, with his bare and sweaty skin can effectively dissipate the heat generated by metabolic activity. To this day, the Kalahari Bushmen pursue and capture large antelope during the heat of the day. However uncomfortable such activities may be for man, they are even more difficult for a bulky fur-covered quadruped which must either seek shade or face heat exhaustion.

While no proof can be offered for our inference, we suspect that the pelvic development in the australopithecines, which eventually allowed an increase in their range of operations, was accompanied by the loss of the hairy coat. Whether due to the advantage this gave to a diurnal hunter or simply to the fact that it merely increased the amount of activity, and hence range of operations, of a simple collector, human hairlessness allows for a relatively greater concentration of subsistence efforts during the heat of the noonday sun.

Human status was denied to the first australopithecines discovered largely because anatomists had preconceived notions as to what size a brain should be before it could deserve the designation of human. The human minimum was established by Sir Arthur Keith as being 750 cc., and, the earliest australopithecines discovered all had cranial capacities below 700 cc. Furthermore, Pithecanthropus was already firmly entrenched as the most primitive of possible humans, at least as far as the generality of anthropological thinking was concerned. Then the pelvic fragments were found, and, when *Paranthropus crassidens* was discovered, Broom claimed a cranial capacity of over 900 cc. While this may have been a little too enthusiastic, even conservative re-estimates place it well above the minimum set by Keith and thus within the very bottom-most part of the normal range of variation of modern man. Since normal functioning can accompany such great differences in brain size in modern men (approximately 800 cc. to over 2000 cc.), no great weight can be placed on brain size as a criterion for determining the humanity or sub-humanity of fossil primates.

Much has been made of the fact that the majority of australopithecine cranial capacities fall at or below 650 cc. This is the approximate upper limit of the range of variation of the living anthropoid apes, although it should be noted that such a capacity is only attained by the largest of adult male gorillas who generally weigh in the neighborhood of a quarter ton or more; the australopithecines ranged from approximately sixty pounds to a little more than twice that weight. Per unit body size, therefore, the australopithecines were much brainier creatures than are the modern apes, although the curve of their body-brain proportion is substantially below that of modern man.

The fact that Schultz has recently described an adult male gorilla skull with a cranial capacity of 750 cc. puts Keith's "Cerebral Rubicon" completely out of business. In addition, it shows that brain size is no indication of mental capacity, and at the same time suggests the kind of variability in brain size that almost certainly characterized the australopithecines.

Attempts have also been made to magnify the importance of the sagittal crest which appears in the larger australopithecines, recalling the condition commonly found in adult male gorillas and orangs, even though the crests are less developed than they are in these pongids. The assumption has been that the saggital crest is a specifically pongid character of great genetic and taxonomic importance which indicates close relationship to the non-human primates, but this ignores the real nature of the crest and its significance. The crest is the result of the extension of the temporal muscle, the muscle that closes the jaws, beyond the limits of its usual attachment on the skull to the midline on top. There further expansion is limited by the meeting of the right and left temporal muscles which now have nowhere to go but up.

If the chewing apparatus grows to such a size that yet larger muscles are required, muscle then piles up on both sides of the skull, and the septum between the two muscles at the midline ossifies into a bony crest which is as high as the muscle mass is thick. The crest, then is simply a reflection of the proportion of cranial to facial size. A primate with a large face and a small brain-case will have a crest, but if the brain-case becomes large then there will be sufficient area on it to provide for adequate muscle attachment without the necessity of the muscle to over-spread the whole skull and meet at the midline on top. The saggital crest should be regarded as a manifestation of functional morphology and not as a feature of much taxonomic significance.

Controversies concerning the interpretation of australopithecine brain size and sagittal crest significance have been generally resolved by most anthropologists. Disagreement, however, remains concerning taxonomic interpretations and relationships. Since we shall use our appraisal of the australopithecine dentitions to indicate our preferred solution to the problems involved, we should now mention the larger issues at stake.

In accordance with the policy pursued by Broom and softened by Dart of proliferating taxonomic categories, all of the South African early Pleistocene hominids have been placed in a separate formal subfamily, Australopithecinae, under the assumption that they were not true men. Dr. J. T. Robinson, Broom's successor, has simplified some of the welter of conflicting names by reducing the numbers of genera to two, *Australopithecus* and *Paranthropus*. As the reader may have guessed, we prefer an even simpler solution. As we have noted, all the evidence points to the fact that the australopithecines must have been using culture as their major means of survival, which would make them, by our definition, members of the genus *Homo*. We not only deny a separate subfamily status to the australopithecines but we further deny that they are generically distinct from modern man.

Formally, we include all of the australopithecines in the designation *Homo africanus* in accordance with the first named species of this type. The species designation is less convincing than that of the genus, and at this taxonomic level or below it there may be some justification in recognizing the distinctions that Robinson

STAGE   SUBSTAGE   SITE

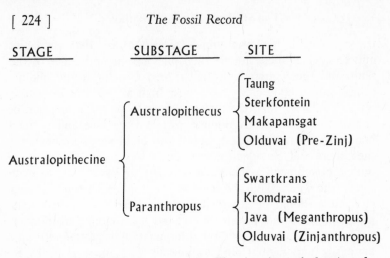

FIGURE 96. Australopithecine taxonomy. The groupings of the Australopithecines.

has raised to the generic level. In any event, we shall use his terms Australopithecus and Paranthropus without the italics to designate the two subdivisions within the Australopithecine stage of human evolution.

Substage Australopithecus includes the finds made at Sterkfontein, the Makapansgat limeworks, and the original Taung discovery, to which we can probably add the Pre-Zinj child found by Leakey in Olduvai Gorge in 1960. Substage Paranthropus includes the Swartkrans and Kromdraai finds as well as Meganthropus of Java and Zinjanthropus of Olduvai Gorge. All the indications point to the fact that Australopithecus occurred at an earlier time level than Paranthropus, and we believe that Australopithecus is the logical ancestor.

The first and most striking difference between Australopithecus and Paranthropus is one of gross size. It has been estimated that the forms included under the term Australopithecus weighed in the neighborhood of sixty pounds while Paranthropus was more than twice that bulk. The material is so fragmentary and postcranial remains are so scarce that these estimates are highly tentative, but it would appear that Paranthropus was of roughly the size of a modern man while Australopithecus was less than half as large. Next, the sagittal crest has been observed for Paran-thropus but not for the earlier form, which, among other things, Robinson has taken to indicate that Australopithecus was closer in form to more modern hominids than Paranthropus.

This brings us to a consideration of the teeth and the adapta-tions indicated. Little Australopithecus had front teeth which were relatively large for his size including canines which gave a hint of projecting above the plane of occlusion, although by their wear patterns it is clear that they functioned in the same manner as incisors. Paranthropus had molars of substantially larger size, while the front teeth remain approximately the same in dimen-sions as those of Australopithecus. Robinson has taken the large molars of Paranthropus to indicate that this form was an habitual

FIGURE 97. Robert Broom (1866–1951), South African paleontologist, with a cast of Plesianthropus. (Courtesy of the American Museum of Natural History.)

vegetarian in contradistinction to the *relatively* larger canines of Australopithecus which he presumes indicates a carnivorous adaptation. He recognizes that the lack of apelike large canines in these bipeds means that they must have been relying on tools for defense, but he refuses to grant the australopithecines the ability to make tools. Tool users but not toolmakers. Robinson then advances his own discovery, Telanthropus, as the first true man and maker of the tools which have now been found in the australopithecine levels of the South African deposits.

In our view, this seems to be another form of hominid catastrophism and we prefer the simpler evolutionary explanation which runs like this. Without the anatomical defensive development of large canines and unable to outrun its enemies, the earliest australopithecine—Australopithecus proper—must have possessed culture in order to have survived in the grassland environment which the fossil animal bones tell us was his habitat. The development of Paranthropus from Australopithecus can easily be explained in terms of the selective factors operating at that time. The increase in body size makes good sense when one realizes that the number of serious potential enemies is greatly lowered by such a change. Such animals as jackals and the smaller hunting cats could give serious trouble to a fifty to sixty-pound primate, even a tool using one, but when body bulk rises to 120 to 150 pounds, the major predatory worries narrow down to leopards, lions, and packs of hunting dogs or wolves. A further increase in size would confer few advantages unless the formidable bulk of a rhinoceros were suddenly attained, and it is apparent that no really major body size change has occurred from the time of Paranthropus to the present day.

As for the increase in molar size, this can best be regarded as the normal result of increasing the size of the whole organism. Certainly it is unlikely that a creature using culture as its primary means of survival, however simple that culture may be, should be limited to the exclusively vegetable diet postulated by Robinson. The change to be explained in the dentition is not the increased size of the molars, but the fact that the incisors and canines remained the same while the rest of the body more than doubled in bulk. This makes sense when we consider the probable length of time that tool using was the primary means for defense. In Australopithecus, the canines are large, but they do not project as significant defensive weapons, and one can infer that the ancestors of the australopithecines had been using tools as defensive weapons for a long enough time so that the accumulation of random mutations could result in the reduction of the canines toward the level of the incisors. If this is the case for Australopithecus, obviously the later Paranthropus had been the beneficiary of such a process for a longer period of time, and this, coupled with the indications of clearly shaped tools, should have allowed still more random mutations to accumulate affecting the front teeth. Because of the reduced importance in maintaining such relatively large teeth as had formerly been valuable, the accumulating random mutations could be expected to produce smaller front teeth—especially canines—and of course this is exactly what the anatomical evidence shows.

We have now accounted by what we believe are morphologically sound and logically valid steps, for the transformation of Australopithecus into Paranthropus with the exception of that part of the anatomy represented by the sagittal crest. This however can be regarded simply as one of the consequences of the increase in size. Large and small members of the same animal group show their largeness and smallness in different degrees in different structures. For example, among human beings, a pygmy who is very much reduced in body size is also slightly reduced in brain size, but the cerebral reduction is less pronounced than the reduction of the body. There are still the same number of fingers and toes and various essential organs which the brain has to administer. In a very large person conversely, arms and legs and face increase relatively more than does brain size. If we regard the major bodily difference between Australopithecus and Paranthropus as primarily one of size, then expectably the limbs and face should be larger in proportion than the brain. According to expectation Paranthropus with more than twice the bulk of Australopithecus has a cranial capacity which runs, at most, only one third larger. This means that the musculature needed to operate a chewing mechanism which has increased in proportion to the body size does not have an equivalently enlarged braincase on which to attach. Not surprisingly, then, the temporal muscles enclose the skull and actually meet at the top where a small sagittal crest forms for their attachment.

Two problems remain to be discussed concerning the australopithecines, their dating, and their distribution. Of these, the most difficult is that of the dating. One of the primary sources of the difficulty is that no two authorities can agree on the age which should be allotted to the Pleistocene. Estimates by the experts have ranged all the way from a few hundred thousand years up to two million, and even the two laboratories which have computed absolute dates by using the Potassium-Argon technique have differed by nearly 100 per cent in their age determinations for the strata of Olduvai Gorge. In the past, many authorities have used for convenience the rough approximation of one million years for the Pleistocene with the feeling that at least this was in the right order of magnitude even if it were not exact. Now, however, it seems increasingly apparent that a two million year extent of the Pleistocene is more nearly correct.

While arguments concerning the absolute age of the various parts of the Pleistocene continue, more vexing are the questions concerning their relative ages. It is true that absolute age determination could tell without question which fossil is older than which, yet this is not possible at the present time and those problems of relative dating remain unsolved. Even if absolute ages can never be precisely established for the Early and Middle Pleistocene, an understanding of the relative ages of the various fossils is crucial. It scarcely needs to be said that the australopithecines could hardly serve as the actual ancestors of the pithecanthropines if both forms lived at the same time. It makes better evolutionary sense to regard the australopithecines as ancestors rather than as contemporaries of pithecanthropines, and, although we are still a long way from having indisputable proof that such was the case, yet the view favored by some authors that they were contemporaries has even less evidence in its favor. One of the problems is that the bulk of the pithecanthropine material has been discovered in the Far East, while, with one exception the australopithecine finds have all come from Africa, and the relationships between the strata of the two areas have not been well worked out.

Whether the Paranthropus substage is late Lower or early Middle Pleistocene is the subject of an argument which has not been resolved on the basis of the South African evidence, but the splendid stratigraphic sequence uncovered by the work of Dr. Leakey in Olduvai Gorge, Tanganyika, offers a solution which is gratifyingly simple and should carry a great deal of weight. His 1959 discovery, which he somewhat prematurely christened Zinjanthropus, is recognizably an australopithecine of the larger and later variety—the Paranthropus substage, as is the Lake Natron find of 1964. The Olduvai specimen found more than twenty feet below the top of Bed I belongs to the upper part of the Lower Pleistocene. In addition, whatever the doubts surrounding the Potassium-Argon method of absolute age determination, the dates yielded by analyses performed in a single laboratory indicate that Zinjanthropus is nearly twice as old as the Trinil layers containing the pithecanthropines of Java. While this all provides evident confirmation for the view that the later australopithecines are substantially earlier than the pithecanthropines, the most conclusive support for this interpretation was Leakey's discovery late in 1960 of a pithecanthropine (Figure 94) in Bed II of Olduvai in a Middle Pleistocene context approximately the same age as the discoveries from Java.

In general our claim for the evolutionary relationship between the australopithecines and the pithecanthropines is supported wherever there is any clearcut evidence. There are some loose ends, however, which cannot all be successfully resolved. Specifically, von Koenigswald's 1939 Pithecanthropus skull came from the Djetis beds underlying the Trinil layers, in which he later found the fragments of two lower jaws he christened Meganthropus. If, as Robinson has claimed and as we agree, Meganthropus represents a Javanese version of Paranthropus, then pithecanthropines and australopithecines might have been contemporaries. The experts are still unagreed as to whether the Djetis beds are early Middle or late Lower Pleistocene, and, besides, the simple fact that two fossils come from the same bed does not constitute assurance that they are of the same age, particularly when the stratum involved may include sediments deposited over a period lasting many tens of thousands of years.

Another loose end concerns the relationship between the Paranthropus group of South Africa and what Leakey has called Zinjanthropus in Olduvai Gorge, East Africa. Anatomically they are similar enough to be considered members of the same evolutionary substage but there has been a disagreement over their relative ages with many experts feeling that the South African finds are much more recent than Leakey's discoveries. This difficulty can best be met by a consideration of the last problem relating to the australopithecines—the problem of their distribution.

When this consideration is limited to the skeletal remains of the australopithecines, only a very incomplete picture can be built of their distribution, although it is a suggestive one. With one exception the finds have all come from Africa. In 1961 the discovery of a Paranthropus-like form at Koro Toro, northeast of Lake Chad, extended the African range from Bechuanaland and the Transvaal up through East Africa and north of the Congo to the edge of the Sahara. The one non-African find, the "Meganthropus" of 1941, suggests that, after an African origin, the australopithecines spread as far as Indonesia, and while this alone is uncomfortably sketchy evidence to go on, it receives a strong boost from the distribution of the much more numerous fragments of the primary adaptive agency of the australopithecines—their culture.

While we must infer that organisms so anatomically ill-equipped as the australopithecines must necessarily have had enough ability to exchange ideas so that they could plan future activities in which different group members performed specific functions, i.e., they must have had some sort of language, however crude, our tangible evidence for their culture is of the simplest sort. The only remains we possess of the complexity of coordinated activities upon which they must have relied for both defense and subsistence are crude stone tools. Even the most carefully made of these tools were simple river pebbles with a few chips knocked off to produce sharp edges and points. There have been continual arguments over the identification of these early human tools, with many skeptics noting that the action of natural forces would produce many such fragments by chance alone in the rocky beds of rapidly flowing streams. On the other hand many archeologists have raised the decisively telling point that crudely-flaked river pebbles are not naturally found in the silt of stoneless lake shores or in other areas where their presence could not be explained without invoking some sort of human agency.

The existence of these undeniable' tools in early Pleistocene strata all the way from the coast of North Africa right down to the Cape proves that some creature was relying upon culture in the broader sense as his primary means of survival. By our definition this creature must be called man. These crude pebble tools belong to a cultural tradition called Oldowan after the clear developmental sequence discovered by Leakey in Olduvai Gorge during the last thirty years. If, as we have argued, the australopithecines must have had culture in order to survive, then the Oldowan tools, constituting the only evidence for the existence of

FIGURE 98. Pebble-tool distribution through the tropics of the world. (Drawing by Mary L. Brace and Richard V. Humphrey.)

culture in the early Pleistocene, must be the products of australo-pithecine manufacture. Consequently, the distribution of pebble tools of the Oldowan type must coincide with the distribution of australopithecines.

The earliest Oldowan tools, although so crude that they are hard to recognize (Figure 89), were apparently restricted to Africa in the Lower Pleistocene (Figure 36). It seems reasonable to regard these as the products of the activities of substage Australopithecus. The success which this survival mechanism conferred upon the possessors can be seen not only in the relative reduction which it allowed to occur in the front teeth of the succeeding Paranthropus substage, but it is particularly apparent in the greatly expanded territory occupied by the advanced Oldowan toolmaking tradition.

At the base of the Middle Pleistocene, stone tools, whose apparent origins are in the early Oldowan, have a distribution which includes all of Africa, extends north to Europe in the form of one of the Clactonian, and then sweeps east encompassing all of India, Southeast Asia, and out into Indonesia. Paranthropus in the west and Meganthropus in the east are simply strategically placed representatives indicating that the originators of this widespread culture were all one kind of early man.

While our sweep entirely encompasses the tropics of the Old World, it is not to be assumed that the archeological remains are particularly abundant or that the human populations represented were ever particularly dense. The evidence, especially the fortunate Zinjanthropus find, indicates that the hunting part of human foraging activities was primarily concerned with immature animals. Apparently techniques had not yet been developed whereby regular and successful hunting of the abundant numbers of Pleistocene mammals could be practiced.

We should repeat that we have presented a picture of australopithecine development and its significance for subsequent human evolution which is not generally accepted at the present time. Not that it is generally believed to be wrong, although there are those who would so argue, but many authorities claim with some reason that the evidence is not at present sufficient to warrant taking any position. However, we believe that the evidence, the logic, and the internal consistency of such an evolutionary view constitute powerful enough arguments to warrant our stand, and that it is the presentation of an alternative view that would require the support of a great deal more than the now available evidence would allow.

2. The Pithecanthropine Stage

The complexities and uncertainties which beset our consideration of the australopithecines necessarily made our presentation relatively long. Although many questions still remain unsolved concerning the Pithecanthropine stage, these are much less bothersome, and there is no necessity for such lengthy treatment.

The greatest number of pithecanthropines so far discovered has come from the Far East. Not only has this large number come from eastern Asia, but the first discovery of a pithecanthropine was made by Dubois beginning in 1890. The confirmation provided by the Choukoutien finds in the late 1920's and in the 1930's led many people to believe that Haeckel had been more or less correct and that Asia was the original "cradle of mankind." The subsequent finds of skeletal material as well as archeological remains in Africa have changed all this, and it is now recognized that the early and abundant discoveries in Asia were the result of great if somewhat misleading good fortune.

Anatomically there are two major differences between the later australopithecines and the pithecanthropines. First, the pithecanthropines possess significantly larger brain cavities without being different in body size. While larger brains do not necessarily imply greater intelligence for their possessors, yet when large differences in cranial capacity exist between otherwise similar groups then one does begin to suspect that mental differences exist as well. With one exception, australopithecine cranial capacity lies below 700 cc. while that of the pithecanthropines is higher. In fact, the pithecanthropines fall within the lower 300 cc. of the range of variation for modern man.

The other major difference appears in the teeth and face. In most respects, the pithecanthropine teeth fall within the upper limits of the modern range of variation. The molars, while large by modern standards, show a marked degree of reduction when compared with those of Paranthropus.

While the remainder of the body is represented by incomplete and highly fragmentary remains, indications are that the adaptive changes in the pelvis had been completed for long-distance walking, and that it does not differ significantly from the pelvis of modern man. Nor does the rest of the skeleton differ from that of men of today. Below the neck the pithecanthropines were not particularly distinctive, but one look at the face and head is sufficient to tell even the most untutored observer that more changes will have to occur before the form we know as modern man is to be attained. The major morphological developments that occurred during the Middle and Upper Pleistocene have been in the head and particularly the face.

The reader will recall that the selective pressures operating on man have been progressively changed by human cultural adaptations, and, with this in mind, one should expect the anatomical differences between the australopithecines and the pithecanthropines to be related to cultural developments. However crude a measure brain size is for determining intelligence—and it does not work at all when the differences are no greater than those between various living peoples—the great changes visible in the human fossil record show that there was a distinct selective advantage to the possession of increased brain size. Since man's primary adaptive mechanism is the behavioral and technological complex we call culture, it is reasonable to suppose that increases in brain size indicate increases in cultural capacities, and since we presume this to have increased human chances for survival, it is to be expected that these two changes should have occurred between the australopithecine and pithecanthropine stages.

The differences of face and head are obvious, but at first glance the cultural differences do not seem correlatedly as great. The chipped pebbles and flakes are scarcely distinguishable from those of Bed I in Olduvai Gorge, but it should be remembered that tools are only a small fraction of the totality of culture, and stone fragments were probably only a fraction of the tools used. We can assume that the non-material part of culture underwent a significant expansion before the Pithecanthropine stage. While this is an inferential assumption, it is not entirely guesswork since there is tangible evidence for the presence of one very significant cultural item which had not been present before—fire.

The earliest evidence for the human use of fire comes from Choukoutien where the numerous hominid fossil fragments of what was originally called *Sinanthropus* were found. Fire implies more than might at first be supposed. The hearths at Choukoutien indicate that it was a campsite which was re-used repeatedly over a long period of time. Re-use of a campsite is not a behavioral characteristic of man's closest non-human relatives, and implies that the ability to communicate the concepts of time and place must have been characteristic of pithecanthropine culture. One of the big advantages to an agreed-upon campsite, as pointed out by Dr. Irven DeVore, is that the amount of food collected by a hunting and gathering group can be greatly increased since the band can then split up for the day, search in different places, and meet to share their food later on. We can infer that the consistent use of a campsite indicates the existence of a division of labor.

Because of the nature of human reproductive physiology, it is inevitable that the simplest division of labor will be by sex. Women, charged with the care of children, cannot be expected to be as effective in the pursuit of game animals as men. In hunting and gathering cultures from the Pithecanthropine stage right up to the present day, women have devoted their subsistence efforts to the collection of vegetable foods and whatever small animals can be caught with the hands, while men have directed their activities to a greater extent toward the capture of larger game. The competitive advantages conferred by even such a rudimentary division of labor as this, must have been an important factor in the successful survival of human groups from at least the early Middle Pleistocene onward. Although it is impossible to identify direct evidence for the sexual division of labor itself, the existence of re-utilized hearths at Choukoutien can be taken as *indirect* evidence for it. It is probable that this aspect of culture became of importance during the Australopithecine stage, but, lacking indications for campsites, this simply remains an educated guess.

The control of fire confers several distinct survival benefits on the possessors, and in addition provides evidence of the increasing complexity of the cultural survival instrumentality. Fire can serve as a source of protection from large predators. Because of his heavy dependence on a visual means of perceiving the world that man has inherited from his arboreal primate ancestry, human beings have always been relatively helpless at night. Fire, in addition to providing illumination by which man can operate, is a substantial deterrent to the depredations of large carnivores.

The protective benefits the control of fire afforded early man resulted in a somewhat unexpected consequence. Fire permitted the possessors to occupy caves and rock shelters in safety, whereas, prior to this time, such areas would have acted more like traps than shelters. To the modern prehistorian this is an enormous help since it means that the number of places where one is likely to discover the remains of Paleolithic populations can immediately be narrowed down. This may in part constitute the reason why remains of the Pithecanthropine and later stages of human evolution are so much better known than those of the earlier stages.

The final benefit the control of fire conferred on its possessors was the freedom to extend their range of habitation into areas normally too cold to permit unprotected humans to survive. Man possesses all the physiological characteristics of a thoroughly tropical mammal, but, as a result of his increasing ability to manipulate his immediate environment, he has been able to move out of the tropics and take advantage of the extensive living areas of the temperate zones and even the arctic. Fire, while it may not at first have been of great importance, must nevertheless have provided enough artificial warmth to allow the pithecanthropines to extend their range into slightly colder climates. Even without a change in population density, more human beings must have been surviving in the world than ever before.

Two aspects of the Pithecanthropine stage remain to be discussed—its dating and distribution. As is so often the case for the earlier stages of human evolution, the general picture appears reasonable, but the amount of specific evidence that can be mustered is uncomfortably small. While the dispute in learned circles

continues as to whether the earliest pithecanthropines belong to
the late Lower Pleistocene (Late Villafranchian) or the early
Middle Pleistocene, it is generally recognized that the pithecanthropines go back at least to a time that would correspond to the
second glaciation of the Alpine sequence.

The earliest skeletal remains assignable to the Pithecanthropine
stage came from Java in the form of the infant Modjokerto skull
of 1936 and the robust but fragmentary pieces of skull and face
of 1939 at Sangiran—both discovered as a result of the efforts of
von Koenigswald. As we have indicated, there remains some doubt
as to exactly how old these fragments are, with von Koenigswald
regarding them as late Villafranchian (Lower Pleistocene), and
other authorities regarding them as early Middle Pleistocene, perhaps of an age equivalent to the early Mindel (second) glaciation
of the Alpine sequence. While some authorities have tried to
claim that the early pithecanthropines were contemporaries of
the late australopithecines, it is evident that the exact dating of
both has not been settled. Even their relative dating is unclear.
While both Meganthropus (australopithecine) and early pithecanthropines occur in the same (Djetis) layer in central Java, the
layer in some places is over a thousand feet thick and must represent accumulation over a considerable period of time—tens, maybe
even hundreds, of thousands of years. Nor is the evidence for
contemporaneity any better in South Africa.

At present it seems most reasonable and in consonance with the
evidence to offer the tentative suggestion that the australopithecines evolved into the pithecanthropines at the end of the Villafranchian. Certainly full-fledged pithecanthropines exist by the
beginning of the Middle Pleistocene, but the exact placement in
time of these two stages will have to await refinements in absolute dating techniques and the accumulation of much more evidence correlating the local stratigraphic sequences with those in
other parts of the world for which the relative dating has been
well worked out.

It is clear, however, that by the time equivalent to the second
glaciation of the Alpine sequence, the pithecanthropines had
spread throughout the tropics of the Old World. Dubois' original
finds as well as those by von Koenigswald from the Trinil layers

in Java all belong to this time level. The "Sinanthropus" finds at Choukoutien may actually be a little more recent since there is a possibility that they belong to the earlier part of the long warm interval between the second and the third glaciations. This fits the anatomical evidence since the Choukoutien men had slightly larger brain cases and slightly smaller teeth than the Java finds, so it is possible on both anatomical and geological grounds to regard them as a later version of the Pithecanthropine stage.

With Java and Peking giving evidence of the existence of early Middle Pleistocene pithecanthropines in the Far East, we turn now to their westernmost representatives.

At the northwestern extreme of the area inhabited by man during the early Middle Pleistocene, the only skeletal fragment discovered so far is the famous Heidelberg mandible of 1907. With so little to go on, any judgment as to whether or not Heidelberg is a pithecanthropine is bound to be tentative. While morphologists have argued long and inconclusively over the nuances of chin formation etc., we believe that the measurements tell the tale. As Table 3 shows, the measurements of the teeth which are

TABLE 3

SINANTHROPUS AND HEIDELBERG MANDIBULAR BUCCAL–LINGUAL
TOOTH MEASUREMENTS

	I_1	I_2	C	PM_1	PM_2	M_1	M_2	M_3
Heidelberg	7.1	7.8	9.0	9.0	9.2	11.2	12.0	10.9
Sinanthropus	6.4	7.0	9.2	9.9	9.8	11.8	12.2	11.2

least subject to modification by wear, that is the width or buccal-lingual diameters, are almost the same for the Heidelberg mandible as the average measurements which Weidenreich discovered from the extensive Choukoutien material. Since a definitive placement within the Pithecanthropine stage requires an appraisal of both face and brain, obviously we cannot be certain that Heidelberg, minus its brain-case, was a pithecanthropine, but the teeth are the right size, the dating is the same, and the evidence for culture in Western Europe at that time are just what one would expect, so we feel fairly confident in assigning the Heidelberg jaw to the Pithecanthropine stage as its most northwesterly representative.

Recently, Dr. Robinson has regarded the Telanthropus material, which he and Dr. Broom found at Swartkrans, as being properly designated Pithecanthropine. While Robinson has claimed that it is contemporary with Paranthropus in an effort to prove that the latter was a blind end doomed to extinction, yet the evidence is far from conclusive. The initial Telanthropus discovery was made in a little pocket of different materials from the top of the Paranthropus-bearing Swartkrans breccia, and as Broom initially realized, it could have been deposited at a later time. Since this is consistent with our interpretations, we shall regard it as probably of later date, and as an indication of the existence of the southwesternmost extent of the Pithecanthropine stage.

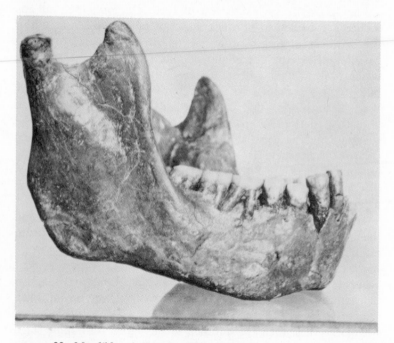

FIGURE 99. Mandible of Ternefine Man (*Atlanthropus mauritanicus III*). (Courtesy of Dr. C. Arambourg.)

Various pieces of evidence have been found in the area between Germany and South Africa, but, these are tantalizingly incomplete and difficult to evaluate. At Ternefine in Algeria the French paleontologist Arambourg was responsible for the discovery of three mandibles and the parietal bone of a human skull in 1954 and 1955. These were associated with crude stone tools including Abbevillian-type hand axes and with what has been considered to be an early Middle Pleistocene fauna. Ternefine, then, is roughly contemporary with Heidelberg and the far eastern pithecanthropines, but since the parietal belonged to an immature individual and in any event represents only a part of the skull, it is not possible to determine with any confidence what the skull looked like. The jaws and teeth fall within the range of variation indicated by the Asiatic finds, and our tentative assumption is that the skulls must likewise have been similar.

Finally Dr. Leakey's discovery in 1960 of a complete skull cap in Bed II of Olduvai provides the most positive confirmation of the existence of pithecanthropines in Africa in association with Middle Pleistocene strata and a hand-axe toolmaking tradition which itself is directly derived from the Oldowan pebble-tool tradition associated with the australopithecines. Although Heidelberg, Telanthropus, and Ternefine are jaws without skulls, and Olduvai Bed II (1960) is a skull without a jaw, nevertheless the time designations are the same as are the evidences for associated cultures where these are present, and we regard them as all belonging to the same Pithecanthropine stage of human evolution. The additional finds of jaws and teeth reported in 1964 promise to confirm this judgment.

The view that the pithecanthropines arose at one point and then spread throughout the range indicated by their maximum extent is now widely held, and is a possible one. Such a picture is, however, more correct for the australopithecines, since it is evident that they arose in Africa and then spread as their cultural adaptive mechanisms developed, but if one envisions the tropics and south temperate areas of the Old World populated, albeit thinly, with australopithecines, then the advance to the Pithecanthropine stage can be regarded as having taken place more or less simultaneously across the whole extent of their range. There is nothing mystical

FIGURE 100. Bifaces in quartzite associated with Ternefine man. (Courtesy of
Dr. C. Arambourg.)

about such a process since it simply reflects the general response
to a change in the most important adaptive mechanism. Contacts
between adjacent bands of australopithecines ensured the rapid
spread of cultural innovations that had particular survival value
throughout the australopithecine world within the space of, at
most, a few thousand years. Since cultural adaptation accounts
for the most marked change in the operation of selective forces,
the big changes in the forces affecting human survival took place
roughly simultaneously, as far as evolutionary time is concerned.
Genetic responses to these simultaneous alterations in selective
factors would necessarily have been similar or identical since any
differing responses would have been selected against. Furthermore,

the intermittent but repeated contact of adjacent groups would have ensured the exchange of significant genetic material throughout the inhabited world providing the basis for Weidenreich's realization that, at any one time level, there has only been one species of man during the course of human evolution. Such simultaneous modification of the forces of selection and the perpetual circulation of genetic material provide the means whereby the Australopithecine stage was transformed into the Pithecanthropine stage—not simply in one place, but throughout the inhabited world.

The next full stage in our scheme is the Neanderthal stage, and while there is relatively extensive evidence for its appearance and date, this does not occur until very near the onset of the last (fourth) glaciation, which means that there is a long gap for which we have relatively little evidence in the form of actual human fossils. There are a few fossils, and, most important, they can properly be placed in the evolutionary continuum because of the existence of an unbroken and increasingly rich archeological record. In Europe and Africa, at least, cultural evolution proceeds from the Pithecanthropine to the Neanderthal stages without break, and what skeletal evidence exists can most conveniently be interpreted as confirming the transition between these two stages.

From North Africa and southern France there are a number of finds that belong to the latter part of the Middle Pleistocene, but these are mainly jaws and teeth. Since there was no important change in jaw and tooth size or shape between the Pithecanthropine and Neanderthal stages, these scattered finds are no help. The Steinheim skull of 1933 and the Swanscombe skull of 1935–1936–1955 furnish the only picture we have of what the human head looked like at the end of the second interglacial, and, as has been already noted in Chapter 6, these constitute the focus of a continuing controversy—Steinheim because it was distorted and Swanscombe because it lacked the frontal and facial portion. These sources of uncertainty have different authorities to interpret them according to their own view of man's evolution, and since some authorities have believed that a modern form of man may have existed much earlier than is generally considered possible, the doubtful, distorted, or missing parts are generally regarded as modern unless proven otherwise. However, examination of the original reports and available evidence does not contradict our expectation that the only cranial material available stands morphologically half way between the pithecanthropines and the Neanderthals in both size and form.

There is one other find prior to those properly associated with the Neanderthal stage which should be mentioned in our survey since so much attention has been devoted to it. This includes the skull cap and the part forehead and eye socket fragment discovered in 1947 at Fontéchevade in the southwestern part of France. Fontéchevade is referred to here, not because it is particularly important, but because of the interpretation which has been attached to it. Most authorities now regard it as the long-sought representative of pre-Neanderthal "sapiens," modern in form and lacking the primitive browridges. It is instructive to note, however, that the author of this interpretation is Professor Vallois of Paris who was much influenced by the teachings of his former mentor Marcellin Boule, whose position he inherited following Boule's death. Since Boule's thinking was implicitly opposed to evolutionary interpretations, it is no surprise that Vallois finds the concept of hominid catastrophism not uncongenial.

A number of difficulties surrounds the attempts to interpret the Fontéchevade remains. First, the human skeletal material was not all found *in situ*, but part was actually discovered in the shade of the laboratory where blocks of the site had been brought for more leisurely study. Unfortunately, no sample section of the site was left unexcavated as a demonstration of what the stratigraphy had been, and, as a consequence a cloud of doubt will always hang over the age of the Fontéchevade human remains, although most authorities agree that they probably belong in the early part of the last interglacial.

The biggest stumbling block to interpretation, however, lies in the fragmentary nature of the skeletal remains themselves. The brainbox represented by Fontéchevade II was soft and crumbly when found and there was no assurance that it was undistorted. Fontéchevade I, the fronto-orbito-nasal fragment was not distorted. While Vallois devoted an exhaustive monograph to their study, only two photographs were included. One was taken before restoration and the other was taken afterward, and while both are not as clear as they might have been, it is still evident that so many changes have been made that even an expert would scarcely guess that the pictures referred to the same individual. Careful consideration of the evidence assembled in Vallois' monograph leads one to the cautious conclusion that there is not enough material from Fontéchevade of known sex, age, form and date to warrant an appraisal of evolutionary stage. Certainly it is questionable whether it offers any support for Vallois' sweeping claims of ancient *sapiens* and hence Neanderthal extinction, i.e., hominid catastrophism.

3. The Neanderthal Stage

Neanderthal man has gone farther toward capturing the imagination of the general public than has any other fossil with the possible exception of the original Pithecanthropus which was hailed as the "missing link." While it is true that many misconceptions are attached to this image—the hairy, slouching, cave man clad in loin cloth, club in hand, anachronistically contemplating a dinosaur—the dim awareness exists that the precursors of modern man were physically distinguishable from men of today and do provide direct evidence that man has evolved much as other organisms have.

Despite the fact that both experts and laymen have recognized the importance of the Neanderthals, few have attempted to define precisely what it is that constitutes a Neanderthal. The definition which we use has recently been proposed by one of us (C.L.B.) and is as follows:

> Neanderthal man is the man of the Mousterian culture
> prior to the reduction in form and dimensions of the
> Middle Pleistocene face.

This recognizes the fact that the only area in which the Neanderthals differ significantly from modern man is in the face. While most of the individual measurements can be equalled in single members of modern populations, yet taken together it would be most remarkable to find them in a living man. Certainly the difference between the Neanderthals as a population and the various modern populations is most striking in the facial dimensions. From the neck down, the Neanderthal skeleton is scarcely distinguishable from that of modern man, although there is a slight tendency for the joints and muscle attachments to be a little more robust. Certainly the bent-knee-gait and semi-erect posture with which the hominid catastrophists have tried to invest the Neanderthals was largely a product of their own wishful thinking. On the contrary, the Neanderthals stood just as erectly as we do today and were never forced to shuffle along, unable to straighten their knees.

When Boule made his study of the famous skeleton from La Chapelle-aux-Saints, he discovered that the cranial capacity was in excess of 1600 cc. which is approximately 150 cc. larger than the average for modern male Europeans. However, since he was so firmly convinced that this large-brained man must have been a primitive and inferior individual, he tried to claim that the organization of the brain was inferior to that of modern man. Boule's claims are without support, for even if one could infer anything whatever concerning the complexity and relative proportions of the various parts of the brain from the impressions on the inner surface of the skull—which one cannot—the range of variation within which perfectly normal and even extraordinary mental ability can occur is so large that no such judgment is possible on skulls differing so little from modern ones as did those of the known Neanderthals. On anatomical grounds there is no reason to regard Neanderthal mental capacity as having been different from that of modern man. The evidence indicates that man's brain reached its present state of development by the Neanderthal stage at least one hundred thousand and perhaps as much as two hundred thousand years ago, and has changed in no significant respect since that time.

It has seemed puzzling to some that the increase in brain size, which was undoubtedly related to an increase in information storage capacity and problem solving ability, should suddenly have ceased. The puzzlement has been due to the assumption that, if brain size and intelligence are indeed related, then further increases should have been of even greater benefit to the possessors.

The answer, while not of a kind which can be subjected to rigorous testing and proof, nevertheless is cogent enough so that there would not seem to be much doubt of its truth. It derives from an appreciation of the nature and mode of operation of man's principle adaptive apparatus which, as we have said, is not brain-power *per se*, but culture.

One of the most important facets of culture is the role that it plays in the acquisition of information by the individual. With cultural traditions forged by the experience of preceding generations, the individual is not obliged to depend upon his own wits and the accident of his own experience to acquire many of the essential facets of knowledge which improve his chances for survival. As soon as language can be developed, the experience of an individual can be shared with other members of his group, and the learning of one is of benefit to all. This has an interesting consequence which is not often mentioned: with just enough intelligence to be able to master one's language and grasp the significance of the insights verbally transmitted from generation to generation, even a relatively unimaginative individual has almost as good a chance for survival as a genuine genius. In the evolutionary process, as soon as culture has achieved notable success as an adaptive mechanism, then, above a certain minimum, an excess of brains or intelligence does not greatly improve one's probability of reproducing and hence of passing such traits on to future generations.

The success of the cultural adaptive mechanism by the time of the Neanderthals is evident in the greatly increased number of Mousterian tools, indicating a significant increase in population density. It is also evident in the fact that man could now successfully survive in numbers in what today is called the temperate zone, despite the lowering of the temperature signalling the onset of the last glaciation. Occupation of such an area meant access to the quantities of game animals that inhabited the periglacial parts of the Old World, but this was only made possible by the solution of certain problems which would normally have prevented a tropical animal like man from being able to survive under such climatic conditions. Clothing and shelter must have been essential.

From the concentration of Mousterian tools in rock shelters and caves, we have pretty good evidence that shelter was being used. It is probable that the cave entrances were modified by brush and skin barriers, and certainly the abundance of hearths indicates that fire was being used as a source of heat. Evidence for the use of clothing is a little less direct, although it can be inferred and no one can doubt that the Neanderthals, with the full cerebral development of modern man, were bright enough not to face the raging blizzard clad only in the fur-lined G-string so mindlessly depicted in cartoon caricatures. The great proliferation of stone scrapers in the Mousterian clearly indicates that considerable attention was paid to the preparation of skins. Furthermore, the remarkable rounded wear on the front teeth of the Neanderthals themselves, as in the present-day Eskimo, suggest that it was at least partially the result of their use in the process of tanning hides by chewing (see Figure 122).

The mention of the wear evident on the Neanderthal incisors brings us to the reason for the difference in face size between the Neanderthals and modern man. Except for the part of the face immediately related to the housing for the respiratory passages, i.e., the nose, the major determiner of face size is the dentition and its supporting architecture. Big teeth with long roots mean a large face, and as can be seen in Figure 101, the forward portion of the late Neanderthal dental arch is substantially larger than even the very largest population average (Australian aborigines) for modern men. Because of the heavy use to which the front teeth were subjected, it is hard to secure figures for unworn teeth, but our use of the buccal-lingual (cheek-side—tongue-side) diameter should minimize this difficulty since this dimension reaches its maximum near the level of the gums.

It is interesting to note that although Neanderthal incisors are about the largest developed during human evolution, they were generally subjected to such heavy usage that they were worn down to the gums by early middle age. Such a heavy, rounding kind of incisor wear clearly indicates that the front teeth were used for something more than simply biting food. One of the keys to man's successful survival has been his developing ability to manipulate his world to his advantage, and it is apparent that

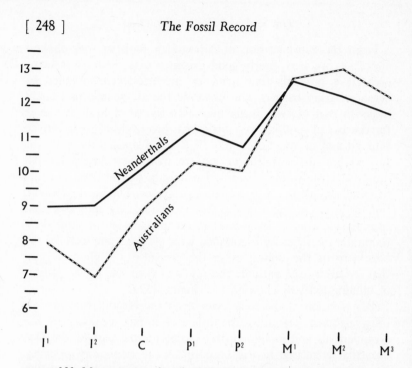

FIGURE 101. Measurements of teeth of Neanderthals and Australian aborigines.

into Mousterian times, the front teeth did heavy duty as manipu-
lators—one might say they were the Lower and Middle Pleistocene
equivalent of the Boy Scout knife. It seems likely that they were
used to crack nuts, peel bark, squeeze, scrape, pry, and cut a
variety of objects, and also to tan rawhide. Evidently the possession of large strong incisors was a necessity if a Neanderthal were
to live through his most productive years.

If the reason for the existence of large incisors at the onset of
the last glaciation is obvious, then the reason for the transformation of the Neanderthal face into the face of modern man should
be equally easy to account for. One need only account for the
suspension of the adaptive significance of the possession of large
incisors, and by the process of the probable mutation effect, the
accumulation of variation will result in their eventual reduction.
Since the only real difference between Neanderthals and moderns
lies in the size of the face, a simple reduction would be all that

was required to effect the transformation. Analysis of the changes in man's cultural adaptive mechanism, as seen in the archeological record, provides the necessary insight; one of the most obvious changes, beginning with the early Mousterian, is the proliferation of cutting and manipulating tools. The technological changes that mark the development of the Upper Paleolithic out of the Mousterian are particularly concerned with the increase in number and variety of cutting, gouging, chiselling, engraving, and scraping tools. As specific tools were made for the purpose of performing specific tasks in the developing Mousterian and more particularly in the derived Upper Paleolithic, there was a gradual reduction in the former extreme of incisor usage and a gradual suspension of the adaptive significance of the enormous Neanderthal front teeth. Now that they were free to vary, the accumulation of random mutations resulted in their inevitable reduction, hence the modern face.

Before leaving the Neanderthals, mention should be made of their dating and distribution. As a group, there is no doubt that they flourished from the end of the last interglacial, about one hundred thousand years ago, up to the beginning of what has been called the Göttweiger Interstadial, which was a climatic amelioration between the early and late parts of the Würm glaciation some forty thousand years ago. Although this places the Neanderthals as a stage, it is hard to be more precise where individuals are concerned. First, the relative placement of the finer subdivisions of the Würm is a source of continuing disagreement among professional geologists and archeologists, and, second, the Neanderthals had instituted the practice of burying their dead. While this assured us of the discovery of more complete skeletons and greater numbers of individuals, it also meant that the actual level of the bones within the ground did not correspond with the time at which the individual had lived. As a result of these two sources of uncertainty, it is not yet possible to discuss the trends of development which must have occurred during the sixty thousand years or more of the Neanderthal stage.

The distribution of the Neanderthals is a little easier to plot since there is abundant archeological evidence for the areal distribution extent of the Mousterian toolmaking tradition and

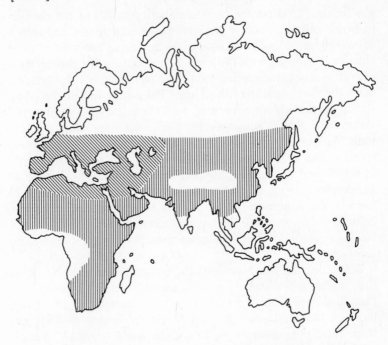

FIGURE 102. Mousterian and derived cultures. Oblique hatching indicates the area of Mousterian concentration; vertical hatching indicates the distribution of other derived cultures.

other contemporary traditions of the same approximate level of technological complexity. The occasional occurrence of skeletal remains with this cultural spread completes the picture with Figure 104 showing the location of the most significant finds. It is evident that the entire inhabited portion of the Old World immediately prior to the Göttweiger Interstadial was peopled by groups at the Neanderthal stage of development. To be sure, some authors have tried to present a modified version of hominid catastrophism claiming that the early Neanderthals, represented by Skhūl and Krapina, appear more modern than the later ones represented by La Chapelle-aux-Saints, La Ferrassie and others. These supposedly early Neanderthals then are presumed to have given rise to true moderns somewhere "in the East" who then swept into Europe and extinguished the late-surviving "classic" Neanderthals. This view cannot be supported since both Krapina and Skhūl properly belong in the early part of the Göttweiger Interstadial rather than the third Interglacial and hence must be accounted later than the so-called "classic" Neanderthals of the La Chapelle type. With both Krapina and especially Skhūl at Mount Carmel showing variations in the direction of modern form, it fits the evolutionary hypothesis to find that they occur halfway between the early moderns and the full Neanderthals in time as well as in form.

4. Modern Man

The first datable appearance of men of relatively modern form is in the latter part of the Göttweiger Interstadial and associated with the earliest true Upper Paleolithic toolmaking traditions. Unfortunately both the skeletal and the archeological evidence for the appearance of modern man is somewhat sketchy. The earliest population which has been called modern is that of Skhūl at Mount Carmel in Palestine, but it is associated with a variety of the Mousterian and most authorities recognize that the skeletal remains are "Neanderthaloid." Clearly Skhūl presents the best picture of a transitional population. Unfortunately there is no good clearly datable population associated with the early Upper Paleolithic although there are a number of hints.

The most famous Upper Paleolithic find is the so-called Old Man of Cro-Magnon discovered in 1868 in Cro-Magnon in the Commune of Tayac near Les Eyzies, Southwestern France. The fame of Cro-Magnon is largely due to the fact that this was the earliest *recognized* discovery of an undoubted fossil man, having been made at a time when most paleontologists still accepted Cuvier's dictum that fossil man did not exist. Natural scientists of nineteenth-century France while dominated by the ghost of Cuvier, could not deny that a genuine fossil man had been uncovered, but, with Darwinian evolution creating a disturbing intellectual furor, at least they could claim that their human fossil was indistinguishable from men of today, and therefore they could strongly imply that evolutionary ideas need not be applied to man.

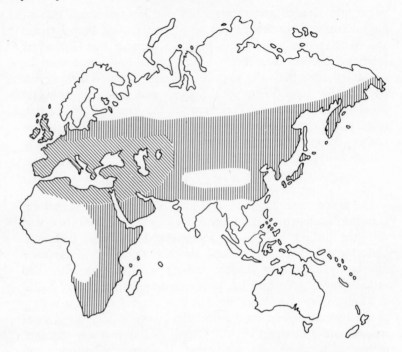

FIGURE 103. Upper Paleolithic and derived cultures. Oblique hatching indicates the area of Upper Paleolithic concentration; vertical hatching indicates the distribution of other derived cultures.

While Cro-Magnon is indeed a genuine fossil man and does belong to the Upper Paleolithic, its exact significance is obscured by a number of factors. It was discovered accidentally by railway workmen, which would not be much of a guarantee of stratigraphic accuracy even today when the importance of precise dating technique is much more clearly realized. Then, too, the other skeletons with which it was found were part of a series of burials, and even under the best of circumstances, burials are often difficult to date precisely. Aside from the uncertainty which surrounds the precise dating of Cro-Magnon, the exact morphological status is subject to a variety of interpretations. There can be no question that the individual was robust, male, and tall (5 ft. 11 in.), but the assertions relating to the noble chin and lofty brow are perhaps overenthusiastic. Evidently Cro-Magnon man did not possess the heavy brow ridges of a Neanderthal nor did he possess the huge Middle Paleolithic dentition which occupied so much jaw space that the chin would be labelled "retreating," but here we run into some difficulty because Cro-Magnon had lost all his teeth. With the teeth lost before discovery, it is somewhat difficult to make an accurate reconstruction of the face. Furthermore, the whole middle part of the face has been etched and pitted by weathering, further adding to the difficulties of reconstruction (see Figure 51). This is not to say that Cro-Magnon was not a characteristic member of an Upper Paleolithic population and hence within the range of variation of modern man, but it is intended to constitute a caution to those who would attempt to construct a rigid picture of what is assumed to be the earliest representative of men of today.

Other Upper Paleolithic skeletons have been discovered, although many of them were found before the turn of the century and are not accompanied by accurate stratigraphic documentation. One population discovered in the mid-1890's at Předmost, in what is now Czechoslovakia, included one specimen with a heavy enough brow ridge and large enough front teeth so that it could very well have been placed in the midst of the Skhūl population without disturbing even the most vigilant hominid catastrophist. While this is the extreme of variation, with the rest of the individuals looking progressively more modern, it does indicate that Upper Paleolithic populations did overlap the range of variation of the Neanderthaloids. This same generalization finds support in the skeletal material found in 1928 at Afalou-Bou-Rhummel, Algeria. Even the late Upper Paleolithic (Magdalenian) male skull from Obercassel, near Bonn on the Rhine, is characterized by a development of jaws and brow which is neanderthaloid, and the same thing can be said for a number of other skulls of probable Upper Paleolithic age, although the exact date of many is in doubt because of the fact that many are burials or were discovered accidentally or under other questionable circumstances.

One of these was the famous Combe Capelle skull of 1909 with a lower face of a neanderthaloid form. Unfortunately this was

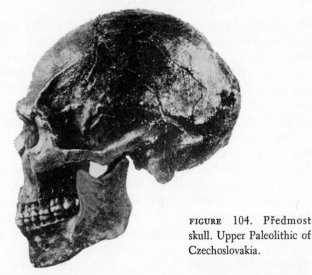

discovered by the pick and shovel technique which Hauser was using to loot the site, so that, even if the skull had not been blown to oblivion in the Second World War, the exact stratigraphy must remain in doubt. Another was the discovery in 1901 of the so-called Negroids, in one of the Grimaldi caves near Monaco on the Riviera. Two skeletons were discovered at this time, one of an adult woman and the other of an immature male. These are of interest since, more than fifty years ago, Boule claimed that these were of the same age as the "classic" Neanderthals despite the fact that an eminent archeologist associated with the discovery had pointed out that they were buried from an Upper Paleolithic level. Furthermore the form of the faces of the Grimaldi remains is subject to some doubt because of the liberties taken in reconstruction. Many authorities, on seeing the reconstruction of the immature male, regard it as an adolescent of fourteen or fifteen years, but most people have overlooked the fact that the deciduous molars were still in place when the remains were discovered. It was only later, in the laboratory, that Boule removed the deciduous molars, elevated the unerupted permanent premolars to the level of the occlusal plane, and restored the entire face by sheer guesswork. The photograph taken before "restoration" shows that the face had been at least 25 per

[254]

cent longer than it was when he had finished. It is evident that not only the dating, but also the form of the Grimaldi remains must remain in doubt—certainly there is no justification for calling them Negroid.

These remarks have been made to show that many problems still becloud attempts to portray the earliest appearance of modern morphology. What there is of reliable evidence shows that the transition from Neanderthal to modern took place gradually at the end of the Mousterian, continuing into the early Upper Paleolithic as a response to the changes in selective factors which have been outlined above.

It has been erroneously assumed by some that there have been virtually no changes in human morphology since the Upper Paleolithic. While no major changes have occurred nevertheless skeletal changes are evident. For example, there has been a slight but definite increase in skeletal robustness, and in the associated structures for the attachment of muscles. There has been a pronounced decrease in the visceral parts of the face, markedly affecting the size of the jaws and teeth. This reduction has occurred to different degrees among the various peoples of the world, varying all the way from no reduction at all for the Australian aborigines, to marked decrease in size and in frequent failures of such teeth as third molars to erupt in peoples in the area from Central Europe over into the Middle East. The differences in the degree of reduction are directly related to the extent to which the various cultural traditions in question have suspended the adaptive advantage inherent in the possession of a large dentition, a matter to be discussed further in Chapter 9.

The final noticeable skeletal change that has occurred since the Upper Paleolithic has been the development of the overbite—again a change related to the dental part of the face. Most of the readers of this book will find that their lower incisors bite behind their upper incisors when mandible and maxilla meet in normal occlusion. This, however, has not been true for the majority of human beings during the course of human evolution. Until recently, the lower incisors met the upper ones edge to edge when the molar surfaces were approximated, and this edge-to-edge bite still is characteristic of the few hunting and food-gathering peoples remaining in the world.

The development of the overbite did not occur until well after the introduction of metal tools in the circum-Mediterranean area, and not until considerably later in western Europe, where the edge-to-edge bite survived in England until after the Norman Conquest. Evidently the change from the edge-to-edge to the overbite did not occur in the westernmost part of Europe until slightly less than a thousand years ago. The initial reason for the development of an overbite was a change in characteristic tooth use, but among people where it has been present for a considerable length of time, genetic changes have occurred which would prevent some individuals from re-acquiring an edge-to-edge bite no matter how hard they might try. To show how the initial loss of the edge-to-edge bite is due to a change in use rather than to genetic alteration, reference may be made to the case of the Alaskan Eskimo who has made the change in one generation. Canned food, store-bought bread, and metal tools have resulted in a radical change in eating and manipulating habits so that, whereas the oldsters all have edge-to-edge occlusions, the younger generation is growing up with an overbite.

The seeds of the change were sown, literally, with the food producing revolution some ten thousand years ago. Prior to this time, human subsistence depended primarily upon success in hunting and gathering. Technological complexity was limited by the fact that groups could not remain for long in any one place, which put rather a restriction upon the total number of possessions which an individual could accumulate. Protein in the form of the products of the chase formed a substantial part of the diet. Since protein requires a minimum of chewing or mixing with salivary enzymes, the main need is to reduce it to bite-sized morsels which can then be swallowed with a minimum of further processing. In this connection it is interesting to note that throughout the Paleolithic the molar teeth show relatively little wear in comparison to the frequently extreme degrees of abrasion exhibited by the incisors. The standard way of producing bite-sized pieces of meat, during the time span before the development of the overbite, was to take a chunk of meat in one hand, stuff it part way into the mouth, clamp the incisors on it, and then saw it off at the level of the lips with a knife or other cutting implement. The same technique is still used among the hunting and gathering peoples of the world, and a residue of it can still be seen in the rural parts of Europe where coarse bread is still a major item of diet. Such a process encourages the edge-to-edge use of the incisors and the flat wear of their occlusal surfaces.

With the coming of the food-producing revolution, man began to exert an increasing amount of control over his future food supply, and the most reliable way in which this could be done was to plant and tend grains and vegetables. As the amount of protein in the diet decreased and the starch and carbohydrate content increased, the amount of chewing for the purpose of increasing the digestibility of the food became relatively greater. Unlike meat, starches and carbohydrates start the process of digestion in the mouth where thorough mixture with salivary enzymes commences their conversion into simple sugars that can then be handled by the stomach.

The food-producing revolution did not immediately result in the loss of the edge-to-edge bite since it took several thousand years before the full possibilities of the change in subsistence began to be realized. With a sedentary existence, the production of food surpluses, and the accumulation of tangible possessions that this made possible, invention and technological progress occurred at an ever increasing rate. The development of metallurgy culminating in the bronze and later iron ages finally gave people a tool-kit which effectively put teeth as manipulating tools out of business, and it is not surprising to observe the cessation of incisor wear and the gradual appearance of partial overbites making their appearance with the beginning of the bronze age.

Primary reliance upon a grain-based diet introduced a degree of fine grinding in the molars not previously needed. This fine grinding involves repeated distal shifts of the mandible, and as the incisors cease to be worn off at the edge, the tips of the lower incisors slide up and back on the lingual (tongue-side) surfaces of the upper incisors. In this way, the upper incisors act as wedges forcing the mandible backwards as it is closed in a fine but powerful grinding motion activated primarily by the big muscles which close the jaws, i.e., bring the lower jaw into relation with the upper jaw.

Among people who have only recently acquired the tooth use habits which allow the overbite to develop, it would be a simple matter to re-acquire an edge-to-edge occlusion merely by changing dental habits. This is also true for many individuals who are members of populations where the overbite has been a characteristic for a millennium or more, but among these latter, there are many individuals who show enough further reduction in the size of the mandibular dental arch so that no amount of changed usage could produce an effective edge-to-edge bite. Among these individuals one can observe the beginnings of a genuine genetic change, and one is tempted to predict that the future of mankind will witness further reductions accumulating in the dental apparatus, to the extent that the overbite and nothing but the overbite will be developed despite the various uses to which the teeth may be put.

While we are also tempted to venture speculations on other changes which the future may bring, we shall here forego that temptation, and leave such speculations to a later section. In the next chapter we shall attempt to summarize the relationships between the changing selective forces and the effects which they have exerted during the course of human evolution from the australopithecines to twentieth-century man.

SUGGESTED READINGS

Brace, C. L. "Cultural factors in the evolution of the human dentition," M. F. Ashley Montagu (editor). *Culture and the Evolution of Man*, Oxford University Press, New York, 1962, pp. 343–354.

The role of culture in influencing the form and relations of the teeth in man.

Campbell, B. *Human Evolution: An Introduction to Man's Adaptations*. Aldine Publishing Co., Chicago, 1966.

An excellent integrated account of man's evolution.

Garn, S. M. (editor). "Culture and the direction of human evolution," *Human Biology*, vol. 35, 1963, pp. 219–311.
Seven studies.

Howell, F. C., and F. Bourlière (editors). *African Ecology and Human Evolution.* Viking Fund Publications in Anthropology, No. 36, 1963.
Contains some fine papers on cultural factors in the evolution of man.

Koenigswald, G. H. R. von (editor). *Neanderthal Centenary 1856–1956.* Kemink en Zoon, Utrecht, 1958.
Thirty valuable contributions on various aspects of Neanderthal man, celebrating the centenary of the discovery of Neanderthal man.

Origin and Evolution of Man. Cold Spring Harbor Symposia on Quantitative Biology, vol. 15, 1950.
A classic symposium dealing with a wide range of topics, especially relevant to those discussed in the present chapter.

Roe, A., and G. G. Simpson (editors). *Behavior and Evolution.* Yale University Press, New Haven, 1958.
A synthesis of evolutionary facts and principles as they bear on behavior, with behavioral facts and principles as they bear on evolution.

Montagu, M. F. Ashley (editor). *Culture and the Evolution of Man.* Oxford University Press, New York, 1962.
Twenty contributions toward the understanding of the role cultural factors have played in human evolution.

Culture: Man's Adaptive Dimension. Oxford University Press, New York, 1968.
Additional contributions supplementing the preceding volume.

Spuhler, J. N. (editor). *The Evolution of Man's Capacity for Culture.* Wayne State University Press, Detroit, 1959.
Six essays.

Washburn, S. L. (editor). *Social Life of Early Man.* Viking Fund Publications in Anthropology, No. 31, 1961.
A highly informative and stimulating series of contributions.

CHAPTER EIGHT ❦
INTERPRETIVE SUMMARY
OF THE FOSSIL RECORD

Our examination of the evidence for human evolution, has led us to the genetic arrangement of the fossil record in four representative stages: Australopithecine, Pithecanthropine, Neanderthal, and Modern. We do not omit to note the possibility that the Australopithecine stage should be further subdivided into early and late phases corresponding to what Robinson would designate the Genus *Australopithecus* and the Genus *Paranthropus*. In our view, however, all the stages and their subdivisions properly belong in the Genus *Homo*, designating those organisms that rely upon culture as their primary adaptive mechanism.

The major morphological changes that have occurred since the beginning of human evolution can be focused on three areas:

1. The Attainment of Erect Posture and a Bipedal Mode of Locomotion

This must have occurred at the very beginning of human evolution, since it was evidently a characteristic of the earliest australopithecines yet discovered. The slightly longer ischium of the known australopithecine pelves indicates that long-distance walking was not perfected to quite the degree that is characteristic of more recent men, but this is a relatively minor change. The evident bipedalism of the australopithecines is one of the indications that points to their essential humanity, since a weaponless biped on the savannas of Eastern and Southern Africa could not have lasted a single generation. The success of the australopithecines points to the likelihood of their use of culture as a major means of adaptation. We have also noted that the increase in size of the later australopithecines doubtless was of survival value, but since this is not quite the same thing as a change in form, we have not equated it in rank with the other three changes.

2. The Increase in Brain Size

The australopithecines, as the earliest human beings, had brains no larger than those of some living anthropoid apes, but while living apes with brains of such size range in the neighborhood of a quarter-ton of gross body weight, the australopithecines go on down to fifty or sixty pounds total. Relatively speaking, the australopithecines were much brainier creatures than any living ape. While the evidence for cultural development as seen in the archeological record reveals only a moderate increase by the time of the second glaciation when the pithecanthropines began to flourish, yet the selective advantage conferred by the possession of more brains was apparently powerful enough for the average brain size to double in volume while body size remained effectively unchanged since the late Australopithecine stage. By the Neanderthal stage, the brain had almost tripled in size when compared with the original australopithecines, while again, culture had shown only a moderate increase in tangible complexity. From this point on, however, culture develops at an ever-increasing rate while cranial capacity does not change at all. We can only infer that some sort of threshold had been passed and that the efficiency of culture in transmitting information among individuals and across generational boundaries was sufficient so that beyond a certain point, marked increases in individual intelligence conferred no particular survival advantages upon the possessors.

3. Various Reductions in the Dentition

The non-projection of the canines, even in the earliest australo-pithecines in whom these were still relatively large teeth, is another reason why all of the fossil stages considered are placed within the Genus *Homo*. Lacking such anatomical means of controlling the environment, we must conclude that the creatures in question relied upon a non-anatomical instrument, i.e., culture. Certainly changes in diet resulted in reduction of the canines, especially since tools began to be deliberately employed to perform, more efficiently, the functions of the canines. Throughout human evolution, the canines have fulfilled the same function as have the incisors.

The molar teeth underwent an initial increase related to the general increase in size of the later australopithecines when compared with the earlier ones. The sharp decrease between the Australopithecine and Pithecanthropine stages is tentatively correlated with the evident increase in hunting efficiency of the pithecanthropines. Protein foods do not require the same amount of crushing and mixing with salivary enzymes as do carbohydrates and starches, and it is reasonable to associate the significant increase of meat in the diet with a reduction in the amount of heavy duty mastication required. Furthermore, the addition of fire to the cultural repertoire indicates that the use of heat to break down the more resistant parts of the utilized foodstuffs would lead to a further reduction in the amount of required chewing, allowing the probable mutation effect to produce a reduction in the size of the molar teeth.

The incisors remained large until manufactured tools could be more effectively utilized for specific tasks. This started in the Mousterian. With the pressure taken off the front teeth, the accumulation of random variation results in their reduction, with the result that the large heavy face of the Pithecanthropine and Neanderthal stages reduces to the form recognizable in modern man. Changes in eating habits and further reduction produce the overbite generally present in modern *Homo sapiens*.

Figure 105 shows graphically the features wherein the major stages of human evolution differ from each other, and conveys some hint of the changes in selective pressures which result in the

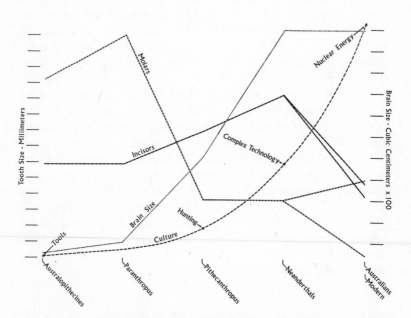

FIGURE 105. Brain, tooth size, and cultural relations in the Pleistocene. Summary chart of the major changes that have taken place in human evolution with their suggested cultural causes. Initial increase in molar size is due to increase in body bulk between the Australopithecus and Paranthropus phases. The drop in molar size to the Pithecanthropine level indicates the addition, with the development of effective hunting techniques, of quantities of meat protein to the diet. The incisor line does not increase with body size between the Australopithecus and Paranthropus phases, which indicates a *relative* decrease in incisor size, possibly due to the use of tools instead of the front teeth. The increase again to a maximum at the Neanderthal Stage reflects the development of tools which assume tasks formerly performed by the teeth. This has been less so in the Australian aborigines, reflected in the fact that the incisors do not decrease so markedly and the molars decrease not at all—technology being at its minimum development in Australia, the burden falls on the teeth. Australopithecus and Paranthropus belong to the Villafranchian, the Pithecanthropines to the Middle Pleistocene, Neanderthals to the Upper Pleistocene, and Moderns to Post-Pleistocene times. The spaces allotted are not to scale.

morphological responses indicated. Doubling of the brain and reducing the molars changes the australopithecines into the pithecanthropines. A further simple increase in brain size produces the Neanderthals out of the pithecanthropines, and finally the reduction of the Neanderthal dentition, particularly at its forward end, and the accompanying adjustments by the supporting facial architecture accounts for the final development of modern form. Treated in this way, the changes which have taken place in man's physical form since the first record of his existence are actually less dramatic than they would at first appear to be. This is because in our intimate familiarity and concern with human morphology we tend to magnify our perceptions of the difference between the several manifestations of human form. As a counteraction to this pardonably egocentric tendency, it is possibly a healthier exercise to reduce the differences to their proper perspective. This we have attempted to do. Differences still remain and they are unquestionably important ones, but, related to the selective pressures and adaptive mechanisms that called them into being, they take their place in the processual continuum of development which is human evolution.

SUGGESTED READINGS

Baker, P. T., and Weiner, J. S. (editors). *The Biology of Human Adaptability*. Oxford University Press, New York, 1966.
On the problems of man in his natural environments and his adaptive responses to them.

Dobzhansky, Th. *Mankind Evolving*. Yale University Press, New Haven, 1962.
On the evolution of man from the genetic point of view.

Dill, D. B., E. F. Adolph, and C. G. Wilber (editors). *Handbook of Physiology, Section 4: Adaptation to the Environment*. American Physiological Society, Washington, D.C., 1964.
The fundamental treatise on the adaptation of mammals, and especially man, to the environment, containing sixty-five contributions by the authorities in their fields.

PART

III

Living People

CHAPTER NINE ❦ HUMAN
VARIATION AND ITS
SIGNIFICANCE

IT IS THE TASK of physical anthropology to further the understanding of human evolution. The investigation and interpretation of the hominid fossil record is clearly one of the ways in which this may be accomplished, but another and equally important approach is through the consideration of physical diversity among the living peoples of the world. Superficially it might seem as though it would be easier to deal with the abundant evidence present in the form of living peoples, but actually this turns out to be somewhat more difficult.

The paleoanthropologist's approach begins with the arrangement of the known fossil record in time, after which the causal mechanisms postulated to produce the changes so observed can be discussed. To many, the analogous procedure on the part of the student of the living is to arrange the peoples of the world according to geographical location, and then to attempt an explanation for the population differences observed. In practice this is far less easy, since a number of problems immediately arise which greatly complicate the issues.

While it may appear simple, it is in reality extremely difficult to determine where one population ends and another begins. An arrangement of world populations based on such characteristics as stature and head form would differ radically from an arrangement based on hair form and skin color. The criterion for the delineation of living human groups is considered to be their breeding behavior, and a population is then considered to be that group of people whose members habitually choose their mates from among themselves. This approach to the identification of meaningful human groups enjoys considerable popularity at the present time since, following the insights which have come from that branch of the biological sciences called population genetics, the unit which is significant for the evolutionary survival of a species has been recognized as the breeding population. This works quite well in delineating meaningful groups in nature such as field mice or fruit flies. Zoologists have used the term "races" to designate breeding populations that share identifiable characteristics, and it has been assumed that a similar practice could be followed in dealing with human groups. When "races" are delineated for mankind by modern biologically oriented physical anthropologists, they are usually defined along these lines.

The use of such an approach as an attempt to discover biologically meaningful human groups usually does not take into consideration the fact that human breeding populations are determined by the dictates of culture rather than by specifically physical features. Certainly the most valid groupings of human beings are based upon cultural criteria. This puts the physical anthropologist in the awkward position of having to base the analysis of human physical diversity upon groupings which are not primarily based upon morphological characteristics.

The result is that "race" has always been a troublesome issue for human biologists, altogether apart from the social and political problems that have been involved. This accounts for the fact that there is such widespread disagreement among anthropologists concerning the definitions of race and the identification of the races of man. Definitions range all the way from the denial that races exist at all to the attempt to define race on an exclusively morphological basis, and, for the majority of anthropologists who recognize some division of *Homo sapiens* into constituent races, the number recognized ranges all the way from three to somewhere in the hundreds. Finally, once a given anthropologist has settled on a definition which suits him he then discovers that there is relatively little that he can do with his races except to list them.

This is all in marked contrast to the convenience which the social scientist finds in the term race. While individual sociologists may have slightly differing definitions, the differences are not significant and in fact disappear in practice. There is virtual unanimity among professionals in the applications and uses of the term. Even those anthropologists who have attempted to define race on biological grounds alone are forced to admit that the sociologist is quite properly within his own province when he studies the problems engendered by race relations. Obviously the concept of race is used in the same way by people concerned with a theoretical as well as an applied interest in politics, i.e., by political scientists as well as by politicians.

The definition of race which we offer is essentially that of the social scientist and is based upon the perception of physical traits which are assumed to characterize human groups. We define a race as being:

A *group of mankind, members of which can be identified by the possession of distinctive physical characteristics.*

The inclusion of the word "distinctive" in this definition is crucial, since the importance of race is primarily in human perception and of course the attitudes and actions of the perceivers. Unless differences are clearly and easily perceived, consistent attitudes and practices cannot be pursued and the race in question loses its identity as far as the people under consideration and also the social scientists are concerned. In some cases what are perceived as racial differences are in fact primarily cultural differences between people whose genetically based physical characteristics are not markedly distinguishable. For example, if one were to send a Sikh man to a barber, give him a shave and a haircut and dress him in a business suit he would be indistinguishable from, say, someone of Italian or any other Mediterranean origin. The same thing would be true for a Sikh woman in, for instance, a bikini and a bathing cap. However, the man in beard and turban and the woman in her sari are immediately recognizable as being racially distinct from people of European origin.

Because human breeding populations are delimited by culturally established boundaries, because of inherent defects in the meaning of the term and because of the inhumanity which has been practiced in the name of race, it has occasionally been advocated that the term be entirely abandoned. One of us (Montagu) has suggested that the significant group to be considered is the human breeding population, noncommittally called an "ethnic group," and that the term race be given up for these reasons.

On the face of it, it might seem that race as we have defined it, namely, as a breeding population with the addition of physical differentiation, would be the most desirable grouping for the exploration of human physical differences. Actually the accumulating evidence from recent research shows to an increasing extent that neither the use of breeding population (ethnic group) nor race is sufficient for the understanding of human diversity. It has become apparent that the assumption that there is something significant in the association of traits in a single group of people obscures the factors influencing the occurrence and distribution of any single trait. *The most important requirement for the analysis of human variation is the appreciation of the selective pressures which have operated to influence the expression of each trait separately.* Since in many important cases the crucial selective factors have no reference to ethnic or population boundaries, obviously an approach that takes population as its unit for study will fail to produce an understanding of whatever is influencing the distribution of the characteristics in question.

At this point the reader will remember that the most significant changes in the human fossil record occurred as a result of changes in the selective pressures affecting particular features which followed improvements in the primary adaptive mechanisms in question. Since the primary human adaptive mechanism is culture, it may be legitimately asked why a culturally defined group should not be the proper unit for the study of adaptively determined human variation. The answer is that for some purposes the presence or absence of the crucial adaptive mechanism may indeed coincide with culturally determined population boundaries, but for most characteristics the adaptive mechanism, while cultural, is quite unrestricted by the boundaries of specific cultures. For instance, metal cutting utensils are as much the property of the Congolese pygmy as they are the property of the Viennese—or Roman or New Yorker. Clearly many adaptively important cultural features are not limited by the boundaries of specific cultures, any more than are the genetic characteristics of particular populations limited by their preferred, but not exclusively practiced, breeding habits.

Human physical variation can best be understood by relating the distributions of specific morphological features to the distribution and history (also the prehistory) of the relevant selective and adaptive forces. In the section which follows we shall discuss a few of the most obvious characteristics of mankind where the distribution parallels the known or postulated distribution of the selective factors involved. Because of the stress which has been placed on characteristics controlled by single genes it has been assumed by many recent authorities that only the study of such traits could produce any precise insight into human diversity. It is apparent, however, that most of the traits by which human races can be easily recognized are not single gene traits, and yet, as we shall see, their distribution is just as revealing as that of the traits which are relatively simpler in their genetic background.

The traits we shall consider first are those that have been traditionally most important for racial recognition (or discrimination, depending on the purpose motivating the making of the distinction). The first such trait which we shall examine is skin color.

Skin Color

Figure 106 shows the distribution of skin color throughout the world just before European exploration and colonization so radically changed human distributions on the face of the earth. It can be seen that dark pigmentation is only found among people who live within fifteen to twenty degrees of the equator although not all people who live in the tropics are dark. Furthermore some people who are generally accounted as being very dark may be partially exhibiting the effects of heavy sun tanning. The aboriginal in-

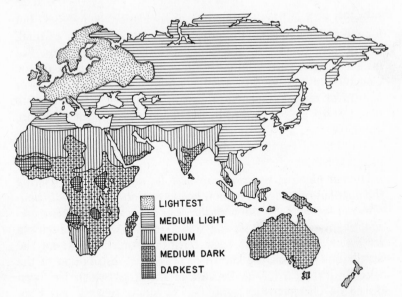

FIGURE 106. Distribution of human skin color before the Age of Discovery.

habitants of Australia, particularly those who did not live in the extreme northern part, frequently give evidence of the fact that their dark color is sometimes due to living out in the sun without any clothing.

In some areas, however, it is clear that people living within twenty degrees of the equator are distinctly not noticeably dark, as is the case with the inhabitants of Indonesia and northern South America. In these cases, the people in question apparently have not been there for a sufficient length of time to have developed pigmentary protection.

The pigment in the human skin is a complex organic molecule called melanin. The exact function of melanin is still a matter of dispute, and, as with many of the other physical differences between men, its significance is largely based on presumptive rather than on scientific evidence. The presumptions, however, appear reasonable and must be given careful consideration.

Where the ultraviolet component of solar radiation is strong, as it is in the tropics, the possibility of damage to the living cells in the dermis of the human skin is always present. Melanin in the outer layer of skin absorbs the harmful ultraviolet radiation and does not allow it to penetrate the living skin. As a result, physicians have long noted the much higher frequency of tissue injury and resultant skin cancer in relatively depigmented as opposed to relatively heavily pigmented peoples where the skin of both has been subjected to excessive amounts of sunshine. Dark skin, apparently, has distinct survival value in the tropics.

Against this it has been argued that many dark-skinned inhabitants of the tropics are not, in fact, much exposed to strong sunlight. The Congo Negro or the pygmy of the Ituri forest spend large parts of their lives sheltered by jungle, nevertheless they are quite well endowed with melanin. The explanation is that neither of these peoples have been forest-dwellers for very long. While this at first seems unexpected in view of the widespread belief that the Negro comes from the jungles of Africa, the fact is that this belief is largely a piece of modern folklore. For one thing, tropical rain forest is relatively restricted in extent, covering far less area than either dry grassland with scattered scrub trees or full desert. For another thing, survival in the rain forest depends on the possession of iron tools and suitable jungle-adapted crops, both of which are relatively recent in Africa. Apparently the Congo area has only recently sustained the populations that now live there, and a consideration of the selective pressures which were important in determining the skin color of the Congolese inhabitants at the present and in the recent past must look instead to the areas from which these people came. There are no historic records placing their origins, but linguistic and cultural evidence all indicates that they came from the area where the grassland merges with the forest to the north and west of the Congo basin and just south of 20° north latitude. The assumption that dark skin has value for individuals who have been adapting for a long time to an environment characterized by an abundance of tropical sunlight is thus not contradicted by the pigmentary characteristics of the peoples of Africa, despite their present distribution.

FIGURE 107. Australian aboriginal elders from the Finke River area, Northern Territory. (Courtesy of the Australian News & Information Bureau.)

FIGURE 108. New Guinea men at Minj, one of them weaving a pas pas, an ornamental amulet worn on the upper arm. (Courtesy of the Australian News & Information Bureau.)

While the equator passes several degrees south of the southernmost parts of India and Ceylon, yet, the whole southern half of the Indian sub-continent from Bombay down lies below the twentieth parallel and one would expect, if our assumptions are correct, that the peoples who have inhabited these regions for the longest period of time, and hence who have been longest exposed to the selective effects of the environment, would exhibit the greatest amount of pigmentation in their skins. As is expected, the peoples whom present cultural and linguistic evidence suggest were the most ancient inhabitants of the area (this is also supported by the myths, legends, semi-historical and historical writings of the ancient Aryan-speaking peoples) are, indeed, the darkest in color, for instance, the Munda speaking people, as relatively northerly outposts in central India, and most particularly, backwoods "hill tribes" such as the Kadar of southern India and the Vedda of Ceylon. In general there is a north-south color gradient with the darkest people in the south. India then supports the generalizations which have been made on the basis of skin color distribution in Africa.

[275]

FIGURE 109. Veddas. (From C. G. and B. Seligman, *The Veddas*. Courtesy of Cambridge University Press.)

In southeast Asia, Indonesia, and the western Pacific, again, the initial impression is one of a great confusion of different colors. The equator runs right through the middle of the big islands of Sumatra and Borneo, just south of the tip of the Malay Peninsula, and just north of New Guinea, and the area bracketed by 20° N. and 20° S. includes mainland southeast Asia, the northern quarter of Australia, and all of the islands in between extending far east into the Polynesian part of the Pacific. There are no really dark-skinned people in Sumatra or Borneo or the parts of Indonesia right on the equator, and it is not until one gets farther away from mainland southeast Asia, such as into parts of the Philippines, New Guinea, Melanesia, and northern Australia, that one finds the kind of really dark brown skin which for purposes of social discrimination is called black. A few peoples in the refuge of the Malay jungles and the inhabitants of the out-of-the-way Andaman Islands between the Malay Peninsula and India also exhibit very dark skins, but with these exceptions the bulk of the people in

Indonesia and southeast Asia range from brown in the south to yellow-brown toward the Chinese border.

The reason why there is so little evidence of dark skin among the inhabitants of the western and northern parts of this area is connected with the history of population movements during the recent past. On the basis of the remnant peoples such as the Semang and Sakai of the Malay Peninsula, the Andaman Islanders, the Aeta of the Philippines and other less adequate indications, it is reasonable to regard the original inhabitants of the whole area as having been dark. Population was not dense because the basic means of subsistence was hunting and gathering, which requires large areas to support limited numbers of people. The development of efficient farming techniques farther north allowed these northern peoples to spread south into what must have been for them relatively unoccupied country, either absorbing or eliminat-

FIGURE 110. Melanesians. Group of Fiji Islanders. (Courtesy of the American Museum of Natural History.)

FIGURE 111. West African Negro. (Courtesy of West African Information Services.)

FIGURE 112. Nilotic Negro, Nuer. (From Evans-Pritchard, *The Nuer*. Courtesy of Oxford University Press.)

ing the few darker people who had formerly had the country to themselves.

Historical records amply confirm the north-south movements of the last two thousand years and the decrease in both cultural and physical resemblances to the mainland becomes more marked the farther east one goes until one reaches New Guinea. For a variety of reasons, the inhabitants of New Guinea and Australia are clearly the most ancient inhabitants of the area under consideration and consistently have dark skins. It seems reasonable to regard the Polynesians who now spread far to the east of New Guinea as being the end product of the first great push from mainland southeast Asia, having passed north of New Guinea itself. If we are correct in regarding the whole area as having been thinly populated with dark-skinned peoples before the migrations, then the present remains of the first light-skinned people to come from the mainland should show the effects of having absorbed darker elements on the way. This certainly is supported by the appearance of the present Polynesians.

In our consideration of the distribution of the various shades of human pigmentation we have made no mention of the Western Hemisphere. In general it appears that the American Indians have not been across the Bering Straits for a long enough time for selection to have much affect on skin color, even in the most tropic parts of Central and South America. The color of the Indians then, like that of the Indonesians, betrays their eastern Asiatic origin.

So far, much of our account has been concerned with light-skinned people moving down into tropic areas where dark people had prevailed. Of course in Africa the formidable barrier of the Sahara desert and the swamps of the upper Nile prevented any such population movements and in the New World there were no preceding dark tropic dwellers, but this picture holds true for Arabia, India, and southeast Asia—Indonesia. This southern expansion of light-colored peoples has been recognized by many generations of geographers, historians, and anthropologists, but very few have grappled with the explanation for it.

There are two basic problems involved. First, what made these people light-skinned in the first place, and second, why did they

FIGURE 113. Pygmy, Belgian Congo. (Courtesy of the American Museum of Natural History.)

FIGURE 114. Andamanese Negritoes. Front individual carries palm leaf umbrella; second holds fire container; third carries wooden bucket. Little Andaman Island, South of Big Andaman Islands in Bay of Bengal. (Courtesy of the American Museum of Natural History.)

press south? The problem of their southerly movement has been treated from time to time, but we shall defer it until we have discussed the source of their depigmentation. Some authorities have simply assumed that "white" was the original color for all mankind, although this still evades the question of what adaptive advantage it must have conferred in order to become originally established.

Another suggestion has been advanced claiming that the reduction in epidermal melanin allows more ultraviolet radiation to penetrate the skin and aid in the formation of vitamin D. This presumably is an advantage in those parts of the north temperate zone where year round cloud cover so reduces the available amount of sunshine that every little bit absorbed is of value. This view runs into difficulty when one realizes that at the time of year when sunlight is at its rarest and weakest, the greatest amount of depigmented skin is securely covered with quantities of clothing. By the same token, the fur-covered members of the animal world should all be showing the effects of a severe vitamin D deficiency.

The mention of clothing brings us to what appears to be the real source of the reduction in skin pigment which is so apparent in peoples whose remote origins were in the neighborhood of 50° north latitude. From our foregoing discussion it seems apparent that a relatively great amount of skin pigment has been of value to a hairless animal living in the sunnier parts of the tropics, and since the fossil record points to precisely this area as the remote

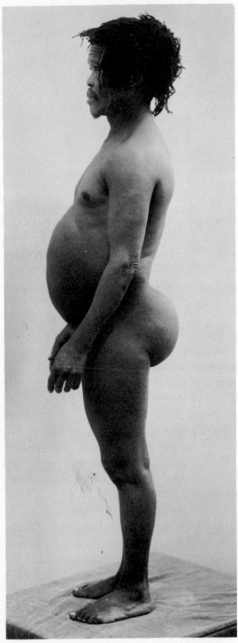

FIGURE 115. Bushman male, South Africa. (Courtesy of the American Museum of Natural History.)

FIGURE 116.. Polynesians. Group of Katiu islanders, Taumotus. (Courtesy of the American Museum of Natural History.)

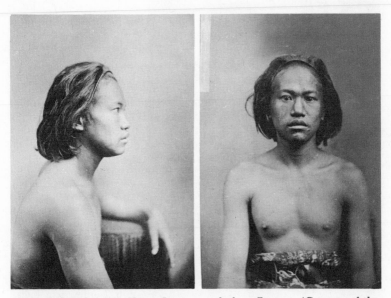

FIGURE 117. Indonesian. Young Javanese male from Bautam. (Courtesy of the Musée de l'Homme, Paris.)

FIGURE 118. Asiatic Indian, Northwestern India. (Courtesy of Information Service of India.)

home for all mankind, there is some basis for the assumption that the remote human ancestors were dark in color. This being the case, our problem is how some of their descendants eventually became light.

While there can be no proof for it, this is how we believe it happened. The archeological record shows that relatively success-ful and extensive human occupation of the north temperate zone as a permanent habitat did not occur until the last glaciation. During the previous glaciations, the onset of cold conditions had forced people back south, but by the end of the third interglacial, the technological facets of developing human culture had just reached the point where, with some refinement, they would allow people to adapt to the cold instead of having to flee from it. People stayed in the north, then, taking abundant advantage of the quantities of big game that lived there.

The archeological record reveals an abundance of scrapers ap-pearing in Europe and the Middle East at the onset of the Würm glaciation, and this clearly shows an increasing preoccupation with the preparation of animal skins. Equally clearly the Neanderthals did not tramp through the snows in the loin-cloth type of garment pictured in the standard cartoon. One of the things which allowed them to survive was the use of adequate clothing. Man presented something besides his own skin to the outer world, which meant that the presence or absence of melanin no longer possessed any importance.

With the adaptive significance of melanin substantially re-duced, beginning with the onset of the last glaciation approxi-mately seventy thousand years ago, the genetic background for melanin production was free to vary, with the eventual result that mutations opposed to melanin production occurred. Since these were not selected against because of the reduction in importance of the protective function formerly played by melanin, such mutations accumulated with the consequence that melanin ceased to be produced with the same efficiency. Thus the cultural factors which allowed human survival in the north temperate zone greatly reduced the survival value of a particular trait—pigmenta-tion—and the resultant accumulation of random mutations meant that the trait was eventually reduced.

FIGURE 119. Amazonian Indian. (Courtesy of the American Museum of Natural History.)

The degree of human depigmentation wherever it is found should indicate the length of time and the extent to which skin pigment has been reduced as an adaptive feature. This is, indeed, borne out by observation since the people with the palest coloring in the world today are those who can trace their ancestry back to the zone stretching from western through eastern Europe and on into southern Russia where the archeological record offers evidence that human survival depended on the use of clothing for a longer period of time than anywhere else in the world. We are tempted to suggest that perhaps this may also be related to the reason why peoples with cultural backgrounds stemming from northern Europe have always been so stuffy about the idea of human nudity, but this is to trespass somewhat beyond the realm of physical anthropology.

It might be asked why the inhabitants of northern China (Manchuria) and Mongolia are not as light-skinned as the Europeans of the same latitude. The answer must be that they have not been where they now live for quite as long, and that their ancestors therefore were not dependent upon clothing for survival for as long a time as the ancestors of the Europeans. The archeological record does not provide the same kind of confirmation for this view which can be seen in the West since the artifacts assignable to the early Würm are notably meager, although this is actually what one would expect if the area were not permanently inhabited at this time. The almost complete absence of evidence for human

FIGURE 120. Tierra del Fuegian Indians, Straits of Magellan. (Courtesy of the American Museum of Natural History.)

FIGURE 121. Plains Indian. Holding Eagle of the Gros Ventre tribe. (Courtesy of the American Museum of Natural History.)

FIGURE 122. Eskimo. Alaskan seamstress chewing the sole of a sealskin boot she was making for the United States armed forces in the north. (Courtesy of the American Museum of Natural History.)

FIGURE 123. Group of Chinese. Staff of Peiping Union Medical College, with Professor Franz Weidenreich in front row center. (Courtesy of the American Museum of Natural History.)

FIGURE 124. Italians from Ischia. (Courtesy of the Italian State Tourist Office.)

habitation at this time in the northern parts of the Far East is in marked contrast to the abundance of Mousterian remains in the West and suggests that the depigmentation process in Asia started substantially more recently.

Eventually the cultural mechanism was developed which allowed the inhabitants of eastern Asia to spread north, and which at the same time allowed for a reduction in their epidermal melanin. In this northward spread during the final stages of the Würm, they encountered the Bering Strait land bridge which then existed, and, as a result, populated the Western Hemisphere. With this background, the depigmentation of the inhabitants of eastern Asia and the New World should have started at the same time and it is no surprise to discover that they are approximately the same color.

Only two areas of the world suggest that the south temperate zone was inhabited in the Pleistocene for any length of time,

[290]

one being South Africa and the other being the southern half of Australia. While neither area shows evidence that clothing was ever sufficiently used to reduce the significance of extensive skin pigmentation, significantly enough both areas are south of the tropics and the intensity of ultraviolet radiation is substantially reduced. We should expect that peoples who are long-time inhabitants of these zones would show at least a partial reduction in pigmentation from the deep pigmentation associated with the descendants of the ancient dwellers in the tropics proper, and this we find, indeed, to be the case. The aborigines of the southern part of Australia are not as dark as the "blackfellow" in the north, and the South African Bushmen and Hottentots are lighter still, being a sort of yellow-brown which accords with the inference, based on archeological evidence, that they have inhabited the southernmost parts of Africa for a longer period of time than the aborigines have lived in southern Australia.

With this explanation of the factors that produced the differ-

FIGURE 125. Scandinavian. A Swedish fisherman. (Courtesy of the American Swedish News Exchange.)

FIGURE 126. Eastern Europeans. Russian stevedores on the Volga, province of Yaroslaf. (Courtesy of the American Museum of Natural History.)

ences in human skin color, it is now appropriate to consider the factors responsible for the extensive movements, in the recent past, on the part of the relatively depigmented peoples south into India and southeast Asia. Our explanation runs as follows: the technological and cultural changes which allowed men to survive in the temperate latitudes during the cold of the last glaciation, and which led to their eventual depigmentation, started trends in cultural adaptation which culminated in the discovery of methods of controlling the food supply after the Pleistocene was over. The Neolithic revolution was a cultural development which was distinguished by the beginning of human endeavors to control the propagation of plants and animals.

The success of this food-producing way of life in contrast to the previous hunting and gathering kind of existence can be seen in the vast increase in numbers of the peoples whose cultural heritage stems from this source. The food-producing revolution occurred earliest in the Middle East, commencing about ten thousand years ago, and before long the area had almost as many people as the existing subsistence techniques could support. Cultural elaboration, including the improvement of farming, was one result, but another was the actual movement of populations producing the kind of color distributions which we see in the world today.

Hair

The form and color of the hair of the head is often given an importance second only to skin color by those who feel impelled to make racial discriminations. The geographical distribution of hair color follows the distribution of skin color without exception, and, in spite of the numerous individuals in whom the two traits appear to be unrelated, it is apparent that this is the one instance where two traits vary together for a biological reason. Pigment in hair itself has no particular significance, but hair is a structure derived from the epidermis and will necessarily share in the processes of the same system for melanin production.

For individuals whose forebears had become adapted to survival in areas of strong sunlight, the well developed melanin production system of the epidermis will certainly ensure that the hair too has its fair share of melanin. Because of the structure of hair and the arrangement of the melanin granules within it, hair with only a moderate amount of melanin will appear black, which is why so many people in the world whose forebears underwent slight to moderate epidermal depigmentation still have predominantly black hair. Where depigmentation has been allowed to become advanced, the hair is affected, and, depending on the degree, all shades can be seen from brown through blond.

Red hair is something else, the existence of red pigment in the skin and hair being not well accounted for as yet. Red hair appears to be due to a deficiency of melanin, with carotene predominating. The deficiency is also seen in the skin, in which the melanin tends to aggregate in numerous small islands as freckles. Owing to the deficiency in melanin the skin of redheads is highly vulnerable to the effects of what would be considered a normal exposure to solar radiation. With respect to the distribution of melanin, redheads appear to stand intermediate between albinos and brunets.

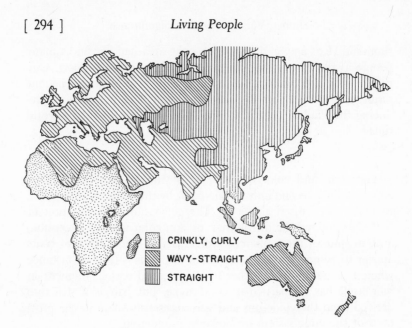

FIGURE 127. Distribution of human hair form before the Age of Discovery. (Drawing by Mary L. Brace and Richard V. Humphrey.)

It seems likely that redness in hair and skin arose as the result of random changes in a different part of the enzymatic substrate normally responsible for melanin production, but this must be accounted an educated guess.

Unlike hair color, hair form apparently has had definite adaptive significance. The top of the head is very vulnerable to blows, scratches, burning, and overheating from direct sunlight. There is only a thin layer of subcutaneous fat beneath the skin. A good hair covering affords protection not only to the soft tissues and bone, but serves as protection against mechanical and radiation injury to that rather vital organ, the brain.

The most striking thing about the distribution of hair form is the tendency for the extremely kinky forms of hair to occur among the same populations in which the very darkest skin pigmentation is to be found. There is no direct correlation between skin color and hair form as is shown by the presence of the most extreme hair form among the only moderately pigmented Bushmen of South Africa, so the suspicion is raised that tightly spiral hair may be an adaptive feature and the reason why its distribution parallels that of dark skin color is that both traits may be responses to related conditions. If dark skin is the adaptive response to high levels of ultraviolet radiation, and the insulation provided by woolly head hair is a response to high levels of solar heat radiation, then it is obvious that both adaptations are responses to different problems raised by living in an area characterized by an excessive amount of sunlight.

In the past, observers have noted the presence of dark skin and kinky hair in Africa, traces of it in southern Arabia, stronger traces among the hill tribes of India, the jungle peoples of the Malay Peninsula, the Andaman and Philippine pygmies, and finally its full development in the inhabitants of Melanesia, and have offered a number of theories involving vast migrations for obscure reasons. It is much simpler, however, to regard these instances of the simultaneous occurrence of extremes of human variation in both skin color and hair form as essentially adaptive responses to similar selective pressures.

One more thing can be added in considering variations related to the hair. If our argument relating to depigmentation is generally applicable, then among those people who have provided cultural means for the protection of the head for the longest period of time, we should find the greatest amount of reduction in the biological adaptations aimed at such protection. The same people who were the first to use clothing extensively may be assumed to have provided protection for the head, i.e., hats, and this assumption receives support from the fact that it is among their descendants today that we observe the highest proportion of deficiencies in the normal head protective mechanism. Not surprisingly, it is among people of European derivation that the highest frequencies of gray hair and baldness occurs.

So far our discussion of human physical variation has dealt with extremes in adaptation which are responses to purely environmental selective forces. To be sure these forces are limited by latitude and not by specific geographic province or breeding population, which means that no nice explanation can be offered which starts with the breeding population as the significant unit. The next facet of human variation which we shall consider will clearly show the futility of beginning one's analysis with "races" or breeding populations, since that variation cuts right across population and even geographic boundaries, and as in the characteristics discussed above, it follows the dictates of selection or its absence.

Face Form

Besides general pigmentation and hair form, the characteristics long considered of greatest importance for racial diagnosis are connected with the form of the face. While the previously discussed characteristics are not merely controlled by single genes or even by the various alleles of a single locus, yet they are genetically much simpler than the complex of anatomy which we call the face. Nevertheless despite the complexities and unknowns which surround the genetic background of face form, an investigation of the variations in the human face shows that the differences can be associated with relatively clear differences in selective factors.

There are two aspects of the face each associated with a different major function subject to important differences in selective forces affecting human survival. These are the parts particularly associated with the respiratory passages and those associated with the whole chewing apparatus. It might be argued that the face is also the locus for the organs of sight, which of course is true, but on the other hand the microscopic complexity of the visual machinery does not allow any gross anatomical differences to occur. Variations in the color of the eye, in color vision, visual acuity, and even in the size of the eyeball can occur without affecting the skeletal housing called the eye socket and without any influence on the anatomy of the adjacent areas. This cannot be said for variations in the nose area and in the jaws and teeth, and it is our intent here to consider such variations and the selective pressures which produce them.

Because variations in the dental apparatus are most clearly related to differences in selective pressures, we shall consider these first. Apart from the existence of an edge-to-edge bite in some peoples but not in others, which is partially but not entirely a matter of the characteristic mode of usage and hence wear, the primary differences in the human masticatory apparatus are simple differences in size. Some peoples have big teeth and others have small teeth, and of course the whole tooth-bearing part of the face is related to the size of the teeth themselves. Not surprisingly, the people in whom the growth process produces large teeth also tend to have large jaws, large chewing muscles, and other evidences of exuberant bone growth associated with the skull and face.

Good studies on the dimensions of human teeth are surprisingly rare in the scientific literature, but enough information is available to enable us to arrive at a quite satisfactory understanding of the relationship between the size of the dentition and the selective factors influencing it. The smallest teeth are to be found among the peoples of Central and Eastern Europe and the Middle East, and the largest teeth are those of the Australian aborigines. Not only are Australian teeth the largest in the world, but under pre-European conditions they regularly showed the most extreme degree of wear.

This amount of abrasion points in a direct and simple manner to the selective forces operating to maintain large teeth. With the largest of human teeth being worn to the gums by middle age, it is easy to imagine what would happen if the teeth had been any smaller. Obviously smaller teeth would wear down at an earlier age leaving the possessor effectively toothless in the prime of life. A toothless person in the Australian "outback," before the advent of European technology had a relatively reduced chance of surviving, and if these circumstances occurred before the normal end of reproductive life, the opportunities for transmitting the traits involving small tooth size to the next generation were materially decreased. The operation of the forces which maintained large teeth in pre-British Australia offers one of the clearest pictures of natural selection at work influencing human form and survival.

Since there are great differences in the amount of tooth wear to be seen among the different peoples of the world, and since extremes of tooth wear can influence the chances for survival, it is instructive to consider the causes for wear in its most pronounced form. Clearly the most important function of the masticatory apparatus is to reduce food to the appropriate form and size for swallowing. The teeth, as the bearing surfaces of this crushing machine, are worn, at least in part, by the abrasive content of the food they are made to chew. In the case of the Australian aborigines, the game they catch is singed by being rolled in the ashes of an open fire, briefly roasted, and then eaten—ashes, grit, and all—with a minimum of assistance from a manufactured cutlery. Of course, the products of the hunt provide only a portion, and even so not the major portion of the aboriginal diet, although it was certainly large enough to account for a substantial amount of dental abrasion. The rest of the diet included varying amounts of seeds, nuts, fruits, berries, insects, roots and vegetable products most of which were eaten without any further preparation. Obviously the eating of the proverbial peck of dirt was the usual experience for the Australian aborigines and not something which took a whole lifetime to accomplish.

While the immense variety of their diet might not qualify the Australians as a literal example of grinding poverty, yet there can be no question that such a regimen can produce a great deal of tooth wear. There is, however, another important source of tooth wear to be considered which has nothing to do with the diet, and this involves the observation, also made on other peoples who show similar kinds of tooth wear, that the aborigines use their mouths like a third hand. When first discovered, the Australian aborigines possessed a culture of a technological poverty greater than that of any other people in the world, being on a par with what we believe the most advanced human technology was like some time during the third interglacial. With such a rudimentary tool kit they frequently avail themselves of the convenient all-purpose tool that heredity has provided in the form of their large and powerful jaws and teeth. As a vise, clamp or pliers, the dentition is frequently used to hold objects which are then manipulated with the hands. The wear thus produced occurs in most pronounced form on the front teeth in contrast to wear produced by heavy duty food chewing which affects the molars, and it is interesting to note that it is the front teeth which show the most extreme degrees of wear by early middle age.

This being the case, one would expect an inverse correlation between the amount of wear on the front teeth and the level of technological development among the peoples of the world, and to a certain extent this holds true. The simplicity of the picture is somewhat spoiled by the discovery that a people such as the Eskimo, with a relatively complex technology for a nonliterate non-industrialized culture, exhibit a quite similar degree of wear on the incisors definitely limiting the chances for survival of the aging Eskimo. The special problems that survival in the Arctic raise mean that, despite the greater technological development, the Eskimo use their teeth extensively in manipulating their environment—untying knots, chewing frozen boots, and, most important of all, tanning skins for clothing. Among most of the peoples of the world, however the greater the technological complexity of their culture, the less the front teeth are worn and the smaller these teeth tend to be.

It is apparent that where the teeth are extensively used as tools a premium is placed on large incisor size. Furthermore, small front teeth are distinctly disadvantageous and are actively selected against by the early deaths and failures to reproduce of their possessors. We have no problem then explaining the existence of large teeth wherever they are found. The existence of small teeth at first seems somewhat less easy to account for, but a little reflection will show that their occurrence follows the same principle governing the distribution of depigmentation. Specifically, where technological development has resulted in the production of tools designed to execute the tasks formerly performed by the teeth, the presence of large front teeth ceases to be important for human survival. Random mutations affecting the teeth can occur without disadvantage, and since, generally, random mutation in reference to any structure eventually results in its reduction, the affected teeth are reduced. As would be expected the people with the smallest teeth in the world are those whose remote ancestors first developed a complex technology.

Technological complexity, however, is not limited by race, and,

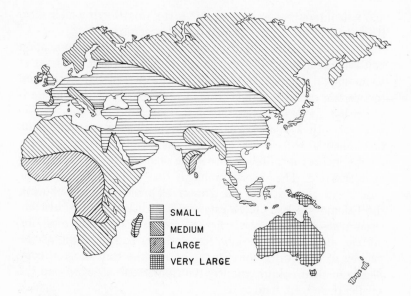

FIGURE 128. Distribution of relative tooth size before the Age of Discovery. (Drawing by Mary L. Brace and Richard V. Humphrey.)

as a result, that part of face size which is contributed by the dentition varies across population boundaries in a manner that would be quite inexplicable if racial group were taken as the starting point for analysis. Any chart attempting to trace the distribution of differences in human dentition size is plagued by two problems. Published information exists for only a few human populations, and second, other things being equal, big people should tend to have big teeth. Figure 128 is based on the available information crudely corrected for body size by showing the relative size of the teeth in proportion to body bulk. For instance, the Bushmen of South Africa have always been cited as having small teeth since their dental dimensions are approximately the same as those of Europeans, but then no consideration is given to the fact that Bushmen are noticeably smaller in gross bulk. In proportion to their body size, Bushman teeth are actually relatively large, although not in the same category as those of the Australian aborigines.

We shall offer a few words of interpretation for Figure 128. The smallest teeth belong to those people whose forebears first enjoyed the benefits of the food-producing revolution. Food producers with their sedentary existence generally accumulate more possessions and can therefore develop a more elaborate technology than hunters and gatherers. In conformity with expectation, then, a broad band extends from central Europe through the Middle East, across northern India into the Far East and Southeast Asia corresponding with the areas where the food-producing revolution has exercised its effects for the longest period of time.

Plotting the distribution of relative gross tooth size in this manner obscures the fact that there is something of a West-East gradient in *effective* incisor size that is not expressed by simple length-width dimensions alone. This is due to a change in the form of the front teeth. Some years ago the American anthropologists Hrdlička noticed that the incisors of American Indians possessed raised margins on the tongue (lingual) side in such a manner that, considering the root to be the handle, they looked like miniature coal shovels (Figure 129). These "shovel-shaped incisors" were then recognized as characteristic of the inhabitants of eastern Asia, a discovery which gave further support to the view that Asia was the area from which the American Indians originated. Subsequently the shovel-shape was recognized in the teeth of Sinanthropus, a fact taken by Weidenreich to indicate that Sinanthropus was the direct ancestor of the modern Asians. Re-examination of material found before shovel-shaped incisors were recognized as significant shows that not only the European Nean-

FIGURE 129. A shovel, a shovel-shaped incisor, and a non-shovel-shaped incisor. (Drawing by William H. Price.)

derthals but also their Upper Paleolithic descendants possessed shovel-shaped incisors, although most modern Europeans do not.

The problem is less the explanation of the origin of shovel-shaped teeth than the explanation of the causes of their disappearance in the areas in which they are now absent. Following our principle of attempting to understand the causes for the existence of specific traits, rather than taking the recognition of difference as a datum of sufficient importance by itself, the significance of incisor form assumes a somewhat different meaning. Instead of constituting an indication of ancestry as was formerly believed, the raised lingual margins of the incisors are in fact an indication that the teeth were formerly (or still are) subjected to heavy usage and great wear. The addition to the total amount of incisor enamel by the elevation of the lingual borders represents a simple adaptive response to increased wear without the increase of overall tooth size and hence increased jaw size.

Although the available material is insufficient for a definitive judgment, it seems likely that all Middle Pleistocene hominids possessed large shovel-shaped incisors. As technology developed and the value of large incisors decreased, particularly in that part of the temperate zone in which the food-producing revolution occurred, selection pressures were relaxed and the teeth were free to vary, with the inevitable result that reduction occurred. There are two ways in which a large shovel-shaped tooth can undergo reduction, one is by the reduction of the overall dimensions, which in our chart (Figure 128) is shown to have occurred all the way across the middle latitudes of the Old World. The other method of reduction is the elimination of the extra enamel in the form of the raised lingual margins. As a reflection of the fact that technological elaboration, in the form of Upper Paleolithic cultures and subsequently the earliest food producers, occurred earliest in the area from the Middle East through central Europe, it is understandable how it has come about that the absence of shovelling makes the effective amount of enamel less among the peoples of these areas than among the peoples farther east whose teeth, in gross dimensions, are of similar size.

A comparison of the tooth-dimension chart (Figure 128) with that representing the distribution of variations in pigmentation shows that the two distributions do not correspond. In fact, starting in the Middle East, where teeth are smallest, and going north and west, it can be seen that teeth in fact increase in size while pigment decreases, with the largest teeth in Europe occurring at the extreme north and west fringes. Evidently while clothing was an ancient feature of cultural adaptation in these areas, the kind of technological complexity associated with a food-producing type of subsistence came much later, a statement which is supported by an abundance of archeological evidence.

The extent of a band of medium-large dentitions down the east part of Africa reflects the spread of effective stone cutting tools, of the sort which allowed the Neanderthal face to change into a more modern form. This occurred more or less contemporaneously with the Upper Paleolithic in the north. This form of technological advance failed to penetrate the edges of the forest region in West Africa and around the Congo drainage basin, perhaps because of a lack of sufficient suitable raw materials; the effect of this was that the dentitions of these peoples remained relatively larger. People with these larger teeth then multiplied in great quantities following the acquisition of farming techniques and suitable food crops, allowing them to spread into the previously unoccupied African rain forests. Extending outward to the south and east, these people moved into the regions in which a moderately large lower face had been characteristic, in this manner creating, so far as the student is concerned, a somewhat confused picture for this trait in the southern parts of East Africa and the eastern parts of South Africa. The relative size of the lower part of the face in Africa remains the same across the boundaries of skin color, hair form, subsistence economy, and geographic province while at the same time varying within each of these. Clearly hair form or skin color or geographic province has no particular biological or adaptive association with the size of the dentition so that any appraisal of human facial variations which begins with sociologically defined races as its basic units will fail to understand the distribution or the meaning of such variations. *It is only by plotting the distribution of such variations in relation to the relevant selective factors that it is possible to appreciate the problems involved.*

Dental variation elsewhere in the world follows the same principles. The parts of India and Southeast Asia in which live remnants of hunting and gathering populations show a relative enlargement of the lower face. When New Guinea and Australia are added to the areas considered, the results are exactly what one would expect with the relative increase in face size, exhibiting a close correlation with the areas in which technological elaboration has been present for the shortest period of time.

The Western Hemisphere is something of a blank so we have omitted it from our picture of the distribution of human dentitions. There is every indication, however, that it follows our principles very nicely, but the lack of precise published studies means that we cannot check the evidence for the kind of correlation we have found elsewhere. Judging from photographs of Indians from both North and South America, it would appear that the smallest faces in the New World are confined to an area running from the highlands of Peru in Western South America north through Middle America to somewhere just south of the boundary between Mexico and the United States. Significantly enough this corresponds with the area in which food-producing cultures have been in existence for the longest period of time in the Western Hemisphere.

The distribution of variations in the size of the human dental apparatus apparently follows the distribution of the factors affecting it in an expected manner despite the sketchy nature of our information for many populations. Skin color also behaves in a similarly predictable manner, but the distribution of dental size bears no relation to that of skin color since the important operative factors vary quite independently.

With two of the most prominent traits in which people can be seen to vary evidently showing no relation to each other, it is not surprising to find that other traits, the operative selective factors of which are known, are also independent. While the shape of the lower part of the human face is determined by the development of the masticatory apparatus, variations in the upper face are dominated by the shape of the nose.

The history of human face form, commencing with the prehuman ancestors of man and proceeding up to the present day,

has been one of varying degrees of reduction. The dental apparatus has undergone reduction as its manipulative functions have
decreased, and the whole supporting facial skeleton has correlatedly decreased along with it, with the exception of its respiratory portion. The result has been the preservation of a relic of
the former extent of facial development which juts out from the
face like a peninsula, and which we now identify as the human
nose.

To a certain extent then, the degree of nasal prominence is a
reflection of the amount of reduction of the rest of the face.
Nose form is also, in part, determined by the relative degree of
development of the immediately adjacent parts of the face, for
instance the peoples who are noted for the possession of particularly broad noses all have particularly large incisors, meaning that
the whole facial skeleton in the area where the nose is widest is
noticeably spread. People such as the Australian aborigines and
various other peoples from New Guinea to western Africa where,
for the reasons mentioned above, the incisors are particularly
large evidently show a widening of the whole lower face including the external form of the nose.

In addition to the differences in the width of the lower part of
the nose, there remain outstanding differences in the length of
the nose and in the height of the nasal bridge which cannot simply be explained by citing different degrees of reduction in the
rest of the face. The distribution of nose form in the world is
shown in Figure 130 as reflected by the various values recorded
for the nasal index. A low index indicates a long narrow nose
while a high index describes a relatively short wide nose. However, since nasal width is at least partially accounted for by another trait which is distributed in correlation with the effects of
its own selective pressures, it is evident that the nasal index is not
the best criterion of nasal length and height. It is, however, the
best measure we have, and will have to serve in lieu of a better
one as the basis for tentative interpretations.

Like dental size, the form of the nose does not correspond very
closely to population boundaries and, apart from that portion of
its variability which is directly related to the size of the lower
face, it appears that nose form responds to another set of influ-

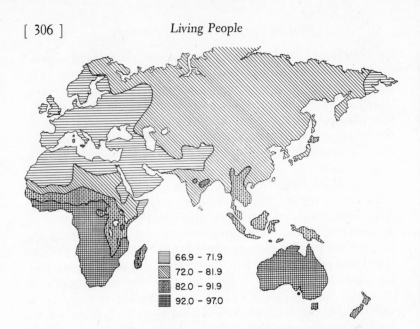

FIGURE 130. Distribution of different values for the nasal index before the Age of Discovery. (Drawing by Mary L. Brace and Richard V. Humphrey.)

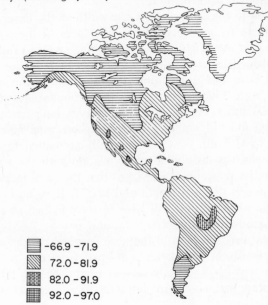

encing forces. A quick glance at Figure 130 will show that the relatively shortest noses occur only in the tropics and observation confirms the fact that the nasal bridges of the peoples in question are low as well as being short. At first it seems as though no consistent sense could be made from such an observation since such people as the inhabitants of East Africa right on the equator have appreciably longer, narrower, and higher noses than the people in the Congo at the same latitude. A former generation of anthropologists used to explain this paradox by invoking an invasion by an itinerant "white" population from the Mediterranean area, although this solution raised more problems than it solved since the East Africans in question include some of the blackest people in the world with characteristically woolly hair and a body build unique among the world's populations for its extreme linearity and height.

While the full answer to nose form distribution is yet to be given, a good attempt supported by some significant research has been made. The point of departure, as with the other traits, for which distributions have been sensibly explained, has been the consideration of the possible functions which differences in nose shape might serve. A long nose lengthens the passage through which inspired air must pass before it reaches the lungs, and this appears to have benefits in two quite different kinds of environments. Where the humidity is extremely low, an elongated respiratory passage serves to moisten the air before it reaches the lungs, and in an area where the temperature is extremely low, a similarly long passage serves to warm the air before it can desiccate the delicate and functionally highly important mucous membranes.

If this explanation is correct, the distribution of big noses should indicate the areas where people have had to cope with either extreme dryness or extreme cold, and by and large the actual distribution more or less fits expectations. The relatively long noses of East Africa become explicable then when one realizes that much of the area is extremely dry for parts of the year. The long noses of the dry Middle East and those of the cold northwest fringe of Europe fit expectations, but there are a number of cases which seem less obvious at first glance.

The Bushmen of the extremely dry Kalahari desert in Southern Africa possess greatly reduced noses seemingly uncorrelated with their habitat. This becomes less of a paradox when it is realized that the Bushmen have only recently been forced to take refuge in the desert by the settlement of the temperate southernmost parts of Africa by peoples possessing more efficient subsistence techniques and weapons. Likewise the inhabitants of the dry central Asiatic plains have only been there for the last few millennia. The Eskimos, also, can be viewed as relative newcomers to the Arctic, and although they do indeed possess long narrow nasal passages, the nasal bridge is not as high as might be expected—perhaps in part due to the fact that the heavy stress placed upon the dentition has meant that the rest of the face has undergone relatively less reduction than among the cold-adapted peoples of northern and western Europe.

The Australian aborigines are the final apparent exception to the presumed association of nasal length with lowered humidity. The Australian desert is one of the driest areas inhabited by man, yet the nasal index is relatively high. In this case, the actual length of the nose is in fact overshadowed by its great width, and this width is probably a function of the fact that the whole lower face is greatly broadened to accommodate the largest incisors possessed by modern *Homo sapiens*. Within Australia itself, however, nose form varies in conjunction with humidity precisely as one would expect. The longest and highest noses occurring in the central desert while the shortest and lowest noses occur in the tropical and humid north.

A final comment on nose form concerns the explanation of the tendency for short low noses to occur among peoples dwelling in the humid parts of the tropics. This again represents an example of the reduction of a character which confers relatively little benefit on the possessors. Long nasal passages are of no particular advantage where the inspired air need be neither moistened nor warmed, so that any variation arising in relation to nose form would be equally likely to survive. Since most naturally occuring variations will tend to reduce the size of the affected structure, the accumulation of their effects in time results in the reduction of the noses of the long-time denizens of the moist tropics.

Body Build

Before turning our attention to a brief discussion of a few of the characteristics for which the mode of inheritance and the genetic basis is known, there is another grossly observable human morphological characteristic which may be considered in terms of its adaptive value. This is body build.

Studies of a generation ago concentrating on variations in human physique tended to attach much importance to human stature. It was eventually shown that there was an inverse relationship between stature and temperature—the colder the habitat the taller the people tended to be. More sophisticated recent studies have shown that if that part of stature change which can be associated primarily with weight change is omitted, then there is no important variation of stature due to changes in temperature alone. Weight, however, does turn out to have a significant negative association with temperature—going up in areas where the temperature drops, and going down where the temperature rises.

There is more to gross variation in human body shapes than simple changes in average weight, and it has become apparent that variation in human body form may well be related to the problems posed by life under conditions which put stress upon the ability of the organism to survive.

One of the problems we must consider is that concerned with body-heat preservation and body-heat loss. Obviously in a cold climate it is desirable to use the heat generated by metabolic activity as efficiently as possible. Conversely it is equally apparent that for people to sustain activities in very hot climates, the major functional development must be some kind of mechanism which promotes the dissipation of the heat generated in metabolizing enough fuel to produce the activity in the first place. Since heat loss occurs at the surface of the body, it is clear that bodies which have different relative amounts of surface area will differ in the speed with which heat dissipation occurs, as a simple example will demonstrate. If one hundred pounds of copper is shaped into a sphere and heated, it will hold its heat for a much longer period of time than one hundred pounds of copper stretched out in a wire a half mile long and heated to the same temperature. As the example illustrates, a sphere presents a minimum amount of surface area per unit mass and thus is the ideal heat-preserving shape.

Not only does shape influence the relationship between surface area and bulk, but as a little reflection will serve to show, differences in gross size can also play a part. It is easiest to envision these relationships in a cube. The surface area is computed by multiplying the area of one side by the number of sides. The surface area of a single side is calculated by multiplying the width by the length and since these are equal in a cube and the number of sides is constant, changes in the total surface area of the cube will be proportional to the square of any linear dimension. Changes in the volume, however, will vary as the cube of any linear dimension, so it is obvious that as the object gets bigger the volume increases much more rapidly than the surface area, although the shape remains the same.

Nineteenth-century biologists noted that these principles can be applied to animal distributions. Other things being equal, members of a species living in the colder parts of the species range will tend to be larger. It was also noted that those parts of the body that present an extensive surface to the air, noses, ears, limbs, tend to be reduced among the members of the colder parts of the species range. These principles also apply to man.

Although there are many individual and group exceptions, it can be said that, on the average, human bulk decreases in the hotter and increases in the colder regions inhabited by man, and the inference has been made that this is related to the greater heat conserving properties of larger bodies. As examples one can cite the Indians of North America from the plains area, on north through the Canadian woodlands and those of the Southern Argentinean pampas and Tierra del Fuego. The Indians of these regions tended to be large and bulky. The southernmost of the aboriginal Australians as also the northernmost of the native Europeans, were relatively large people. But not only are there size differences, there are also differences in shape. Long slender arms and legs are clearly associated with desert-living peoples while short limbs and heavy bodies can be seen in the Arctic. A number of objections have been raised against considering the short limbs of Arctic peoples as adaptive, but it seems quite clear that the danger of frostbite makes long arms and legs considerably less desirable in cold climates.

Against the adaptive value of specific body form in the tropics, the fact has been cited that the tallest as well as the smallest peoples in the world live cheek by jowl by each other right on the equator in east central Africa. It can, of course, be argued that both extremes in body build are different ways of handling the heat dissipation problem. One way of presenting a maximum amount of surface area to the air is to stretch a given mass into an elongated shape, and certainly the immensely tall East Africans of the Upper Nile area are about as linear and elongated as people can get. The other way of influencing the mass-surface area ratio is to change the size. Increasing gross size without changing form was seen greatly to increase mass in proportion to surface area. This being true, the converse evidently is that a decrease in size will greatly decrease the mass (proportionate to the cube root of any linear dimension) in relation to the surface area, thus accomplishing the same effect as modification of shape.

The pygmy simply by being small acquires the same surface-mass ratio achieved by the Nilotic African who is normal in bulk but greatly elongated in shape. Since both are equally efficient heat-dissipating mechanisms, the factors influencing the appropriate adaptation will stem from other sources than a simple response to heat regulation. The tall East Africans generally are food producers whose subsistence is derived from their cattle. This means that the food supply is relatively assured and that they obtain regular amounts of protein from their diets. Pygmy subsistence however, is less assured, and there may be long periods when food is not plentiful and little protein is eaten. This kind of problem would be particularly hard on people who are large enough so that they need a regular and substantial food intake, and, of course, would be especially difficult for the rapidly growing child. A people having low nutritional requirements as adults, and whose members grow less rapidly during the critical phases of development, will have a better chance of surviving as marginal hunting and gathering populations in the fringes of tropical forests.

With small size being both efficient for heat dissipation and the best assurance for survival in an area characterized by periodic nutritional bottlenecks, it becomes possible to understand why peoples within the pygmy stature range exist in such places as the eastern edge of the Congo basin, southern India and Ceylon, the Andaman Islands, Malaya, the Philippines and the remote parts of New Guinea. With the limited amounts of big game in these areas and before the recent advent of iron tools and weapons in many of them, the survival value of being small was considerable.

Former explanations for the distribution of pygmies relied on postulations of vast migrations of a single stock of small-statured people throughout the tropics of the Old World, but it makes much better evolutionary sense simply to regard the pygmies, wherever they occur, as size adaptations made *in situ* by the local populations of the areas in question. The Congo pygmy is simply the small end and remnant of a distribution of hunting and gathering peoples that extended, prior to the diffusion of an agricultural subsistence base, into sub-Saharan Africa, around the edges of the Congo forest and on through the edges of the West African forest where it merges with the savanna. In southern India, Ceylon, and southeast Asia the peoples of pygmoid stature are the remnants of hunting and gathering populations which, because of the great southward push of food-producing techniques and peoples into the more desirable areas, are confined to the more inaccessible and heavily forested areas. Only in the Andaman Islands did pygmies remain unaffected by the unequal competition with food-producing peoples, although here the only choice for habitat was necessarily tropical forest with no big game and the same sort of occasional nutritional bottlenecks that plague hunting and gathering peoples in the tropical forests elsewhere.

For the reasons discussed in our treatment of skin color and hair form, the remnants of the ancient inhabitants of southern India and southeast Asia are all very dark in color and possess very tightly curled hair. In contrast to this, some of the jungle inhabitants of central Borneo and the Philippines have the reduced coloring and reduced hair curl which is more characteristic of the peoples who have arrived from the north in relatively recent times. At the same time, they are of extremely small size, illustrating the selective effect that the problems of survival in such an environment exerts on the human physique regardless of the differences in other traits which may have developed in diverse geographical areas. In the highlands of New Guinea, as well, there are people of pygmy stature but again with very different faces from those of the short peoples of either Africa, southeast Asia, or Borneo since they came closer to resembling smaller versions of the faces of the aborigines of Australia. Again the effects of this kind of environment have determined the pygmy physique despite the differences in technological selective factors which have resulted in marked facial differences in the areas considered.

Central New Guinea is a particularly interesting case since there has been no overwhelming invasion of peoples whose characteristics developed in response to selective pressures elsewhere, as was true for southeast Asia and Indonesia, nor have new subsistence techniques been in effect for a long enough time for a substantial change in the distribution of local groups to have been distorted beyond the possibility of recognizing its original form, as has been the case in Africa. As a result the New Guinea pygmy represents neither a discontinuous nor an isolated phenomenon, either culturally or physically, as is now general for the small peoples elsewhere in the world. Because New Guinea has been less overwhelmed either by invading peoples or by the effect of diffusing cultural features than other parts of the world, it is interesting to note that only here is there the completely gradual cline, i.e., the gradient of differences, from the local normal-sized peoples to the pygmies without break in precisely the manner which we assume was once the case for all the regions that now give shelter to isolated pygmy populations.

Before leaving the subject of the significance of variations in human physique, another set of influencing factors must be considered. While the pygmies appear to represent a response to problems stemming from both periodic food shortages and the necessity for the efficient dissipation of metabolically generated heat, and other differences in physique appear to be adaptive, there seems to be another factor affecting human survival in parts of the north temperate zone. A belt of chronic overpopulation and undernourishment extends from Egypt through India and into southern China and southeast Asia, but the people, while small, have not become pygmoid in size. While it is impossible to do anything more than suggest the answer, it would appear that any further reduction in size would decrease the potential for the amount of work and nourishment people must produce in order to survive. These people seem to be able to produce a maximum amount of work on the smallest possible number of calories per day. If they were larger they would eat more than they could cultivate, if smaller they could not sustain the amount of labor necessary to support a family, so a close adjustment is made, and, despite the different origins of the peoples in this belt, there is a remarkable similarity in bodily proportions.

We have said enough about the gross morphological variations visible in mankind. Others exist which we have not treated, and much of what we have said has been obvious but undocumented by the kind of solid evidence which is usually demanded of biological interpretations. Our purpose has been not only to touch on the major observable variations in man, but also to demonstrate that the various traits in which people differ are distributed in accordance with the selective factors responsible for their expression, and not as a result of any association with socially delimited boundaries such as the perception of "race." Where the selective factors are related or happen to vary together, then the traits they influence will likewise vary together, but as we have shown, it is more common to see the selective forces and their corresponding traits varying more or less independently of each other and crossing geographical and population boundaries without regard to the supposed limits of human gene pools or areas of mating preference.

If this approach to understanding human variation is clear when gross morphology is the subject under consideration, it is at least as obvious when characteristics are investigated for which a precise knowledge exists concerning the genetic background. In fact in much recent biological thinking there has been the feeling that morphological variation is difficult to appraise, since the precise mode of inheritance of morphology is so poorly known. The result has been the abandonment of morphology as a valid area of investigation by many recent students. This in part explains the reason why the data on which our appraisal of human morphological variation is based were collected primarily a generation or more ago and remain so incomplete.

Single Gene Traits

Within the last two to three decades there has been a belief among biologists, and particularly biological anthropologists, that the simple understanding of the genetics of a trait was sufficient reason for acquiring information concerning its occurrence in different human populations. Accordingly, the energy which had previously been devoted to morphological trait gathering in generations gone by has recently been transferred to genetic trait gathering. The result has been the collection of an enormous amount of information relating to human characteristics with a simple mode of inheritance. Recalling the role of the basic genetic material in the production of protein molecules, it is not unexpected that many of the features which are inherited as single gene characters turn out to be proteins or closely related molecules.

Within the last few years the realization has grown that the distribution of some of these traits corresponds with the distribution of recognized and important selective factors. Now at last some evolutionary sense can be made out of what formerly seemed to be merely biochemical oddities.

The first such primarily physiological trait which we shall consider is color blindness. The exact biochemical deficiency which produces failures to see colors is unknown, but the mode of inheritance is clear and simple. Contrary to popular assumptions, failure to see red and failure to see green are not due to the same genetic deficiency, although the genes controlling each type of vision occur at loci on the X chromosome and hence are examples of the phenomenon of ordinary genetic linkage as well as sex-linkage. Apparently there are at least two alleles at each locus.

While genetically these are actually two separate traits, yet as far as the individual possessing either is concerned, failure to see colors, whatever the genetic source, is subject to the same kind of selection and for purposes of distribution studies there is some justification for lumping the two. Furthermore, many studies have failed to recognize the differences and have lumped them anyway. It seems obvious that visual acuity, including color vision ability, is highly desirable for a people depending on hunting and gathering as a mode of subsistence. As pointed out by Dr. Richard H. Post of Michigan, any deficiency in vision in such a group would be detrimental and would be selected against. For people at a food-producing level of subsistence, the penalties for poor color vision would be less severe, and one would expect mutations affecting vision to accumulate in time, and eventually result in a reduction of visual efficiency in the same manner in which skin depigmentation occurs following the relaxation of the significant selective pressures.

Theoretically, then, the highest percentage of deficiencies of color vision would be expected to occur among people whose forebears were the first to forsake a foraging for a food-producing mode of subsistence. It would, therefore, also be expected that the distribution of increasing color vision deficiency would be correlated with the cline of dental reduction. In most cases the expectation is completely fulfilled, with the highest percentages of color blindness occurring among people of European and Middle Eastern origin followed closely by Chinese. This, of course, is quite to be expected since, as with the slightly lesser degree of dental reduction in the Far East, the food-producing revolution occurred slightly later in China than it did in the Middle East.

The lowest percentages of color vision deficiency occur among modern hunting and gathering populations although there is some confusion in the evidence where the samples tested are too small to be reliable. Clearly, then, the distribution of color blindness frequencies, in cutting across boundaries of socially perceived racial differences, behaves in the same manner we have already demonstrated for morphological features. Again, the most important criterion to consider is the distribution of the selecting factor.

One of the classic cases of the interaction of biological and cultural selective factors can be seen in the distribution of abnormal hemoglobins, in spite of the first impression that this must be something difficult and obscure. This trait was first recognized more than half a century ago with the description of a form of anemia which was usually fatal. At first it was thought to occur only among people of African descent but subsequent work has shown the trait to be more widely distributed. Not only is the sufferer afflicted with severe anemia, but when a sample of his blood is placed in a low oxygen environment, the red blood cells become twisted into a variety of angular shapes, many of which suggested the form of tiny sickles to the early observers. This latter characteristic, frequently encountered when samples were prepared on slides under glass covers for microscopic examination, earned the disease the name "sickle-cell anemia."

Sickle-cell anemia was eventually shown to be a single gene characteristic determined by the form of hemoglobin carried on the red blood cells. Hemoglobin is the complex organic molecule which forms a temporary bond with free oxygen, enabling the red blood cells to pick up oxygen at the lungs and deliver it to the tissues where it is needed to burn (oxidize) the fuels which run the machinery of the body. Like so many other characteristics whose form is controlled by single genes, hemoglobin is basically a protein molecule, and, as such, it is chiefly made up of a series of amino acid units. Recent analysis has shown that normal hemoglobin differs from the hemoglobin which produces sickle-cell anemia at the location of only a single amino acid. At a specific point in the amino acid chain, normal hemoglobin has glutamic acid, while sickle-cell hemoglobin has the amino acid valine.

While there are now about two dozen kinds of abnormal hemoglobins known, our primary concern will be for the normal form and for the kind which is responsible for sickle-cell anemia. Normal hemoglobin is designated hemoglobin A, while sickling hemoglobin by convention is called hemoglobin S. Since chromosomes are double structures, the locus for hemoglobin always has two genes. The genotype for normal hemoglobin is AA while the genotype for a person who is afflicted with sickle-cell anemia is SS. This makes the cross between the two—the heterozygote—AS, which also can be induced to show the sickling phenomenon in blood samples but which in the carrier does not show the anemic symptoms. The heterozygote AS is said to show the "sickle cell trait," and, since the homozygote SS generally dies in early childhood, most of the hemoglobin S in existence is that possessed by heterozygotes.

This brings us to the puzzling problem which has only recently been solved, namely, why the percentage of abnormal hemoglobin should be so high in some parts of the world. High frequencies for hemoglobin S occur in parts of Africa, southern Europe especially Sicily, southern Italy, Greece, Asia Minor, southern Arabia, India, and southeast Asia, and in some places in East Africa the gene frequency rises as high as 20 per cent. Since almost all the occurrences are in the form of heterozygotes that should mean that as much as 40 per cent of the people in such a population are heterozygotes. By chance matings, somewhat less than 5 per cent of the next generation should be SS, but since this is not viable, the genes should be eliminated from the common pool. The problem is why, with this constant drain, is S maintained at a 20 per cent level.

Recurrent mutation is obviously not a factor since even the most extreme mutation rate is many thousand times too low. To maintain such a frequency, something must be eliminating the homozygote AA at a rate which balances that for the elimination of SS. The answer to this puzzle began to emerge when it was suspected that the heterozygote AS might be particularly resistant to malaria. Certainly the highest frequencies of hemoglobin S, all present in heterozygous form, occur exclusively in areas where falciparum malaria is a major hazard for human survival. While it is true that no high frequencies of hemoglobin S persist for long outside malarial areas it is also true that people with very low percentages of abnormal hemoglobin exist in the tropics and in areas where malaria is a severe problem. Since the proof of an adaptation can only stem from the correlation between the selective force and the presumed biological response, the spotty occurrence of hemoglobin S through the malaria belt of the Old World led to some skepticism concerning the proposed association.

Many important aspects remain to be accounted for, but the principal lines of the solution were worked out as a result of the brilliant work of Dr. Frank B. Livingstone at Michigan. Dr. Livingstone's studies have revealed the relationship between the spread of malaria and the impact of human activities in shaping the environment at present and during the recent past in Africa.

The most serious and widespread form of malaria is caused by the parasite *Plasmodium falciparum* which is spread among the human hosts by the mosquito *Anopheles gambiae*. Curiously, these mosquitoes do not thrive in the tropic rain-forests since environments lacking sunlight and standing water are among the few in which they cannot thrive. The deep shade produced by uncut tropical jungle and the highly absorbent humus of the forest floor discourage the breeding of *Anopheles gambiae* and it appears that falciparum malaria must therefore be a recent introduction to much of tropical Africa. Hence the pygmies of the Ituri forest in the eastern Congo and the remnants of former hunting and gathering populations of the Ivory Coast of West Africa have been until recently much less troubled with malaria than the Africans who practice slash-and-burn agriculture.

The practice of chopping down a patch of forest and burning it means that a rich harvest can be reaped after planting in the ashes. The heavy tropic rainfall soon dissolves the nutrients in the topsoil and within a very few years the ground is leached out and unproductive. Furthermore the disappearance of the absorbent humus leaves a soil which is impervious to water, so that the rain collects in puddles under the open air providing an ideal mosquito breeding ground. As slash-and-burn farmers move from plot to plot over the years they create an environment in which malaria thrives, and it is clear that, despite the high cost in human mortality, the incidence of Hemoglobin S has been spreading in the rain-forest areas because of the protection it gives to the heterozygotes.

The spotty distribution of Hemoglobin S in West Africa and the Congo is due to the fact that slash-and-burn agriculture as a means of subsistence is very recent. The simple business of cutting down the enormous jungle trees would be unprofitably laborious with stone axes and depends on the availability of iron tools. Iron apparently was used and worked in the savanna land south of the Sahara as long as almost twenty-five hundred years ago, but the invasion of the forest has occurred only within the last thousand years. The kind of farming which spread to the savanna land from Egypt was based on grains which yield very

poor returns in the wet forest areas, so it was not until the do-
mestication of the West African yam that Africans possessed both
the tools and the crops necessary to enable them to penetrate the
rain-forest environment.

Livingstone, by piecing together information from linguistic
and cultural distributions and what historical accounts there are,
has managed to reconstruct the history of the recent past for West
Africa. The percentages of Hemoglobin S correspond exactly according to expectation. The peoples who are believed to have
invaded the West African rain-forest bringing slash-and-burn agriculture and malaria possess the highest percentages of Hemoglobin S. The peoples indigenous to the coastal area that have
acquired slash-and-burn agriculture, and hence malaria by diffusion, also seem to have had sufficient contact with the invaders
to have acquired the abnormal hemoglobin, for while its frequency is not as high as among the newcomers, it is decidedly
higher than among the few remaining representatives of the
original hunting and gathering forest dwellers where it apparently
had been absent.

Of the nearly two dozen known abnormal hemoglobins, several others now appear to be associated with resistance to malaria
conferred by the heterozygous state, with other types of malaria
parasites and other kinds of mosquitoes implicated. The case for
Hemoglobin S, however, remains the best worked out and best
documented. It represents something more important than a
trait for which the distribution in relation to the selective factors
is known, although that is important enough in itself. Of greater
interest is the fact that through Livingstone's careful work we now
have a well documented picture of the spread of a trait not only
by actual population movement but across population boundaries
as a result of the inevitable genetic exchange which adjacent
populations practice, and the subsequent selective advantage that
it confers. Since the genetics of this trait are simple and the selective forces involved are so strong, it can be quantified in a way
that is not possible for the morphological traits we have previously
discussed. Because of this, Hemoglobin S can serve as a model for
understanding the mechanisms underlying the distribution of any
trait whose expression is subject to natural selection, whether it

be a single gene character or one controlled by an unknown number of genes and loci.

With the insights gained from the successful interpretation of the various conditions relating to the abnormal hemoglobins, it is now becoming possible to foresee the explanation of some other characteristics which have been known for some time. Specifically, the near future may produce an understanding of the distribution of the various human blood groups. Information concerning blood groups began to accumulate in 1900 at which time it was discovered that, when the blood from one person was mixed with that from another individual, a clumping or agglutination reaction occurred in some cases. Where agglutination occurred the blood samples in question were said to be of different types.

Blood types remained a minor medical curiosity until the first World War when it suddenly became of vital importance to the military to know the blood types of combat personnel. If transfusion were needed, it was most desirable not to introduce blood of an incompatible type to the recipient since a fatal reaction could occur. Continued research and discovery following the war demonstrated that the various blood types had a simple mode of inheritance, and since they have been identified as mucopolysaccharides, which are organic molecules closely related to proteins, this makes good sense. As the genetics were worked out, it was discovered that the blood types discovered were all the result of three different alleles at the same chromosomal locus. This was the famous A B O blood group system.

Because of its importance in transfusion, an enormous number of blood type determinations has been made during the last third of a century and today more is known about the distribution of the various allelic frequencies in the A B O system than for any other human trait. Somewhat paradoxically, virtually nothing was known about the significance of the distribution. Part of the reason why no effort was made to understand the meaning of blood groups lay in the erroneous assumption that some of the major biological differences between men were nonadaptive in character. The anthropologists who made this assumption were primarily interested in traits that they could use to distinguish what they believed to be the races of mankind. For this purpose they used traits which they assumed were uninfluenced by environmental or selective forces and which were presumably established in remote antiquity. Since blood groups seemed quite removed from the action of selective influences and since they were so clearly inherited, they were seized upon with enthusiasm as the best of racial markers.

There were two consequences of this approach to the study of human diversity. First, the fact that biologists commenced with the assumption that racial groups (breeding populations) were the significant units for analysis provided fuel for those individuals and groups who for their own profit wished to believe that human races are of different innate worth, hence justifying existing practices of racial discrimination. The second consequence was that by restricting consideration to breeding populations it was difficult to appreciate the covariation of selective factors and the respective human adaptations where these crossed population boundaries, as they do in so many cases. This meant that a full understanding of human variation and how it arose was not possible.

Recently, however, there has been a change in the orientation of students of man's diversity. It has been realized that a simple naming of human groups or races has no particular significance as a biological aim, although the study of human group relations and hence group identification has real significance for the sociologist and for other social scientists. In addition, human biologists have increasingly realized that their primary task is the explanation of how human variations arose, and it is obvious that the assumption that human differences are nonadaptive defeats any such effort before it is begun. If man's form is the product of evolution, then man's differences must represent evolutionary responses to different selective pressures. It should, therefore, be possible to explain differences in the frequencies of what were once considered the least adaptive of nonadaptive characters, the various blood types.

With this revitalized evolutionary view in mind, some effort has been made to discover what selective factors could account for the marked differences in allele frequencies which the A B O system exhibits in the various parts of the world (Figures 131-2-3). Among other things, it has been noted that there is a slightly

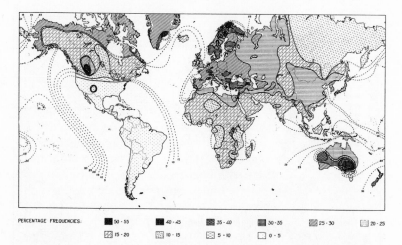

FIGURE 131. Distribution of the A blood groups. (Courtesy of Dr. A. E. Mourant.)

higher than expected chance that people with blood type A will suffer from intestinal cancer, and there is a slightly higher than expected chance that those with blood type O will develop peptic

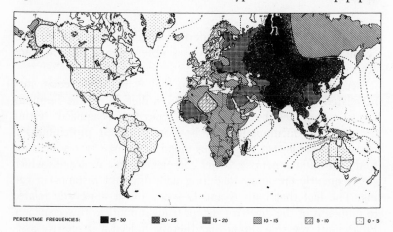

FIGURE 132. Distribution of the B blood groups. (Courtesy of Dr. A. E. Mourant.)

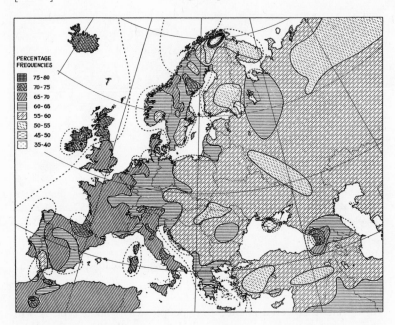

FIGURE 133. Distribution of the O blood groups. (Courtesy of Dr. A. E. Mourant.)

ulcers. Neither condition is important enough to account for the evolution of the various differences observed and clearly some other factor must be sought.

Recently the suspicion has arisen that A B O differences may be related to characteristic differences in diet. With the immunological techniques, by which blood types are recognized, testing primarily for incompatibilities in closely related proteinoids, it seemed probable that the various blood types may have something to do with adjustments to other complex organic molecules which are frequently encountered during daily life—for instance in eating. The fact that both A and O types are in some way related to problems of the digestive system lends support to this suspicion. Preliminary research shows that there is indeed a suggestive association between various frequencies of the A B O system and major population differences in characteristic amounts in fat, carbohydrate, and protein intake. Further work may show that different kinds of protein may correspond to particular A B O frequencies—for example some peoples may derive most of their proteins from animals while others obtain the greater quantity from such vegetable foods as beans or lentils. This research, however, has only been initiated recently, and while it is most exciting and suggestive, nothing has been proven yet.

For the first time, however, investigation is proceeding along fruitful lines, and we can foresee vast increases in the understanding of facets of human diversity in the near future. The A B O blood group system has been mentioned especially because we seem to be on the verge of a solution, but we should note that there are many other blood group systems as well. The Rh system is another for which a great deal of information exists. The reader should not suppose that one is either A B O *or* Rh-something. There are separate loci for each system and every individual has one or another of the alleles for both. The Rh system has been considered important because of the effect which Rh incompatibilities can have on the fetus during pregnancy, but the reasons for the existence of differences in the system in the first place remain entirely unknown. Other systems include M N S, Duffy, Kell, Diego and a host of others whose number is limited only by the ingenuity of people interested in their discovery. Everyone has alleles for one or another type within each of these systems, but the selective conditions for the existence of these different types and for the significance of all these blood group systems remain as yet undiscovered. However with this new approach to understanding human diversity, we can look forward to an enormous increase in our understanding of human physical variation in the very near future—in fact, the research is being carried on at this moment and new insights are being reached even as this is written.

SUGGESTED READINGS

Brace, C. L. "A non-racial approach toward the understanding of human diversity," M. F. Ashley Montagu (editor). *The Concept of Race*. The Free Press, New York, 1962.
A new approach to the study of human diversity.

Livingstone, F. B. "Anthropological implications of sickle cell gene distribution in West Africa," M. F. Ashley Montagu (editor). *Culture and the Evolution of Man*, Oxford University Press, New York, pp. 343–354.
A demonstration of the manner in which genetic differences become established in adaptation to environmental pressures.

Loomis, W. F. "Skin pigment regulation of vitamin-D biosynthesis in man," *Science*, vol. 157, 1967, pp. 501–506.
On the possible mechanism of skin color differences in man.

Newman, M. T. "The application of ecological rules to the racial anthropology of the aboriginal new world," *American Anthropologist*, vol. 55, 1955, pp. 309–327.
——— "Adaptations in the physique of American aborigines to nutritional factors," *Human Biology*, vol. 32, 1960, pp. 288–313.

Newman, R. W. and E. H. Monro. "The relation of climate and body size in U. S. Males," *American Journal of Physical Anthropology*, vol. 13, 1955, pp. 1–17.
Three papers on the relation between climatic factors and form and size of the body.

Post, R. H. "Population Differences in Red and Green Color Vision Deficiency," *Eugenics Quarterly*, vol. 9, 1962, pp. 131–146; vol. 10, pp. 84–85, 1962.
——— "Population differences in vision acuity," *Eugenics Quarterly*, vol. 9, 1962, pp. 189-212.
——— "Hearing acuity variation among Negroes and whites," *Eugenics Quarterly*, vol. 11, 1964, pp. 65–81.
Three papers indicating some of the factors probably operative in the evolution of certain functional differences between populations in vision and hearing.

Roberts, D. F. "Body weight, races, and climate," *American Journal of Physical Anthropology*, vol. 11, 1953, pp. 533–556.
——— and **D. R. Bainbridge.** "Nilotic physique," *American Journal of Physical Anthropology*, vol. 21, 1963, pp. 341–370.
Two papers on climate and physique.

CHAPTER TEN ❧❧ CONTINUING
EVOLUTION

T HE MOST REMARKABLE THING about the creature man is the cultural adaptive mechanism which he has created in order to increase his chances for survival. The realization of this fact constitutes the justification and the basis for the fascination exerted by the social sciences and humanities. In the preceding pages we have attempted to give some indication of the role that culture has played in not only ensuring· man's survival but also in altering the selective pressures that have operated on man and thereby influenced the course of his physical evolution.

Initially culture provided the tools and verbal means of coordinating group activities which served to increase the chances for group survival in the face of possible predation by carnivores, and which increased the efficiency of the acquisition and distribution of food. With culture as man's principal adaptive mechanism, it was important that the individual be able to acquire an adequate command of his culture before it became his responsibility to nurture the next generation. Up to a point, there was a selective advantage in favor of those individuals best able to master the necessary cultural adaptations.

Making a rough correlation between brain size and learning ability, it is obvious why cranial capacity increased during the greater part of the Pleistocene. Eventually a level was reached where the efficiency of the cultural adaptive mechanism was such that it benefited even those individuals who were not completely able to master it. At such a point, individuals who were just up to acquiring the necessary requirements of their culture would have just as good a prospect for survival, and transmission of their characteristics to the next generation, as were those who could master their culture with ease. With no adaptive advantage inherent in further increases in learning ability, brain size ceased to increase and has remained effectively unchanged since the Middle Pleistocene. This also is the basis for the fact that there exists no demonstrable difference between the average intelligence of the various groups of people present in the world today.

One might even go a step further and offer the prediction, admittedly a speculation, that if any differences in intelligence are discovered in the future they will be inversely proportional to the efficiency of the cultural adaptive mechanism of the group in question. Highly effective cultures ensure it that even the dull-witted shall survive and enjoy their opportunity to reproduce, provided they are at least capable of mastering the rudiments of their language and the mechanics of their social system. This provides a mental minimum, and, although modern technology has succeeded in lowering this somewhat, there is a limit below which effective participation in one's culture is so severely reduced that the chances for genetic perpetuation become negligible.

In literate cultures with an elaborate division of labor, it is distinctly possible that the "average" level of intelligence necessary for effective survival may be somewhat lower than is the case for those cultures where the problems involved in simple survival are much more immediate, and the advantages in the possession of a large store of accurate information about one's environment are much more apparent. The premium placed on human intelligence in the face of prolonged scarcity in the Australian desert or at the edge of the polar ice cap, where the penalty for stupidity is death, is almost certainly greater than it is for even the most downtrodden inhabitants of western Europe or North America. Even the most irresponsible and basically incompetent denizen of the slums of Chicago or Naples or Liverpool is capable of reproducing a dozen times over or more with a good chance that the greater part of the offspring will survive to do likewise.

While this situation has been frequently viewed with alarm by "racists," advocates of strict eugenics (control over who shall breed and in what number), and other alarmists, the consequences are certainly less serious than is often feared. For one thing, intelligence is such a complex phenomenon and under the control of so many genes that the genetic reshuffling which necessarily accompanies sexual reproduction makes it more probable that the offspring of the mentally semi-competent will be closer to the population average than their parents were. Despite the high rate of reproduction of members of the lower socioeconomic strata, the basic biological nature of the population remains relatively unchanged.

Increased intelligence apparently had adaptive value up to the Neanderthal stage. Since that time, however, a balance has been maintained with, if anything, a slight reduction of the premium placed on "brains" and a possible slight reduction in the average intelligence particularly of the members of the more effective cultural systems. Unless man discovers a means of manipulating his genes in a way that is as yet unforeseen, the future should certainly see no increase and probably a slight decrease in basic intellectual ability, however it is defined. Ultimately this should be relatively unimportant because of the social limit imposed on total mental incompetence.

From the very beginning of human evolution, the reliance on cultural rather than anatomical means for the manipulation of the environment meant that the significance of large projecting canine teeth had been suspended. As a result of the probable mutation effect, the accumulation of random mutation produced a reduction in canine tooth size until these teeth were functionally the same as incisors. Throughout the record of human evolution afforded by the known fossils, the canines have responded to the same forces that have influenced the form of the other teeth in the forward part of the dental arch, although they still retain a vestige of their prehuman importance in the fact that their roots are distinctly larger than is the case for the incisors, and their tips usually project beyond the occlusal level of the other teeth.

As culture took over the roles formerly performed by the teeth alone, the dentition underwent concomitant reductions. The increase in animal protein in the diet and possibly the use of fire by the Pithecanthropine stage meant that the burden placed on the molars was greatly reduced, and the operation of the probable mutation effect assured the subsequent reduction of both molar size and crown pattern complexity. The advent of specialized tools for cutting, chiselling, gouging, and scraping starting with the Mousterian had the same effect on the incisors. While all this has resulted in the transformation of the more than horsey Middle Paleolithic face into that relatively reduced anatomical complex which sets the standards for modern "beauty," the prospects for the future, while somewhat uncertain, are not calculated to generate quite so much enthusiasm, except perhaps in the members of the dental profession.

Two centuries ago, rotting teeth exposed a person to the possibility of all kinds of secondary infections and distinctly lowered one's chances for survival. With the perfection of the technology of dentistry, all sorts of abnormalities can now be ameliorated to the detriment of nothing more than the owner's pocketbook. Reflect for a moment on the effect that would follow the complete cessation of dental care. How many among us reach voting age without a cavity? Admitting that the diet of the American teen-ager is rapidly approaching "one vast milkshake" and that the quantity of refined sugar ingested is partially related to the incidence of dental decay, nevertheless the suspension of all dental repair work would result in the untimely demise of an appalling number of people. One may surmise that the probable mutation effect is operating at this very moment to reduce the quality of the teeth of civilized peoples. The prophet of gloom could project this into the future and foresee a toothless species in another half-million years, but by that time there will have been enough other changes accumulated so that our present standards of what is "good" will not apply, and our remote descendants may be able

to look back with pity on us their ancestors who had the misfortune to grow up with thirty-two unnecessary sources of potential pain in the permanent teeth, not to mention the twenty
milk teeth. Even now, some individuals never develop lateral incisors, and many more fail to acquire third molars (wisdom [sic]
teeth), while the dental profession becomes ever more adept at
repairing or replacing the crumbling teeth that remain to us.

Other parts and functions of the human body can also be predicted to undergo reduction: pigmentation for the darker immi-
grants into the temperate zone, head hair for men and women
everywhere, visual acuity, resistance to various diseases, and general physical robustness. The adaptive value of these features will
be more or less cancelled out and replaced by clothes, hats, lenses,
medicine, and power tools. Differentiation of this kind has been
proceeding among the peoples of the world depending on precisely how long the adaptive value of the traits in question has
been reduced, and it seems inevitable that the future will see
further changes in the directions indicated. Unquestionably the
people of 1,000,000 A.D. will be radically different from the people
of today—possibly different enough to warrant a new specific
designation within the Genus *Homo*, should we say *Homo dura-
bilis?*

There is one other change which has been occurring recently
and in which a somewhat misguided pride has been taken. This is
the undoubted increase in size which has occurred during the last
century, and which has occasioned the unwarranted feeling that
the twentieth century is generating a better breed of people.
While all the reasons for this change are not fully understood,
most of it can be accounted for by two main factors. First is the
undoubted increase in both the quantity and the quality of the
diet. Second and often overlooked is the fact that under most
of the conditions which have prevailed during human history,
extraordinary size has been a distinct handicap. Imagine the
despair of a family in the Middle East, southern India or China
in attempting to meet the nutritional requirements of a child
genetically destined to grow to a height of 6 ft. 8 in. with a weight
of 250 pounds. Imagine further the despair of said growing child
during the lean year when the per capita consumption averages

eight hundred calories a day or less for an appreciable length of time. Furthermore, individuals who become especially large must necessarily grow more rapidly during youth than others, a fact which makes them particularly vulnerable to a variety of diseases which are less serious for those who grow at a more normal rate.

Until recently, both health and nutritional problems were more serious for the youngster destined to be large. At least part of the recent increase in overall size visible in modern populations is due to the fact that improved standards of food and medical care have allowed genetic combinations to survive which would have been selected against in ages past. Not only do modern men tend to be larger and somewhat softer than was the case in days gone by, but the cessation of the survival value of physical performance has allowed the survival of a degree of variation in human physique and proportions that did not formerly occur. The number of individuals who sport wide hips and narrow shoulders, big hands and thin arms, heavy legs and lean trunk, and other such dysplasias is much greater among "civilized" peoples than is true for, say, the inhabitants of central New Guinea who, small though they may be, possess uniformly imposing and well-proportioned physiques.

What this all portends for the future is not altogether clear, although it seems apparent that, at the moment, the suspension of stringent physical selection and the improvement of medicine and nutrition is permitting a general increase in size, an increase in the variability of physique, and a reduction in muscularity. For the distant future, however, the crystal ball grows hazy and the picture dims. There are simply too many unknowns, and we feel that we have already extended our speculations far enough.

One thing is certain. There are going to be too many people. It is estimated that the present population of three billion includes nearly one third of all the people who ever trod the earth. At the present rate of increase, world population bids fair to multiply some fifteen times within the next century. By the year 2050, the number of people alive would be five times the entire cumulative total of all the people who have ever existed since the beginning of human history. Perhaps the efficient utilization of our present food resources could feed double our present population. Increased food-producing efficiency might feed triple the number of people in the world, but no conceivable development will enable the world to support 15 times its present population. While we may be venturing into the territory of the cultural anthropologist, the sociologist, and the moral philosopher, yet, in the perspective of human evolution, it seems inevitable that man who has exerted increasing control over the conditions of his survival—including the regulation of the rate of reproduction of many of the plants and animals of the earth—will have to take some responsibility for the regulation of his own reproduction simply to ensure that he shall survive. Birth control is a necessity simply to keep human numbers manageable. Perhaps in the future the science of genetics will provide the means whereby some control can be exerted over the quality of human reproduction, but, at the present time, birth control is necessary simply in order to ensure the probability that there will be any future at all.

SUGGESTED READINGS

Bressler, J. B. (editor). *Human Ecology.* Addison-Wesley, Reading, Mass., 1966.
A collection of readings on the effect of environmental factors on the development of man.

Daniels, F., Jr. "Man and radiant energy: solar radiation," D. B. Dill *et al.* (editors), *Handbook of Physiology, Section 4: Adaptation to the Environment.* American Physiological Society, Washington, D.C., 1964, pp. 969–987.
A good discussion of the effects of solar radiation on the skin of man.

Dobzhansky, Th., and M. F. Ashley Montagu. "Natural Selection and the mental capacities of mankind," *Science,* vol. 105, 1947, pp. 587–590.
On the plasticity of human beings and the relation of that fact to the evolution of the mental capacities of the varieties of man.

Hardin, G. (editor). *Population, Evolution, & Birth Control.* Freeman & Co., San Francisco, 1964.
An excellent collage of stimulating and controversial readings.

Montagu, M. F. Ashley. *Man's Most Dangerous Myth: The Fallacy of Race.* 4th ed. World Publishing Co., Cleveland & New York, 1964.

An examination of the fatal difficulties inherent in any attempt to use a concept of "race."

Montagu, M. F. Ashley, (editor). *The Concept of Race.* The Free Press, New York, 1964.

A critical examination of the anthropological concept of race.

Simons, R.D.G.PH. *The Colour of the Skin in Human Relations.* Elsevier Publishing Co., Princeton, N.J., 1961.

An interesting monograph on the behavioral effects of skin color upon whites.

GLOSSARY

Adaptation   A trait of the organism which, in the environment it inhabits, improves its chances of leaving descendants.

Adaptive radiation   Evolution, from a primitive type of organism, or from a basically successful adaptation, of divergent forms adapted to distinct modes of life.

Allele   One of the two or more forms of a gene.

Amino acid   One of a number of organic acids from which proteins are formed.

Anthropoidea   Suborder of the Order Primates. Includes the monkeys, anthropoid apes, and man.

Apes   Members of the family Pongidae, consisting of the gibbons, orang, chimpanzee, and gorilla.

Arboreal   Adapted for living in trees.

Australopithecine   A member of the African hominid forms of the Villafranchian.

Bacteriophage   A virus that destroys bacteria.

Brachiation   Progression in trees by swinging by the arms from branches.

Buccal   Toward the cheek side.

Carbon 14 dating   A method of determining the age of material by determining the amount of radioactive Carbon 14 which has been lost.

Cell The living active unit of all plants and animals, consisting of many specialized parts.

Chromosome One of a number of double-thread shaped bodies possibly made of protein, situated in the nucleus of the cell and carrying the genes. A code center.

Clactonian Lower Paleolithic flake-tool industry of northwest Europe dating from the Middle Pleistocene Mindel-Riss interglacial. Characterized by choppers, scrapers, and knives. A wooden spear is also known from this culture, a culture probably associated with the first inhabitants of Britain.

Cline A gradation of form differences or in the frequency of a trait within a species over a geographical area.

Codon A set of three bases that codes one amino acid. The *bases*, in DNA, are adenine, thymine, guanine, and cytosine.

Competition The process whereby those organisms possessing the adaptive fitness, in the environments they inhabit, are able to leave a larger progeny than those not possessing such fitness. Neither conscious "struggle" nor "survival of the fittest" is implied, but survival of the fit.

Crossover The shifting of genes from one chromosome to another.

Culture The part of the environment that is learned, shared, and transmitted in society. The man-made part of the environment.

Cytology The study of cells.

Deoxyribonucleic acid, DNA The principal constituent of the gene, believed to be the material of heredity itself. DNA carries the master plan or code containing the information that determines the order in which the amino acids fall into place in the protein molecule for which it is responsible.

Dryopithecine A taxon of Miocene apes which may be ancestral to both the later apes (pongids) and man (hominids).

Ecological niche The position occupied by an organism in relation to its total environment, but more especially to the particular situation of the environment which it actually occupies.

Ecology The study of the interactions between organisms and their environment; the economics of organisms.

Environment The conditions acting upon the organism. Such conditions may be internal as well as external.

Enzyme Any of various organic compounds secreted by the body cells that act as catalysts causing the chemical processes of the body to be carried on.

Entropy The tendency of any system to dissipate heat, decrease in organization, and increase in randomness. That part of the heat or energy invested in the body or any system which cannot be taken out and is therefore unavailable for work.

Eocene Geological period, subdivision of Tertiary, lasted approximately from fifty-five to thirty-five million years ago.

Euhominid Used by some authors to refer to the stage of man immediately above that of the Australopithecines, e.g., *Homo* (*Pithecanthropus*) *erectus*.

Evolution Development, by descent, with modification.

Falciparum mosquito *Plasmodium falciparum* is the parasite that produces a particularly virulent form of malaria. It is transmitted by the mosquito *Anopheles gambiae*.

Fossil Remains of an organism or direct evidence of its presence preserved in rocks.

Gene The physical unit of heredity, a small region in a chromosome consisting mainly of DNA. The minimal hereditary unit determined by crossover. Possibly a section (codon) of a DNA molecule.

Gene flow Relating to the dissemination of genes from one population to another.

Gene frequency Relating to the frequency of certain genes in certain populations.

Genetic drift or the Sewall Wright effect The nonselective random distribution, or extinction or fixation of genes in a population.

Genotype The genetic constitution, determined by the number, types, and arrangement of genes.

Gene pool The genes present within a given population.

Genosorption The incorporation of the genes of one population into the gene pool of another.

Gonad The sex gland; the ovary in the female, the testis in the male.

Göttweiger Interstadial A warm period of the Würm Glacial. Würm Interstadial I–II, 38,000 B.C.

Grade   A general term referring to developmental level, e.g., the prosimian grade, the monkey grade, the ape grade, the hominid grade.

Habitat   The particular kind of environment inhabited by an organism.

Hemoglobin   The red respiratory protein coating red blood cells, serving to carry oxygen to and carbon dioxide from the cells of the body.

Heterozygous   Carrying different forms of a gene (allele) on both homologous chromosomes.

Hominine   Synonym of *Euhominine* (see *Euhominid.*)

Hominid   A member of the family *Hominidae.*

Hominidae   The family name of all species of man, including the Australopithecines.

Hominoidea   The superfamily including the Hominidae and the Pongidae, i.e., man and the apes.

Homo habilis   Name given to a form of man, at present inadequately described, possibly an advanced Australopithecine, perhaps approaching the Pithecanthropine stage, with status at present undetermined.

Homo sapiens   The living species of the genus *Homo*, as well as several extinct forms of this species.

Interstadial   The temperate or cool period between phases of a single glacial period. Interstadials are shorter and cooler than interglacial periods.

Labial   Toward the lips.

Lingual   Toward the tongue.

Linkage   Genes situated on the same chromosome are said to be linked. The linkage is broken by crossing-over.

Locus   A particular place on a particular chromosome that always contains one kind of gene or one of a particular set of alleles. Homologous chromosomes usually have identical sets of loci.

Mammal   A member of the class of Mammals, characterized by hair, milk secretion, diaphragm used in respiration, lower jaw made up of single pair of bones; presence of only left systemic arch, and three auditory ossicles in each middle ear connecting eardrum and inner ear.

Meiosis The two successive cell divisions from a cell containing the full complement of chromosomes (forty-six in man) preceding formation of the gametes. Both divisions resemble mitosis, except that while there are two divisions of the nucleus, in the second meiotic division the chromosomes are not duplicated, hence resulting in the formation of gametes with half the number (haploid) of chromosomes from the mother cells with the double number (diploid) or full complement of chromosomes.

Metacarpals The bones of the hand between the wrist and the fingers.

Metatarsals The bones of the foot, between the tarsal bones and the toes.

Miocene Geological period of the Tertiary, lasting from about twenty-five to twelve million years ago.

Mitosis The process of cell division during which the genes and chromosomes duplicate, migrate to an equatorial plane, and separate to opposite poles, and the cell splits and forms two new cells.

Monkey A grade of the Anthropoidea characterized by tails, comprising the New World monkeys (Ceboidea) and the Old World monkeys (Cercopithecoidea).

Morphology The study of form, usually involving the study of the relation between function, structure, and form.

Mucopolysaccharide A carbohydrate containing a large number of compound sugars with their bases made up of repeating units that include an amino sugar.

Mutation A change in the structure of a gene resulting in a transmissible hereditary modification in the expression of a trait.

Mutation pressure The measure of the action of mutation in tending to alter the frequency of a gene in a given population.

Natural selection The fact that those organisms that possess a trait or traits that enable them to adapt better to the environment than those organisms lacking such a trait or traits are more likely to leave a larger progeny. As Darwin put it: "As many more individuals of each species are born than can possibly survive; and as, consequently, there is a frequently recurring struggle for existence, it follows that any being, if it vary how-

ever slightly in any manner profitable to itself, under the
complex and sometimes varying conditions of life, will have a
better chance of surviving, and thus be *naturally selected*. From
the strong principle of inheritance, any selected variety will tend
to propagate its new and modified form." *The Origin of Species*,
1859, p. 5.

Neanderthal man   The man of Mousterian culture (in the Upper
Pleistocene) prior to the reduction of the face and teeth of the
Middle Pleistocene.

Neanderthaloid   Possessing some features resembling the true
Neanderthals.

Nucleic acid   Family of substances of large molecular weight,
of double helical form, composed of nucleotides, found in chromosomes, viruses, etc.

Nucleotide   One of three units of which nucleic acids are composed. Consists of a phosphate and a sugar with an organic
base attached to the sugar. There are four different kinds depending on the nature of the base (adenine, guanine, cytosine,
thymine) (See Fig. 14).

Nucleus   The structure of the cell containing the chromosomes.

Occlusion   The relation of the upper and lower teeth to each
other when the bite is closed or "occluded."

Occipital bone   The bone at the back of the head.

Oligocene   Geological period of the Tertiary, lasting from about
thirty-five to twenty-five million years ago.

Order   A systematic category embracing families, genera, and
species, and their subdivisions, such as the order Primates, consisting of the lemurs, lorises, tarsier, monkeys, apes, and men, all
characterized by a basic structural patterning of traits.

Oreopithecus   An anthropoid genus of the Pliocene.

Orthogenesis   A not widely accepted theory of the tendency of
groups of organisms to evolve consistently in the same direction
over prolonged periods of time without any discoverable reason.

Paleocene   Geological period of the Tertiary, lasting from about
seventy to fifty-five million years ago.

Pangenesis   Darwin's outmoded theory that heredity might be
accounted for by gemmules, set free from all the cells of the
body, to be aggregated in ovum and sperm, so that in conjuga-

tion of the latter all the elements of the body would be recombined.

Paleontology The science that deals with the life of past geological epochs.

Phenotype The manifest characteristics of the organism; the product of the joint action of environment and genotype.

Phylogeny The study of the historical development of the line or lines of evolution in a group of organisms.

Pithecanthropine Resembling *Homo erectus*.

Pithecanthropus Preferably now known as *Homo erectus*, extinct form of man of Middle Pleistocene age.

Platyrrhine Broadnosed, the monkeys of the New World.

Pliopithecus A fossil Primate with gibbonlike teeth which lived during the Miocene and Lower Pliocene.

Pluvial A rainy period.

Polymer One of two or more isomeric substances (i.e., having same percentage composition, but differing in their physical properties), usually of high molecular weight, made up of a chain of repeated units.

Population The group of individuals which forms a single interbreeding community.

Polymorphism Individual variability, having several different forms; the presence of two or more alleles at the same loci of homologous chromosomes ensures variability for specific traits in the same population.

Polytypic A genus with several species or a species with several subspecies or varieties.

Pongidae The family of apes, orangs, chimpanzees, and gorillas.

Potassium-Argon dating A method of determining the age of fossils by measuring the transformation of potassium into argon.

Preadaptation A term not really possessing any significantly different meaning from the term *Adaptation* (*q.v.*). Here taken to mean the reapplication of structures or functions to life in a new environment.

Primate A member of the order Primates, consisting of the lemurs, lorises, tarsiers, monkeys, apes and men.

Probable Mutation Effect The effect of accumulated randomly produced mutations. Where selective forces are relaxed, this results in structural reduction.

Proconsul An apelike fossil form from the Lower Miocene of East Africa.

Propliopithecus An Oligocene anthropoid, which may be ancestral to the hominoids.

Protein Any of certain nitrogenous substances consisting of a complex union of amino acids, a chief constituent of chromosomes and of plant and animal bodies.

Proteinoids Proteinlike substances.

Race Used in many senses, by geneticists to mean any population that differs from other populations in the frequency of one or more genes, and by anthropologists to mean a population whose physical characteristics distinguish it from other populations, and finally, by the layman, in any sense in which he desires to use the term. A term that has outlived any dubious use it may once have had.

Rhinarium The moist patch present at the tip of the snout, as in lemurs.

Ribonucleic acid or RNA The form of nucleic acid (see DNA) synthesized in the nucleus on a DNA template, and responsible for directing protein synthesis.

Ribosome A morphologic unit of the cell machinery in the cytoplasm where amino acid units are linked together to form proteins.

Riss The penultimate glacial period, in the roughly upper two-thirds of the Middle Pleistocene.

Savanna A grassland characterized by scattered trees, especially in tropical and subtropical regions, a cross between a woodlands and a desert.

Selection The maintenance of certain genotypes having adaptive value in contrast with others that do not, and which therefore are not likely to do as well by way of leaving a progeny.

Selection pressure The measure of the action of selection in tending to alter the frequency of a gene in a given population.

Sexual selection Conscious selection on the basis of some preferred sexual trait as a factor of evolution. A widely discredited theory once held by Darwin.

Sickle cell A red blood cell which in the absence of oxygen assumes bizarre shapes often resembling those of a sickle.

Sicklemia Sometimes known as *sickle cell anemia,* due to sickle cells in the blood inherited as incompletely recessive, and homozygous in the sicklemic, the sicklemic rarely survives beyond childhood.

Sinanthropus Preferably now known as *Homo erectus pekinensis,* fossil hominid of Middle Pleistocene age, found at Choukoutien, S.W. of Peking in China.

Specialization A much overworked term, used relative to an actual or presumed ancestral form to mean the development of special adaptations to a particular habitat or mode of life, thus resulting in divergence of characteristics from ancestral forms.

Species A group of actually or potentially interbreeding natural populations, which is more or less reproductively isolated from other such groups.

Suture The edges at which the different bones of the skull come together, and with age mostly unite.

Taxon A taxonomic unit or category.

Taxonomy The science of classification of organisms.

Tetrapod Four-footed animals; all the essentially land-living vertebrates characterized by two pairs of pentadactyl limbs. Includes amphibians, reptiles, birds, and mammals.

Therapsida Mammal-like reptiles; extinct groups of reptiles that lived from the Permian to the Triassic. The main reptile group until the appearance of the dinosaurs. Therapsids were ancestral to the mammals.

Villafranchian The earliest part of the Pleistocene before the first glaciation (Günz).

Virus A minute living parasite composed of nucleic acid and protein that can be seen only by the electron microscope.

Würm The fourth and last of the Alpine glaciations.

Zinjanthropus An australopithecine of the Lower Pleistocene age, found in Olduvai Gorge, Tanganyika.

Zygote The fertilized ovum, the product of the union of the ovum and the spermatozoon.

❧ INDEX ❧

[345]

Parapithecus, 118
Paviland, 135
pea, garden (*Pisum sativum*), 27–30, 38
Pei, W. C., 176, 178
Pekin man, (*see also* Sinanthropus), 177–179
pelvis, *see* bipedalism and long-distance walking
pebble tools, *see* Oldowan
Perthes, Boucher de, 123, 124, 126, 135, 203
phenotype, 28, 29, 341
physical anthropology, 13–17, 267, 268, 315
pigmentation, 56–58, 271–279, 281, 285–287, 290–296, 303, 304, 312, 331
Piltdown, 154, 165–171, 174, 185, 188, 213
Pithecanthropine stage, 148, 177, 183, 189, 190, 193, 200, 208, 210–212, 215, 216, 228, 229, 260–264, 330, 341
    characteristics, 190, 233, 234
    distribution, 175, 236–240
Pithecanthropus, 143–150, 153, 161, 175–177, 180–183, 191, 192, 209, 221, 233–244, 341
Pleistocene, 99, 103, 107, 110, 112, 120, 152, 153, 169, 170, 180, 191, 203, 205, 208, 215, 216, 228, 262, 263, 290, 292
    Early Pleistocene, 170, 185, 186, 188, 193, 196, 199, 209, 223, 228, 229, 231, 232, 237, 248, 263, 328
    Middle Pleistocene, 153, 169, 180, 188, 190, 228, 229, 232, 234, 235, 237, 238, 240, 242, 244, 248, 263, 302, 328
    Upper Pleistocene, 201, 232, 263
Plesianthropus, 192, 193, 197, 225
Pliocene, 99, 112, 115, 119, 120, 170
Pliopithecus, 107, 115, 118, 241

polymorphism, 52, 341
Polynesia, 279, 283
population, breeding, 268, 270, 295, 296, 314, 322, 341
    genetics, 268
Post, Richard H., 316, 326
posture, 53, 113, 160, 192, 260
    Australopithecine, 192, 197, 207
    Neanderthal, 160, 245
Potassium-Argon dating, 98, 196, 208, 209, 229, 341
preadaptation, 53, 114, 341
Předmost, 253, 254
prehensile tail, 73, 74, 120
Pre-Zinj. child, 210, 211, 224
Prichard, James Cowles, 11
primate characteristics, 64–66
primate taxonomy, 64, 66, 88, 89, 342
probable mutation effect, 55, 57, 58, 60, 114, 227, 248, 262, 329, 330, 341
Proconsul, 117, 118, 342
Propliopithecus, 118, 342
Prosimii, 64, 66–73, 91, 108–111, 118
protein, 38, 40, 42, 43, 56, 57, 315, 321, 342
    as food, 256, 262, 263, 311, 317, 325, 330
pygmies, 227, 271, 273, 280, 281, 311–313, 319

La Quina, 162–164

Rabat, 175
race, 268–270, 296, 303, 314, 321, 322, 342
radioactive dating, 95–98
Ray, John, 5
recessiveness, 29
reptiles, 102–104
rhinarium, 69, 109, 342
Rhodesian skull, 164
RNA, 42, 43, 342
Roberts, D. F., 326

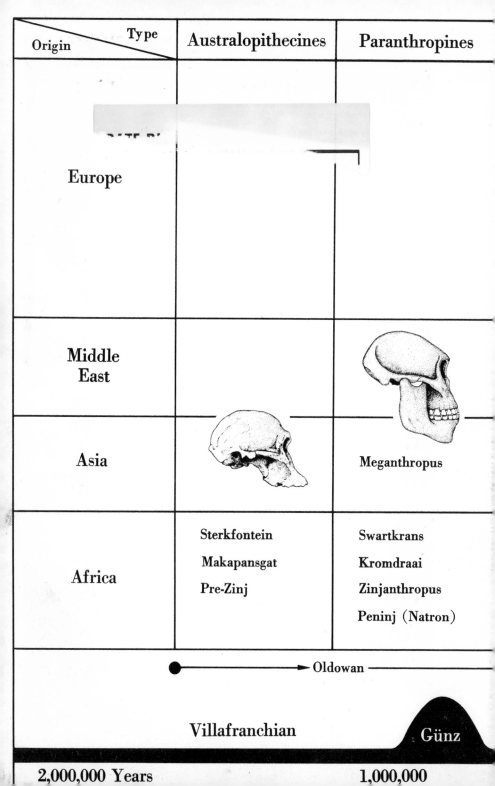

Origin \ Type	Australopithecines	Paranthropines
Europe		
Middle East		
Asia		Meganthropus
Africa	Sterkfontein Makapansgat Pre-Zinj	Swartkrans Kromdraai Zinjanthropus Peninj (Natron)

● ────────────→ Oldowan ────────────

Villafranchian   Günz

2,000,000 Years   1,000,000